MATERIALS SCIENCE AND TECHNOLOGIES

PROPERTIES OF FLUORITE STRUCTURE MATERIALS

MATERIALS SCIENCE AND TECHNOLOGIES

Additional books in this series can be found on Nova's website
under the Series tab.

Additional e-books in this series can be found on Nova's website
under the e-book tab.

MATERIALS SCIENCE AND TECHNOLOGIES

PROPERTIES OF FLUORITE STRUCTURE MATERIALS

PETER VAJDA

AND

JEAN-MARC COSTANTINI

EDITORS

nova publishers
New York

For permission to use material from this book please contact us:
Telephone 631-231-7269; Fax 631-231-8175
Web Site: http://www.novapublishers.com

NOTICE TO THE READER

Additional color graphics may be available in the e-book version of this book.

Library of Congress Cataloging-in-Publication Data

ISBN: 978-1-62417-458-2

Published by Nova Science Publishers, Inc. † New York

CONTENTS

INTRODUCTION

When, in 1974, was published by Clarendon Press (Oxford) the book "*Crystals with the Fluorite Structure*" edited by W. Hayes, the research had appeared sufficiently mature in order to be able to summarize some fundamentals of these CaF_2-type compounds, such as the definition and description of color centers and other point defects, their thermodynamics and kinetics, as well as some theoretical background concerning electronic properties.

Now - four decades later - the domain has experienced such a broad evolution as concerns the application of these materials, both in the modern energetics and in the safety context that it seemed useful to recapitulate the situation afresh by collecting the most recent new and important data on them. In the present work, we have focused on two fluorite-structured groups of materials: the hydrides of the rare earths (and actinides) and some specific metal oxides. By contrast to the former book dealing mainly with alkaline-earth halides, non-stoichiometry appears as a key issue for both groups of materials treated here.

The former group has attracted recently particularly close attention because of its possible candidature as hydrogen storage material within the vast prospect of the clean energy economy. In addition, the amazing property of transiting from metallic to semiconducting state and back by simply changing the hydrogen concentration between dihydride and trihydride had led to the development of the so-called "switchable mirrors" (SWIMs) evolving between opaque or reflecting and optically transparent. Other unexpected before possible applications concern specific optic, magnetic and nuclear properties used for example in magnetic refrigeration, photo-chromism, and neutron generators. Newly discovered structural and electronic modifications under high pressure had prompted us to dedicate a specific chapter to this phenomenon. On the other hand, the essential role played by the non-stoichiometry in these compounds and by the order/disorder processes in the hydrogen sublattice for the understanding of their behavior had demanded for two general chapters - one experimental and one theoretical.

In the second group, we are first dealing with the (antifluorite-type) lithium oxide, Li_2O, a candidate for (super)ionic batteries (again interesting for the clean energy technology) and as a tritium "breeder" in fusion reactor walls, but also a source for the formation of metallic lithium colloids with exciting properties when irradiated with electrons. Moreover, the increasing interest for power generation by fuel cells with high efficiencies and reduced harmful emissions in the atmosphere, leads to the development of solid oxide fuel cell (SOFC) ceramic materials with high ionic conductivities, such as oxygen-defective oxides. Among these high-temperature materials, yttria-stabilized zirconia (ZrO_2) or YSZ, and ceria

(CeO_2), with large deviations from the stoichiometry, are considered as the most promising ones. Lastly, but not the least, for nuclear applications, YSZ is envisioned among other radiation-tolerant oxides, as an inert confinement matrix for actinide immobilization or transmutation in reactors. Further, YSZ and ceria can also be used as non-radioactive surrogates for the actinide dioxide nuclear fuels, such as urania (UO_2) with the same structure, as regards their in-pile behavior under irradiation. A first chapter is thus dedicated to the radiation damage in YSZ and ceria, and a second one is devoted to the behavior of actinide dioxides under irradiation.

In: Properties of Fluorite Structure Materials
Editors: Peter Vajda and Jean-Marc Costantini

ISBN: 978-1-62417-458-2
© 2013 Nova Science Publishers, Inc.

Chapter 1

FLUORITE-TYPE RARE-EARTH HYDRIDES STUDIED FROM FIRST PRINCIPLES

Gunther Schöllhammer,[*] *Ferenc Karsai*[§] and *Peter Herzig*
Institut für Physikalische Chemie, Universität Wien, Austria

Abstract

The dihydrides of the rare-earth metals, except for Eu and Yb under normal pressure, set up a class of isostructural chemical compounds. The stoichiometric compounds possess fluorite-type crystal structures. First-principles calculations for rare-earth hydrides are the subject of this chapter. After a short review of the literature, we present results from investigations of the electronic, energetic, structural, and elastic properties of the stoichiometric and non-stoichiometric dihydrides of four selected rare-earth metals: Sc, Y, La, and Lu. Due to the fact that the hydride phase with a cubic close-packed metallic substructure is extended to the trihydride composition for the La–H system contrary to the H systems of the other selected metals, the stoichiometric and hypostoichiometric trihydride of La is also covered by our discussion.

PACS 81.05.Je, 71.15.Mb, 71.15.Nc, 61.72.J–, 78.20.Bh.

Keywords: Hydrides of rare-earth metals, electronic properties, non-stoichiometry, defect clusters, computer simulations

1.   Introduction

The reaction of a rare-earth metal R = Sc, Y, La, or one of the lanthanide elements, with H_2 is exothermic and leads, depending on the experimental conditions, to a solid solution RH_x or to an in general non-stoichiometric hydride with a hydrogen concentration between slightly less than two and three equivalents.

At ambient conditions, the rare-earth metals, except for body-centered cubic Eu, possess close-packed structures (hexagonal, cubic, hexagonal with doubled c-axis, or the α-Sm

---

[*]E-mail address: gunther.schoellhammer@univie.ac.at

[§]Present address: Technische Universität Wien, Institut für Materialchemie, Getreidemarkt 9, 1060 Wien, Austria

structure). The H atoms of RH_x are interstitially bonded in the matrix of R atoms, which retain the structure of the pure element.

The dihydrides of the rare-earth metals, except for Eu and Yb under normal pressure, show metallic behaviour and – in an idealized picture – the stoichiometric dihydrides crystallize with a fluorite-type structure, in which the H atoms completely occupy the tetrahedral interstitial sites of the cubic close-packed (ccp) metal atoms, whereas the octahedral interstitial sites are vacant. The hydrides are consequently not formed just by hydrogen absorption into the metallic matrix, but their formation induces the convergency of crystal structures and therefore in general the transformation of the metallic substructure. The same is true in the case of the formation of the dihydrides of the hexagonal close-packed metals of group IVB and the body-centered cubic metals of group VB (these compounds, however, are not in the scope of this chapter). They also have the fluorite-type structure or a closely related tetragonally distorted structure (see, e.g., references 1, 2, and the references therein). The dihydrides of the divalent rare-earth elements Eu and Yb possess orthorhombic structures isotypic with the dihydrides of the alkaline-earth metals Ca, Sr, and Ba [3,4]. The properties of the hydrides of Eu and Yb are therefore excluded from the further discussion.

The R–H systems can be divided in two classes depending on the occurrence of a two-phase region in the temperature-composition phase diagrams for hydrogen concentrations between two and three equivalents, separating from each other a phase of a metallic hydride with hydrogen concentrations around two equivalents and a phase of an insulating hydride with compositions closer to three equivalents. In the hydrogen systems of Sc, Y, and the heavier lanthanides, such a two-phase region exists [5, 6]. Except for high-pressure conditions, an essentially hexagonal close-packed arrangement of the metal atoms is typical for the trihydrides of these elements contrary to the fluorite-type dihydrides. The HoD_3 type [7] with $P\bar{3}c1$ space-group symmetry and a triplicated hcp unit cell is frequently considered as a prototype for the structures of these trihydrides; the H atoms occupy off-center positions within distorted tetrahedral and octahedral interstitial sites as well as sites with trigonal-planar coordination. In various experimental and theoretical studies [8–12], structures with space-group symmetry $P6_3cm$ or $P6_3$ were proposed for the trihydrides of different rare-earth metals. These hexagonal structures with broken hcp symmetry are closely related to the HoD_3 structure. For the trihydrides of Sc, Y, Sm, Gd, Ho, Er, and Lu, a transformation leading to structures with cubic close-packed metal atoms was observed by means of X-ray diffraction measurements at high pressure (see references 13, 14, and the references therein). The onset pressure for this transformation decreases with increasing molar volume of the compound and ranges between about 30 GPa for ScH_3 and about 2 GPa for SmH_3 at room temperature. From optical measurements, the closure of the band gap was inferred for the ccp high-pressure systems YH_3 [15, 16] and ScH_3 [17] at pressures of roughly 25 and 50 GPa, respectively. The dihydrides of La and the light lanthanides Ce and Pr, i.e. the rare-earth elements with the largest effective size, can be continuously loaded with hydrogen up to the trihydride composition. Thereby, the octahedral interstitial sites become occupied, and the metallic substructure remains basically ccp over the whole concentration range of the hydride phase, i.e., the arrangement of the metal atoms does not undergo a fundamental change. The complete occupation of the octahedral sites of RH_{2+x} maintaining the cubic symmetry leads to a structure of the $D0_3$ type (Strukturbericht notation). However, in the concentration range between the dihydride and the hydrogen-rich phase boundary of the ccp phase – or the trihydride in the case of La and the light lanthanides – ordering of the octahedrally coordinated H atoms has been observed in the case of several lanthanides at low temperature leading to the formation of tetragonal superstructures, see reference 6 and the references therein. Furthermore, for LaH_{2+x}, the H atoms occupying the octahedral interstitial sites were found to be displaced along the $\langle 111 \rangle$ directions [18,19], and a structure-optimization of LaH_3 by means of first-principles techniques led to an orthorhombically distorted structure [20].

The hydrides of La and the lighter lanthanides undergo a concentration-dependent metal–insulator transition, e.g. for LaH_{2+x}, this transition occurs for $0.6 \leq x \leq 0.9$ depending on the temperature [21].

It has been demonstrated, that the metallic state and the transparent insulating state can be reversibly switched into each other by varying the hydrogen concentration in thin films of hydrides of La and other rare-earth metals [22–25]. This so-called switchable-mirror effect may be of use in sensor technology, see reference 26 and the references therein.

LaH_{2+x} ($x \approx 0.3$) was found to undergo a phase separation at high pressure, which is interpreted as a disproportionation reaction yielding cubic LaH_3 and a solid solution of H in ccp La with octahedral site occupation [27]. It is worth mentioning in this context, that first-principles investigations of LaH_x [28] have shown that H atoms display an energetic preference for octahedral sites compared to tetrahedral sites at low hydrogen concentrations – contrary to the expectations for the solid solution of H in a rare-earth metal (see reference 6).

2.   Electronic-Structure Calculations: Historic Survey

This section provides a short summary of electronic-structure calculations for hydrides of rare-earth metals reported in the literature. Our selective treatment of the subject does not claim to be complete.

First band-structure calculations for rare-earth hydrides were published by Switendick [29] in 1970. At that time, the non-self-consistent augmented plane wave (APW) method was used to calculate the electronic structure of fluorite-type YH_2 and of PrH_3 with $D0_3$ structure. These two hydrides were chosen as model compounds for hydrides of a smaller and a larger rare-earth metal atom. With the crystal potentials constructed by superposition of atomic potentials for the trivalent configuration of the metal and for the neutral H atom, a band gap was obtained for PrH_3. In a further paper [30] Switendick treated the whole series from hypothetical ccp-YH_0, YH_1 (NaCl structure) to cubic YH_3 ($D0_3$ structure) including YH_2 (in the experimentally observed fluorite structure) using a similar procedure. For yttrium trihydride he obtained a band gap of roughly 2 eV in agreement with experiments performed on hexagonal YH_3 [31]. Using a similar but slightly improved method, Gupta investigated the electronic structure of ErH_2 [32] as well as LaH_2 and cubic LaH_3 [33]. Sen Gupta and Chatterjee [34] performed APW calculations for LaH_2 and NdH_2. A comparison of the calculated band structures and densities of states with optical measurements for LaH_{2+x} ($-0.1 < x < 0.9$) was made by Peterman et al. [35]. For the dihydrides, two bands are observed energetically lowered due to the interaction of H s and metallic d states. The wave function of the lower of the two bands is symmetrical (s-/d-like) and for the higher band anti-symmetrical (p-/f-like) with respect to the metal atom. All the other bands have mainly metal d character. Since there are five valence electrons for the dihydride, the third band is occupied by one electron and therefore metallic behaviour is observed. For LaH$_3$, however, a band gap of more than 1 eV was found.

When the first self-consistent band-structure calculations became available, a much reduced direct band gap (ca. 0.17 eV) was obtained for cubic LaH$_3$ [36] by the Korringa–Kohn–Rostocker method. Later, density-functional calculations within the local-density approximation (LDA) showed a band overlap for LaH$_3$ (and YH$_3$) of roughly 1 eV [37], compared to the observed optical gap of 1.87 eV for LaH$_3$ (2.63 eV for YH$_3$) [31].

Because standard density-functional calculations could not reproduce a correct band gap, some authors were considering different theoretical concepts. Ng et al. [38, 39] started from insulating LaH$_3$ and introduced vacancies which are highly localized. The corresponding vacancy state, which donates electrons to the conduction band, is extremely small in size and therefore, according to the Mott criterion, the critical impurity concentration at which the system becomes metallic is unusually high (about 0.25 equivalents) compared to conventional semiconductors (e.g. 10^{-3} for Si:P). The arguments by Eder et al. [40] are based on the "breathing" hydrogen model which takes into account the large variation of radius of the H $1s$ orbital depending on the occupation. Therefore mean-field theory cannot be applied anymore. Using such a model the authors found that the ground state of the system corresponds closely to a state with two electrons forming a tightly bound singlet with one electron primarily on H and the other primarily on the neighbouring metallic ligand. Such a state corresponds to a Kondo-lattice insulator ground-state. Although both approaches have common features and arrive at similar conclusions, there is a remarkable difference. Ng et al. [38, 39] obtained a narrowing of the H bands, while Eder et al. [40] found a downward shift of the H bands.

It is interesting in this context that not only the above-mentioned approaches by Ng et al. [38, 39] and Eder et al. [40] can lead to band gaps in rare-earth-metal trihydrides. In the particular case of hexagonal YH$_3$, Kelly et al. [8] performed first-principles Car–Parrinello calculations based on LDA and found a structure with lower energy (12 meV per formula unit) than the HoD$_3$ structure. For this structure the authors obtained a band gap of ca. 1 eV which is caused by symmetry breaking, whereby the space-group symmetry is lowered from $P\bar{3}c1$ to $P6_3$. Essentially, the gap appears, because due to the symmetry change from $P\bar{3}c1$ to $P6_3$ the bands near the Γ point close to the Fermi level are not allowed to cross anymore, because they belong to the same irreducible representation in the $P6_3$ structure. The comparison of calculated and experimental phonon densities of states by van Gelderen et al. [41] shows better agreement for the $P6_3$ structure.

Most investigations of the optical properties of rare-earth-metal trihydrides have been performed for YH$_3$. These results are also of some relevance for the cubic trihydrides. In 2000 Miyake et al. [42] performed quasiparticle band-structure calculations for hypothetical cubic and hexagonal YH$_3$, assuming the LaF$_3$ structure for the latter, within the GW approximation and the linear-muffin-tin-orbital method. Since the authors did not perform calculations for the crystal structures actually observed, their results cannot directly be compared with experiment. They concluded that the missing band gap in LDA calculations is not an electron-correlation but a self-energy effect, because GW tends to narrow bands whose width is overestimated by LDA. Van Gelderen et al. [43,44] arrived at similar conclusions from their parameter-free GW calculations for YH$_3$ (LaF$_3$ and HoD$_3$ structures). On this level there are no pronounced differences between the HoD_3 and the broken-symmetry structure (apart from the fact that the latter has a larger fundamental and a smaller optical gap than the former). The authors argued that the failure of LDA to describe the H $1s$ eigenvalue is well resolved by the GW method. A different, and slightly faster, procedure was adopted by Wolf and Herzig [45, 46]. These authors used the screened-exchange local-density approximation (sX-LDA) in which one part of the exchange-correlation operator is treated exactly by the non-local Hartree–Fock operator calculated with a screened Coulomb interaction. The other part, which is only weakly wave-function dependent, is still calculated as a local-density functional. No empirical parameter is used, because the Thomas–Fermi screening is evaluated from the average density. For YH_3 in the $P6_3cm$ structure the sX-LDA method yields a larger fundamental gap [45] than the GW method gives for the $P\bar{3}c1$ structure, but the energy of the second conduction state at the Γ point is at a value comparable to the one obtained by GW [43]. Similar sX-LDA calculations showing comparable results were made for the structure with space group $P\bar{3}c1$ and for the $P6_3$ structure [46]. Alford et al. [47] calculated quasiparticle band-structures and band gaps for cubic YH_3 and LaH_3. These calculations are based on pseudopotentials. Although band gaps were found for both compounds, the quantitative results for YH_3 are different from earlier results [42], whereas good agreement with previous work [48] was obtained for LaH_3. Using the weighted-density approximation for hexagonal and cubic YH_3 as well as for LaH_3, Wu et al. [49] obtained band gaps smaller than the experimental ones. The latter authors did not find evidence for strong correlation in H $1s$ states, which is in contrast to what Racu and Schoenes [50] concluded from Raman-spectroscopy experiments. This controversy has not yet been resolved.

3. The Fluorite-Type Hydrides of Sc, Y, La, and Lu: Stoichiometric and Non-Stoichiometric Compounds

In this section, results from current first-principles studies [51, 52] of stoichiometric and non-stoichiometric dihydrides of selected rare-earth metals are presented. We have chosen Sc, Y, La, and the heaviest lanthanide metal Lu for our investigations. The stoichiometric and hypostoichiometric trihydride of La has been included into the discussion because of the close structural relation between the $D0_3$ structure of cubic LaH_3 and the fluorite structure.

3.1. Computational Details

Structure optimizations as well as the calculation of total energies, band structures, partial charges, and densities of states (DOS) have been performed for the fluorite-type dihydrides of Sc, Y, La, and Lu as well as for defect-models derived from these dihydrides by using the Vienna Ab-initio Simulation Package (VASP) [53–56]. The Kohn–Sham equations of density-functional theory [57, 58] with periodic boundary conditions have been solved within a plane-wave basis set with electron–ion interactions described by potentials constructed according to the projector-augmented-wave method [59, 60] with a $[Ne]4s^2$ core for Sc, an $[Ar]3d^{10}$ core for Y, a $[Kr]4d^{10}$ core for La, and a $[Xe]4f^{14}$ core for Lu. Scalar relativistic terms (mass velocity and Darwin terms) have been included. Exchange and correlation have been treated within the generalized-gradient approximation (GGA) according to reference 61 in the case of structures involving Sc, Y, and La and according to reference 62 in the case of LuH_{2+x} structures. An energy cut-off of 500 eV has been chosen for the plane-wave basis set. Spin-polarization has been excluded. The reciprocal-space sampling has been performed using Monkhorst–Pack k meshes [63]. $19 \times 19 \times 19$ meshes have been used in the case of calculations for the primitive and conventional unit cells of the fluorite-type dihydrides, $19 \times 19 \times 9$ meshes for the $1 \times 1 \times 2$ supercell of the conventional unit cell of LaH_2, and $13 \times 19 \times 25$ meshes for the *Pnma* structure found for LaH_3 (see section 3.6.1.). In the case of structure optimizations and total energy calculations for defect structures derived from the $2 \times 2 \times 2$ supercells of the conventional cubic unit cells, $3 \times 3 \times 3$ meshes have been used for optimizations and total energy calculations, and $9 \times 9 \times 9$ meshes for the calculation of the *DOS* for selected structures. Reciprocal-space integration has been carried out with the first-order Methfessel–Paxton method [64] with a broadening parameter of 0.2 eV. Structural parameters have been optimized by the minimization of the atomic forces and the stress tensor with respect to the crystallographic degrees of freedom applying the conjugate gradient technique implemented in VASP.

The minimum of the Γ-point energy (not spin-polarized) of a H dimer enclosed in a sufficiently large and otherwise empty cubic unit cell (lattice parameter $a = 10$ Å or larger in order to exclude the interaction between translation-equivalent molecules) as a function of the bond length calculated with VASP has been used as reference energy for molecular H_2.

Furthermore, band structures, partial charges, *DOS*, and charge-density plots for the fluorite-type dihydrides of Sc, Y, La, and Lu have been computed with the full-potential linearized augmented plane-wave (FLAPW) method (see references 65–68 and the references therein). Thereby, the exchange–correlation potential by Hedin and Lundqvist [69, 70] based on the local-density approximation (LDA) has been applied. [Ar] in the case of Sc, [Kr] in the case of Y, and [Xe] in the case of La and Lu have been treated as core states. For the expansion of the potential and the electron density inside the atomic spheres, spherical harmonics with orbital quantum number $l \leq 8$ have been taken into account. For reciprocal-space sampling $19 \times 19 \times 19$ Monkhorst–Pack meshes have been used. The reciprocal-space integration has been performed with the linear tetrahedron method [71, 72]. The atomic sphere radii have been set to 1.191 Å (Sc), 1.403 Å (Y), 1.609 Å (La), 1.391 Å (Lu), and 0.706 Å (H).

3.2. Formation Energies of the Stoichiometric Dihydrides

From the total energies $E(RH_2)$ of the fluorite-type dihydrides of $R =$ Sc, Y, La, and Lu with optimized cubic lattice parameters a, the total energies $E(R)$ of the respective elemental metals with optimized structural parameters, and the reference energy $E(H_2)$ of molecular hydrogen, the dihydride-formation energies $E_f(RH_2)$ have been calculated according to

$$E_f(RH_2) = E(RH_2) - E(R) - E(H_2). \tag{1}$$

Lattice-parameter optimizations and total-energy calculations have been performed by using VASP (see section 3.1. for details). The obtained lattice parameters, together with experimental values for comparison, and the calculated dihydride-formation energies are given in table 1. The involved metallic elements with the exception of La are hexagonal

Table 1. Calculated cubic lattice parameters a, corresponding experimental values (room temperature), and formation energies $E_f(RH_2)$ per formula unit computed according to equation (1) for R = Sc, Y, La, Lu. For LaH$_2$, the formation energies with respect to elemental La with dhcp and ccp structure are given.

R	$a/\text{Å}$		$E_f(RH_2)/\text{eV}$	Remarks
	calculated	experimental		
Sc	4.771	4.784 [73]	−2.126	
Y	5.207	5.208 [74]	−2.219	
La	5.648	5.666 [75]	−1.999	dhcp La
			−2.002	ccp La
Lu	5.023	5.034 [76]	−2.040	

close-packed (hcp) at ordinary conditions. The low-temperature structure of La is double-hexagonal close-packed (dhcp), i.e. hexagonal close-packed with doubled c axis; a cubic close-packed (ccp) modification exists at higher temperature. The formation energy of LaH$_2$ has been calculated with regard to both close-packed allotropic modifications. A value of -1.982 ± 0.013 eV per formula unit has been determined for the formation energy of LaH$_2$ with respect to the ccp metal by means of calorimetric measurements at 917 K [77].

Phonon-dispersion relations without imaginary modes have been obtained for the selected dihydrides from first-principles by means of the direct method, i.e., these fluorite-type dihydrides are dynamically stable.

3.3. Elastic Properties and Volume Effect of Non-stoichiometry

From a comparative study of the elastic properties of stoichiometric and non-stoichiometric dihydrides of the selected rare-earth metals [51], the bulk moduli and the elastic constants of cubic $RH_{1.75}$, RH_2, and $RH_{2.25}$ have been extracted. These values have been derived from the stress tensors σ calculated for the systems under investigation as described in reference 78. For the cubic crystal system, Hooke's law in Voigt notation [79] is written as follows:

$$\begin{pmatrix} \sigma_1 \\ \sigma_2 \\ \sigma_3 \\ \sigma_4 \\ \sigma_5 \\ \sigma_6 \end{pmatrix} = \begin{pmatrix} C_{11} & C_{12} & C_{12} & 0 & 0 & 0 \\ C_{12} & C_{11} & C_{12} & 0 & 0 & 0 \\ C_{12} & C_{12} & C_{11} & 0 & 0 & 0 \\ 0 & 0 & 0 & C_{44} & 0 & 0 \\ 0 & 0 & 0 & 0 & C_{44} & 0 \\ 0 & 0 & 0 & 0 & 0 & C_{44} \end{pmatrix} \begin{pmatrix} \varepsilon_1 \\ \varepsilon_2 \\ \varepsilon_3 \\ \varepsilon_4 \\ \varepsilon_5 \\ \varepsilon_6 \end{pmatrix}.$$

We have used three different distortions: (i) $\varepsilon_1 = \varepsilon_2 = \varepsilon_3 = \delta/3$, $\varepsilon_4 = \varepsilon_5 = \varepsilon_6 = 0$, (ii) $\varepsilon_1 = \varepsilon_2 = \delta/2$, $\varepsilon_3 = -\delta$, $\varepsilon_4 = \varepsilon_5 = \varepsilon_6 = 0$, and (iii) $\varepsilon_1 = \varepsilon_2 = \varepsilon_3 = \delta^2$, $\varepsilon_4 = \varepsilon_5 = \varepsilon_6 = 2\delta$. The parameter δ has been chosen as 0.5%. The systems $RH_{1.75}$ and $RH_{2.25}$ serve as simple models for hypostoichiometric and hyperstoichiometric rare-earth dihydrides. One has to bear in mind that – except for hyperstoichiometric La dihydride – the degree of non-stoichiometry represented by these structures (±0.25 equivalents) most likely oversteps the homogeneity limits of the cubic hydride phase. The corresponding unit cells have been constructed by removing a H atom from the conventional unit cells R_4H_8 of the fluorite-type dihydrides or by placing an additional H atom at an octahedral interstitial site, respectively. The calculations have been performed by using VASP (see section 3.1. for details).

Two general trends can be figured out by examination of the data for the elastic properties given in table 2. *(i)* The bulk moduli and the elastic constants of systems with the same hydrogen concentration decrease with increasing unit cell volume. *(ii)* The hydrides become stiffer with increasing hydrogen concentration.

Concerning the variation of the unit-cell volumes (also given in table 2) with the hydrogen concentration, it is stated that whereas the insertion of an additional H atom involves a unit-cell contraction by 0.5–1.4% for all investigated systems, the introduction of a hydrogen vacancy leads either to a reduction ($R = $ Sc, Y) or an increase ($R = $ La, Lu) of the unit-cell volume by 0.2–0.4%. The volume contraction of the hyperstoichiometric dihydrides contrary to Vegard's rule is in agreement with experimental findings. In sections 3.5.2. and

Table 2. Space-group symmetry, optimized unit-cell volume, bulk modulus B_0, as well as the independent elastic constants (Voigt notation) for cubic $RH_{1.75}$ (unit cell R_4H_7), RH_2 (conventional face-centered unit cell R_4H_8), and $RH_{2.25}$ (unit cell R_4H_9) with $R = $ Sc, Y, La, and Lu derived from the calculated stress tensors.

System	Space group	$V/\text{Å}^3$	B_0/GPa	C_{11}/GPa	C_{12}/GPa	C_{44}/GPa
Sc_4H_7	$P\bar{4}3m$	108.45	91	149	61	74
Sc_4H_8	$Fm\bar{3}m$	108.63	96	163	63	78
Sc_4H_9	$Pm\bar{3}m$	108.12	99	160	69	88
Y_4H_7	$P\bar{4}3m$	141.52	78	122	56	63
Y_4H_8	$Fm\bar{3}m$	141.18	83	132	59	68
Y_4H_9	$Pm\bar{3}m$	139.98	88	134	64	77
La_4H_7	$P\bar{4}3m$	179.48	55	78	44	41
La_4H_8	$Fm\bar{3}m$	180.21	62	88	49	48
La_4H_9	$Pm\bar{3}m$	177.77	66	91	54	55
Lu_4H_7	$P\bar{4}3m$	127.00	86	134	62	72
Lu_4H_8	$Fm\bar{3}m$	126.71	90	140	65	77
Lu_4H_9	$Pm\bar{3}m$	125.83	96	146	71	87

3.5.3., the energetics of defect models for hypostoichiometric and hyperstoichiometric dihydrides of Sc, Y, La, and Lu based on the $2 \times 2 \times 2$ supercells of the conventional unit cells of the cubic dihydrides is discussed. The optimized unit-cell volumes of these structures are plotted vs the hydrogen concentration in figure 1. The unit-cell contraction of the hyperstoichiometric dihydrides is evident for all hydrides under consideration. For $n < 0$, the values scatter widely. In the case of LaH$_{2-x}$, the smallest unit-cell volumes correspond to the most favourable defect structures among the 53 structures with $n = -3$ and the 602 structures with $n = -4$. In the case of the remaining systems, such an energy–volume relation is not appropriate because the competing structural effects determining the relative stability have different influence on the unit-cell volume (see section 3.5.2.).

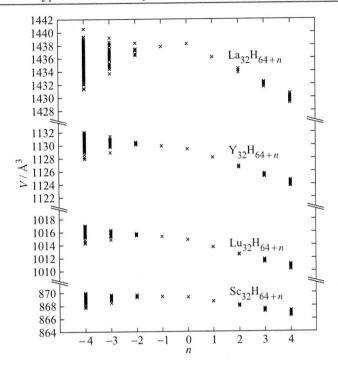

Figure 1. Unit cell volumes of the defect structures $R_{32}H_{64+n}$ discussed in sections 3.5.2. and 3.5.3. vs n.

3.4. Electronic Structure of the Stoichiometric Dihydrides

Self-consistent band-structure calculations applying the FLAPW method and the local-density approximation (LDA) for exchange and correlation were performed for the dihydrides of Sc, Y, Ti, V, Zr, and Nb with fluorite-type or related structures by Wolf and Herzig [2]. Recently, this study has been extended by performing LDA calculations for LaH_2 and LuH_2 based on the same methodology as well as by electronic-structure calculations for ScH_2, YH_2, LaH_2, and LuH_2 by using VASP within the generalized-gradient approximation. For details of the calculations, see section 3.1.

In figure 2, the valence-band structures and the corresponding total *DOS* are shown for ScH_2, YH_2, LaH_2, and LuH_2. Selected partial *DOS* for the systems under consideration are displayed in figure 3. The band structures of ScH_2, YH_2, and LuH_2 vary only slightly. This observation, which also holds true if the fluorite-type dihydrides of Ti, V, Zr, and Nb are taken into account, implies the validity of the rigid-band model for these compounds. The two lowest bands in the band structure of LaH_2 show weaker dispersion than the corresponding bands in the band structures of the other considered dihydrides. The four selected compounds, however, possess analogous bonding properties, which are therefore discussed in a collective way.

The two lowest bands appearing in their band structures have prominent H s character, whereas in the energy region of the band crossing the Fermi energy, only insignificant H s contributions are observed, as can be seen from the partial *DOS*. For the lowest band, almost exclusively H s and metal s contributions are found in the bottom part, which has a

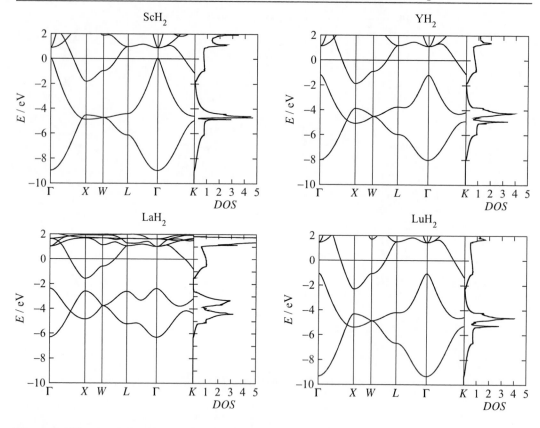

Figure 2. Electronic band structures and total *DOS* (VASP) for the fluorite-type dihydrides of Sc, Y, La, and Lu along high-symmetry directions through the Brillouin zone corresponding to the cubic face-centered Bravais lattice [80]. The energy is measured relative to the Fermi energy. The *DOS* is given in units of number of states per eV per primitive unit cell.

width of roughly 1 eV. Partial electron-densities calculated for the energy interval between the lowest eigenvalue and 1 eV above are shown in figure 4. The charge distribution implies the presence of bonding H–H s–s σ states at the bottom of the band. In the energy range between the minimum of the *DOS* (or gap in the case of LaH$_2$) at about -2 eV and the Fermi energy, e_g–e_g interactions between second-nearest neighbour R atoms and t_{2g}–t_{2g} interactions between nearest neighbour R atoms are relevant, as can be followed from the partial *DOS* and the partial electron densities calculated for this energy range, which are shown in figure 5. Thereby, the e_g–e_g interactions are prevalent. The partial electron densities for the intermediate valence range between 1 eV above the lowest eigenvalue and the minimum of the *DOS* (or gap), are displayed in figure 6. Bonding H–H and R–H interactions become perceptible from the charge distribution.

3.5. Defect Structures for Stoichiometric and Non-stoichiometric Dihydrides

In this section, defect-model structures for the stoichiometric, hypostoichiometric, and hyperstoichiometric dihydrides RH_{2+x} with $R =$ Sc, Y, La, and Lu and $-0.125 \leq x \leq 0.125$ that are derived from the $2 \times 2 \times 2$ supercells of the conventional face-centered unit cells

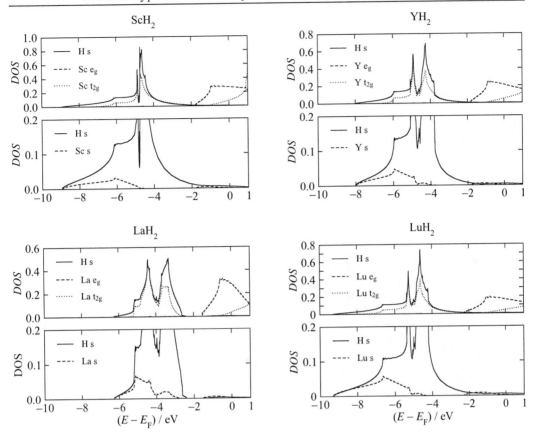

Figure 3. Selected partial *DOS* (VASP) for the fluorite-type dihydrides of Sc, Y, La, and Lu in units of number of states per eV per atom.

are discussed. This supercell of cubic RH_2 contains 32 R atoms and 64 tetrahedrally coordinated H atoms. Defect structures have been constructed by the removal of H atoms from tetrahedral interstitial sites and/or the insertion of octahedrally coordinated H atoms. For LaH_{2+x}, structures based on the $1 \times 1 \times 2$ supercell of the conventional unit cell with 8 La atoms have been considered in addition. Model structures are designated by using formulae representing the unit cell. Thereby, the coordination of the H atoms is indicated by superscripts. The formula

$$R_m H_o^{\text{oct}} H_{2m-t}^{\text{tet}}$$

stands for a structure with o octahedrally and $2m - t$ tetrahedrally coordinated H atoms, i.e. a structure with $o + t$ defect sites. $\square^{\text{tet}}$ symbolizes H a vacancy at a tetrahedral site. Formally, the formation of this defect structure is treated as the following reaction

$$R_m H_{2m}^{\text{tet}} + \frac{o - t}{2} H_2 \longrightarrow R_m H_o^{\text{oct}} H_{2m-t}^{\text{tet}},$$

where $R_m H_{2m}^{\text{tet}}$ and $R_m H_o^{\text{oct}} H_{2m-t}^{\text{tet}}$ represent the supercell of the stoichiometric fluorite-type dihydride with optimized lattice parameter and the optimized defect structure, respectively. This reaction is associated with the defect-formation energy E_{df} calculated from the respec-

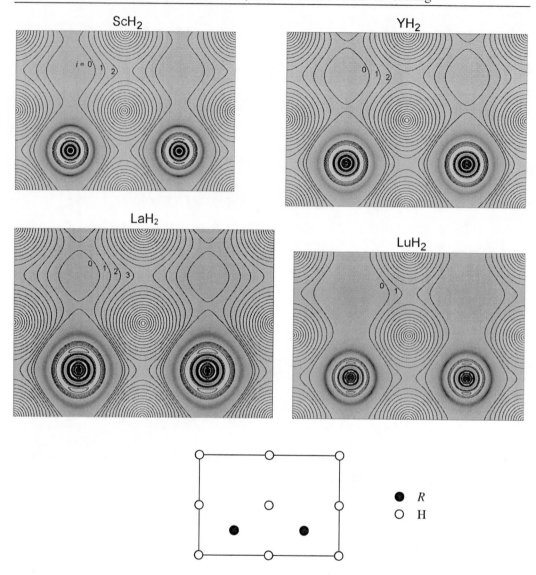

Figure 4. Partial electron densities (FLAPW) in the (110) planes for the energy range of 1 eV above the lowest eigenvalue at the Γ point for the fluorite-type dihydrides of the rare-earth metals R = Sc, Y, La, and Lu. The sections are true to scale. The positions of the atoms in the (110) plane are shown in the sketch below. Contour lines are shown for the densities $n_i = n_0 \times 2^{i/3}$. n_0 has been chosen so that $n_0 \times \Omega = 2.25\ e$, where Ω is the volume of the conventional unit cell. The first few contour lines are labelled. The superimposed grey shadings may help to discern the areas of higher density (lighter grey areas) close to the nuclei and in the H–H bonding regions.

tive total energies,

$$E_{df}\left(R_m H_o^{oct} H_{2m-t}^{tet}\right) = E\left(R_m H_o^{oct} H_{2m-t}^{tet}\right) - \left[E\left(R_m H_{2m}^{tet}\right) + \frac{o-t}{2}E\left(H_2\right)\right]. \quad (2)$$

The defect-ordering energy E_{ord} of a particular structure is defined as its defect-formation

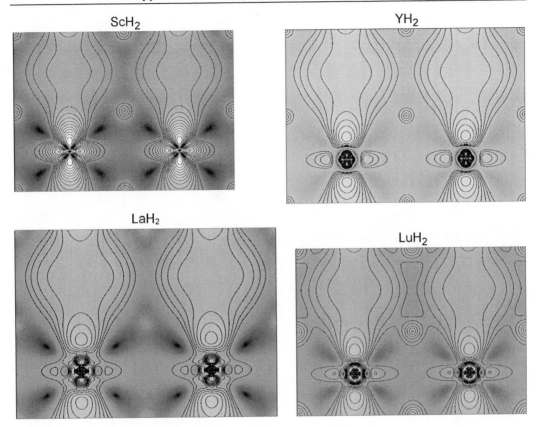

Figure 5. Partial electron densities (FLAPW) in the (110) planes for the energy range between the minimum of the *DOS* (or gap in the case of LaH$_2$) at about -2 eV and the Fermi energy for the fluorite-type dihydrides of the rare-earth metals $R =$ Sc, Y, La, and Lu. The sections are true to scale. For the positions of the atoms in the (110) plane, see figure 4. Contour lines are shown for the densities $n_i = n_0 \times 2^{i/3}$. n_0 has been chosen so that $n_0 \times \Omega = 18\,e$, where Ω is the volume of the conventional unit cell. The superimposed grey shadings may help to discern the areas of higher density (lighter grey areas) close to the nuclei and in the R–R bonding regions.

energy relative to the defect-formation energies of the structures with only one defect per unit cell (see sections 3.5.2. and 3.5.3.),

$$E_{\text{ord}}\left(R_m \text{H}_o^{\text{oct}} \text{H}_{2m-t}^{\text{tet}}\right) = E_{\text{df}}\left(R_m \text{H}_o^{\text{oct}} \text{H}_{2m-t}^{\text{tet}}\right) - \left[o \times E_{\text{df}}\left(R_m \text{H}^{\text{oct}} \text{H}_{2m}^{\text{tet}}\right) + t \times E_{\text{df}}\left(R_m \text{H}_{2m-1}^{\text{tet}}\right)\right]. \quad (3)$$

Structure optimizations with respect to all crystallographic degrees of freedom under the constraint of point-symmetry conservation and total-energy calculations of the optimized structures have been performed for more than 3000 defect models $R_{32}\text{H}_o^{\text{oct}}\text{H}_{64-t}^{\text{tet}}$ by using VASP (see section 3.1.). All geometrically independent structures with $o + t \leq 4$ that can be derived from the supercells $R_{32}\text{H}_{64}^{\text{tet}}$ have been determined. For $o + t > 2$, however, only structures with exclusively tetrahedral defects (vacancies in the hypostoichiometric

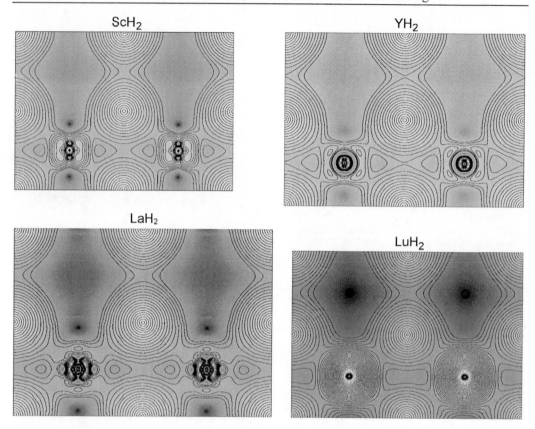

Figure 6. Partial electron densities (FLAPW) in the (110) planes for the energy range between 1 eV above the lowest eigenvalue at the Γ point and the minimum of the *DOS* (or gap in the case of LaH$_2$) at about -2 eV for the fluorite-type dihydrides of the rare-earth metals $R = $ Sc, Y, La, and Lu. The sections are true to scale. For the positions of the atoms in the (110) plane, see figure 4. Contour lines are shown for the densities $n_i = n_0 \times 2^{i/3}$. n_0 has been chosen so that $n_0 \times \Omega = 50\ e$, where Ω is the volume of the conventional unit cell. The superimposed grey shadings may help to discern the areas of higher density (lighter grey areas) close to the nuclei and in the bonding regions.

dihydrides) and structures with exclusively octahedral defects (occupied octahedral interstitial sites in the hyperstoichiometric dihydrides) have been considered not only because of the high number of structures with both tetrahedral and octahedral defects, but also because pairs of tetrahedral vacancies and octahedrally coordinated H atoms had turned out to be energetically highly unstable (see section 3.5.1.). The number of investigated structures for each metal R is given in table 3 for different values of o and t.

3.5.1. Stoichiometric Dihydrides

Four different configurations consisting of H^{oct} and $\square^{\mathrm{tet}}$ can be realized in $R_{32}\mathrm{H}^{\mathrm{oct}}\mathrm{H}^{\mathrm{tet}}_{63}$. A defect-pair that is not stable with respect to the performed structure optimization results if a H^{tet} atom is shifted into a coordination octahedron sharing a triangular face with the original

Table 3. Number N of investigated $R_{32}H_o^{oct}H_{64-t}^{tet}$ structures for different numbers of octahedral H atoms (o) and vacant tetrahedral interstitial sites (t).

o	4	3	2	1	1	0	0	0	0
t	0	0	0	0	1	1	2	3	4
N	71	14	5	1	4	1	10	53	602

tetrahedron. For each of the investigated metals, the corresponding structure transforms to the fluorite-type dihydride $R_{32}H_{64}^{tet}$.

In the case of the remaining H^{oct}–$\square^{tet}$ configurations, the coordination numbers of the H atoms remain unchanged. The formation of a H^{oct}–$\square^{tet}$ pair in the stoichiometric dihydrides of the considered rare-earth metals appears to be highly endothermic. The following defect-formation energies have been obtained: $E_{df} \approx 1.1$ eV for $R =$ Sc and Y, $E_{df} \approx 0.9$ eV for $R =$ La, and $E_{df} \approx 1.0$ eV for $R =$ Lu. The calculated ordering energies E_{ord} lie between 0 and 10 meV, therefore no indications for the formation of relatively favourable H^{oct}–$\square^{tet}$ pairs have been found on the basis of the investigated $R_{32}H^{oct}H_{63}^{tet}$ structures.

3.5.2. Hypostoichiometric Dihydrides

For all hypostoichiometric dihydrides considered in this chapter, positive defect-formation energies E_{df} have been obtained. E_{df} per defect site has been found to increase with increasing lattice constant of the dihydride, i.e., the bonding of the H atoms becomes stronger in the sequence $ScH_2 < LuH_2 < YH_2 < LaH_2$.

There is some relaxation of the metal atoms close to the H vacancies in $R_{32}H_{63}^{tet}$. It is directed away from the empty H site and lies between 0.01 and 0.05 Å. The effect on the lattice parameter is smaller than in the case of the hyperstoichiometric structures with the same defect concentration (see figure 1).

From the calculated E_{df} values for $R_{32}H_{62}^{tet}$, it has been concluded that two structure elements, A and B, are involved in the stabilized structures. A consists of two H vacancies at the shortest possible distance of about $a/2$, where a is the lattice parameter corresponding to the conventional unit cell R_4H_8. B is a linear arrangement of two H vacancies at a distance of about $\sqrt{3}\,a/2$ with a metal atom in the center. A and B are realized in structures $R_{32}H_{62}^{tet}$-1 and $R_{32}H_{62}^{tet}$-2, respectively, which are depicted in table 4. The most favourable structures in the $R_{32}H_{62}^{tet}$ series are $R_{32}H_{62}^{tet}$-2 followed by $R_{32}H_{62}^{tet}$-1 for $R =$ Y, La, and Lu. The difference between $La_{32}H_{62}^{tet}$-1 and $La_{32}H_{62}^{tet}$-2 is 240 meV; the difference between the corresponding Y and Lu structures is one order of magnitude smaller. A rather weak stabilization of the most favourable vacancy-pair structure has also been found in the case of $Sc_{32}H_{62}^{tet}$. The energetic sequence, however, is different: $Sc_{32}H_{62}^{tet}$-1 comes first, is followed by a structure with a vacancy–vacancy distance of about a and $Sc_{32}H_{62}^{tet}$-2, which are less stable by 22 and 35 meV, respectively.

The configurations of 3 and 4 vacancy sites have been found to follow similar energetic trends. In LaH_{2-x}, predominantly the maximization of the number of structure elements B leads to stabilization. $La_{32}H_{61}^{tet}$-2 and $La_{32}H_{60}^{tet}$-2 are most stable for $t = 3$ and $t = 4$, respectively. They are associated with the maximum number of B elements per unit cell. Apart from the zig-zag configuration in $La_{32}H_{60}^{tet}$-2, it is possible to arrange 4 vacancies in

Table 4. Intersection of the unit cell and the (110) plane defined with respect to the cubic axes of the supercell $R_{32}H_{64}^{tet}$, space-group symmetry, number of structure elements A and B, and defect-formation energy E_{df} according to equation (2) for selected defect models of the hypostoichiometric dihydrides of Sc, Y, La, and Lu.

Structure	(110) section	Space group	#A	#B	E_{df}/eV Sc	Y	La	Lu
$R_{32}H_{63}^{tet}$		$P\bar{4}3m$	0	0	1.225	1.414	1.435	1.343
$R_{32}H_{62}^{tet}$-1		$Cmmm$	1	0	2.365	2.687	2.773	2.546
$R_{32}H_{62}^{tet}$-2		$R\bar{3}m$	0	1	2.400	2.662	2.533	2.527
$R_{32}H_{61}^{tet}$-1		$P\bar{4}2m$	2	0	3.481	3.904	4.122	3.638
$R_{32}H_{61}^{tet}$-2		$Cmm2$	0	2	3.573	3.919	3.738	3.711
$R_{32}H_{60}^{tet}$-1		$P4_2/mcm$	4	0	4.578	5.057	5.406	4.636
$R_{32}H_{60}^{tet}$-2		$Pmma$	0	4	4.665	5.028	4.724	4.748

● R
• H^{tet}
□ vacancy

a helical way, such that the number of B elements present in the unit cell is maximized, as illustrated in figure 7. The corresponding structure is less stable than La $_{32}H_{60}^{tet}$-2 by only 36 meV. From figure 8, the energetic effect of the structure elements of types A and B in LaH$_x$ becomes apparent. It can be approximated that the formation of a B element lowers the energy by about 0.2 eV (decrease of E_{df} with increasing number of B for constant number of A). The decrease of E_{df} with increasing number of A elements is much weaker. In the case of ScH$_{2-x}$, YH$_{2-x}$, and LuH$_{2-x}$, the stabilizing effects due to the formation of structure elements A and B cannot be properly separated because of their rather small energetic difference. The remarkable feature of the favourable structures with 3 and 4 vacancies is the accumulation of A and/or B. Sc$_{32}H_{61}^{tet}$-1 and Sc$_{32}H_{60}^{tet}$-1 are the energetically most favourable models in the respective series. The structures with 3 and 4 vacant sites presented in table 4 and the helix model are the energetically most favourable for Y and Lu.

The accumulation of A and B leads to unit-cell expansion and contraction, respectively.

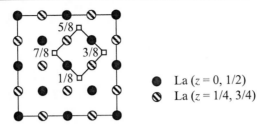

Figure 7. $R_{32}H_{60}^{tet}$ structure with helical arrangement of tetrahedral vacancies ($\square$) projected onto the (001) plane. The z components of the vacancy positions are indicated. The positions of the H atoms are not shown.

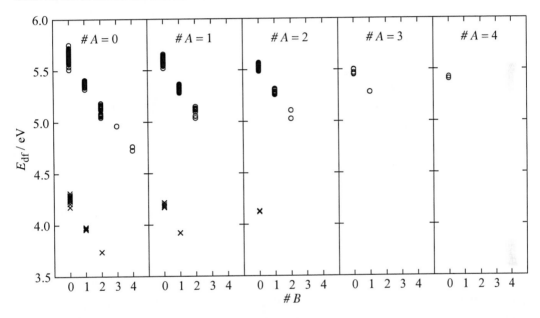

Figure 8. Defect-formation energies E_{df} of $La_{32}H_{61}^{tet}$ ($\times$) and $La_{32}H_{60}^{tet}$ ($\circ$) according to equation (2) vs number of structure elements B per unit cell for different numbers of structure elements A per unit cell.

The $La_{32}H_{60}^{tet}$ and $La_{32}H_{61}^{tet}$ structures with a relatively low defect-formation energy are those with a small unit-cell volume for the respective H concentration ($n = -4, -3$ in figure 1). For the other hypostoichiometric dihydrides, where A and B are in competition, such a correlation between energy and volume does not exist.

It is worthy of remark, that the formation of pairs and chains of H atoms that are geometrically equivalent to the favoured vacancy configuration in LaH_{2-x} have been found to be associated with a lowering of the total energy in the solid solution of H in ccp-La [28], i.e., linear H–La–H arrangements are favoured in LaH_x.

3.5.3. Hyperstoichiometric Dihydrides

Exothermic defect-formation energies E_{df} have been obtained for the investigated hyperstoichiometric dihydrides of Sc, Y, La, and Lu. For selected $R_{32}H_o^{oct}H_{64}^{tet}$ structures, the calculated E_{df} values are given in table 5. The absolute value of E_{df} per H^{oct} atom increases

Table 5. Intersection of the unit cell and the (110) plane defined with respect to the cubic axes of the supercell $R_{32}H_{64}^{tet}$, space-group symmetry, number of structure elements A and B, and defect-formation energy E_{df} according to equation (2) for selected defect models of the hyperstoichiometric dihydrides of Sc, Y, La, and Lu.

Structure	(110) section	Space group	E_{df}/eV			
			Sc	Y	La	Lu
$R_{32}H^{oct}H_{64}^{tet}$		$Pm\bar{3}m$	-0.133	-0.358	-0.510	-0.348
$R_{32}H_2^{oct}H_{64}^{tet}$-1		$Cmcm$	-0.268	-0.712	-1.028	-0.692
$R_{32}H_2^{oct}H_{64}^{tet}$-2		$P4/mmm$	-0.225	-0.702	-1.037	-0.684

● R
• H^{tet}
○ H^{oct}

with increasing lattice constant of the dihydride, i.e., the hyperstoichiometric H atoms are more tightly bonded in LaH_{2+x} than in YH_{2+x} and LuH_{2+x} analogous to the situation in the respective hypostoichiometric dihydrides. The absolute value of E_{df} per defect site, however, is much larger in the hypostoichiometric case. The bonding of H^{oct} atoms in ScH_{2+x} is relatively weak. This can be seen in connection with the fact that ScH_3 is formed only under high pressure [73] and in the context of the Switendick criterion [81], which implies a repulsive interaction between H atoms in interstitial metal hydrides leading to a minimum H–H distance of about 2.1 Å. The distance between H^{oct} and the surrounding H^{tet} atoms in the relaxed structure is 2.13 Å.

The structural relaxation taking place in the vicinity of the defect site in $R_{32}H^{oct}H_{64}^{tet}$ is characterized by an elongation of the shortest distance between H^{oct} and the 8 neighbouring H^{tet} atoms by 0.05–0.06 Å and by a shortening of the distance between H^{oct} and the coordinating R atoms by 0.02–0.03 Å.

The H^{oct} pair configurations that are present in $R_{32}H_2^{oct}H_{64}^{tet}$-1 and $R_{32}H_2^{oct}H_{64}^{tet}$-2 (see table 5) have turned out to be structure elements determining the relative stability of the investigated $R_{32}H_o^{oct}H_{64}^{tet}$ structures. Energetically relatively favourable structures correspond to H^{oct} arrangements giving rise to a large number of these pair configurations. Among the structures with 2 H^{oct} atoms per unit cell, $R_{32}H_2^{oct}H_{64}^{tet}$-1 is most stable for the considered hydrides except for LaH_{2+x}. The linear H–La–H arrangement of $La_{32}H_2^{oct}H_{64}^{tet}$-2 is favoured. Endothermic ordering energies between about 0 and 80 meV per H^{oct} atom have been obtained for the investigated $R_{32}H_o^{oct}H_{64}^{tet}$ structures in the case of $R =$ Sc, Y, and Lu. The ordering energies of $La_{32}H_o^{oct}H_{64}^{tet}$, on the contrary, are partially exothermic; they lie between -16 and 45 meV per H^{oct} atom. Consequently, some H^{oct} configurations are stabilized with respect to a single H^{oct} atom per unit cell. This effect is most pronounced for the

$La_{32}H_4^{oct}H_{64}^{tet}$ structure shown in figure 9, in which the number of linear H–La–H arrangements is maximized. It can be described as La_8H_{17} on the basis of the $1 \times 1 \times 2$ supercell

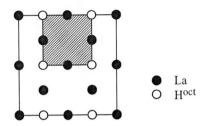

●	La
○	H^{oct}

Figure 9. (001) section of the most stable $La_{32}H_4^{oct}H_{64}^{tet}$ structure. The shaded area corresponds to the smaller unit cell $La_8H^{oct}H_{16}^{tet}$. The symmetry of the structure is $P4/mmm$.

of the conventional face-centered unit cell of LaH_2 and a space group of the type $P4/mmm$ (no. 123). This is interesting because ordered structures have been found at low temperature for $LaH_{2.25}$ [82] and $LaH_{2.50}$ [83] with the same tetragonal unit cell and space groups of the types $I4/mmm$ (no. 139) and $I4_1/amd$ (no. 141), respectively, by means of neutron powder-diffraction investigations of the corresponding deuterides. These superstructures are characterized by ordering of the H^{oct} atoms on the (044) net planes. The octahedral sites on a particular (044) plane are either completely vacant or completely occupied. In the $I4/mmm$ structure, a net plane with occupied octahedral sites follows three net planes with vacant sites. In the $I4_1/amd$ structure, two net planes with occupied octahedral sites follow two net planes of the other type. H^{oct} of the $P4/mmm$ structure La_8H_{17} shown in figure 9 occupies the Wyckoff position $1a$, the vacant octahedral interstitial sites correspond to the positions $1b$, $1c$, $1d$, and $4i$ ($z = 1/4$). The occupation of $1b$ or $1c$ with a second hydrogen atom leads to smaller unit cells La_4H_9 and space groups of the types $Pm\bar{3}m$ (for $c/a = 2$) or $P4/mmm$, respectively. If the second H atom is placed at $1d$, the aforementioned $I4/mmm$ structure is obtained. For a second H atom at one of the sites of position $4i$, a La_8H_{18} structure with $Pmma$ symmetry results. The defect-formation energies have been calculated for $La_8H^{oct}H_{16}^{tet}$ and the derived $La_8H_2^{oct}H_{16}^{tet}$ structures. The results are given in table 6. The ex-

Table 6. Defect-formation energies E_{df} according to equation (2) and defect-ordering energies E_{ord} according to equation (3) of $La_8H^{oct}H_{16}^{tet}$ and the $LaH_{2.25}$ structures resulting by inserting a second H atom at different octahedral sites. The $LaH_{2.25}$ structures with space groups of the types $Pm\bar{3}m$ and $P4/mmm$ have smaller unit cells; for comparison, they are described as $La_8H_2^{oct}H_{16}^{tet}$.

Structure	Space group	E_{df}/eV	E_{ord}/eV	Remarks
$La_8H^{oct}H_{16}^{tet}$	$P4/mmm$	−0.531	—	
$La_8H_2^{oct}H_{16}^{tet}$	$Pm\bar{3}m$	−1.073	−0.010	$2 \times La_4H^{oct}H_8^{tet}$
$La_8H_2^{oct}H_{16}^{tet}$	$P4/mmm$	−0.937	0.126	$2 \times La_4H^{oct}H_8^{tet}$
$La_8H_2^{oct}H_{16}^{tet}$	$I4/mmm$	−1.105	−0.042	experimental structure [82]
$La_8H_2^{oct}H_{16}^{tet}$	$Pmma$	−1.038	0.025	

perimental structure has turned out to be the most stable one. The ordering energy obtained for this structure is negative. The cubic $LaH_{2.25}$ structure, in which the number of linear

H^{oct}–La–H^{oct} units is maximized, and which is also associated with exothermic ordering, is less stable by 32 meV. In the case of the remaining structures, $E_{ord} > 0$ holds. In the relatively unstable $P4/mmm$ and $Pmma$ structures, rather short nearest-neighbour distances between H^{oct} atoms occur, which are avoided in the structures with $I4/mmm$ and $Pm\bar{3}m$ symmetry.

3.6. Lanthanum Trihydride

3.6.1. Stoichiometric Trihydride

Phonon calculations have shown that LaH_3 with $Fm\bar{3}m$ symmetry (DO_3 type) and an optimized volume of $V = 171.61$ Å^3 is an dynamically unstable structure [20].

The $2 \times 2 \times 2$ supercell of the conventional face-centered unit cell of DO_3-type LaH_3 has been structurally optimized without any point-symmetry constraints, i.e. for $P1$ symmetry and a constant number of atoms per unit cell [20]. As a consequence of the structure optimization, the total energy has decreased by 21 meV per formula unit LaH_3. Structure relaxation and total energy calculations have been performed by using VASP (see section 3.1.). Higher symmetrical structures have been found that differ only slightly from the $P1$ structure with respect to the geometrical parameters and the total energy. These higher symmetrical approximants can be described on the basis of unit cells La_4H_{12} and space groups of the types $P1$, Pm, $Pmc2_1$, and $Pnma$. To simplify matters, the $Pnma$ structure, which is characterized and compared to the DO_3-type structure in table 7, will be discussed in the following.

Table 7. Parameters of the La_4H_{12} structure with $Pnma$ symmetry found in optimized $La_{32}H_{96}$ and structural parameters for cubic LaH_3 with the same unit-cell setup.

La_4H_{12} (optimized)	$Pnma$, no. 62	$b = 5.28879$ Å	$a/b = 1.51470$ $c/b = 0.77104$
La @ Wyckoff position	$4c$	with	$x = 0.12974, z = 0.71477$
H1	$4c$		$x = 0.36438, z = 0.15679$
H2	$8d$		$x = 0.11804, y = 0.00209, z = 0.20169$

La_4H_{12} (DO_3 type)	equivalent $Pnma$ setup		$a/b = \sqrt{2}$ $c/b = 1/\sqrt{2}$
La @ Wyckoff position	$4c$	with	$x = 1/8, z = 3/4$
H1	$4c$		$x = 3/8, z = 1/4$
H2	$8d$		$x = 1/8, y = 0, z = 1/4$

The formation energy of LaH_3,

$$E_f(RH_3) = E(RH_3) - E(R) - \frac{3}{2} E(H_2) = -2.455 \text{ eV}, \qquad (4)$$

has been calculated in the same way as described for the dihydrides in section 3.2. Thereby, $E(RH_3)$ is the total energy per formula unit of LaH_3 with $Pnma$ structure, $E(R)$ is the total energy of dhcp-La per atom, and $E(H_2)$ is the reference energy for the hydrogen molecule.

The dihydride formation, which is connected with a formation energy of -1.000 eV per H atom (see section 3.2.), is stronger exothermic than the reaction

$$\mathrm{LaH_2} + \frac{1}{2}\mathrm{H_2} \longrightarrow \mathrm{LaH_3}$$

corresponding to the reaction energy

$$E_\mathrm{f}(RH_3) - E_\mathrm{f}(RH_2) = -0.456 \,\mathrm{eV}. \tag{5}$$

In this sense, the additional H atom in $\mathrm{LaH_3}$ is less tightly bonded than the H atoms in $\mathrm{LaH_2}$.

The orthorhombic distortion of the lattice parameters a, b, and c by $+1.9\%$, -4.8%, and $+3.8\%$ with respect to the cubic unit cell corresponding to a volume increase of about 0.7% is accompanied by significant changes of the interatomic distances. The coordination numbers of the constituent atoms, however, remain unchanged. The H atoms at Wyckoff position $4c$ and $8d$ occupy distorted octahedral and distorted tetrahedral interstitial sites, respectively. The coordination environment of the H atoms is shown in figure 10.

The structure relaxation is not only associated with a lowering of the total energy but also with the opening of a band gap of slightly more than 1 eV within density-functional theory. The band structures of the $Pnma$ structure and of cubic $\mathrm{LaH_3}$ are displayed in figure 11. Unlike the cubic structure, which is dynamically unstable, no imaginary frequencies have been obtained in phonon calculations for the $Pnma$ structure [20].

3.6.2. Defect Models for the Hypostoichiometric Trihydride

Structure optimizations and total-energy calculations have been performed for vacancy models derived from the $2 \times 2 \times 2$ supercell of the face-centered $D0_3$-type unit cell of cubic $\mathrm{LaH_3}$ applying VASP (see section 3.1.). The structure relaxations have been carried out without restrictions concerning the point-symmetry but keeping the lattice parameters constant. The involved structures have a pseudo-cubic lattice parameter of $a = 11.140$ Å.

Model structures for $\mathrm{LaH_{3-x}}$ are designated by using formulae representing the unit cell, similar to the notation introduced in section 3.5. for dihydride structures. The formula

$$\mathrm{La_{32}H_{32-o}^{oct}H_{64-t}^{tet}}$$

stands for a structure with o octahedral and t tetrahedral vacancies, the formation of which is treated as the following reaction

$$\mathrm{La_{32}H_{32}^{oct}H_{64}^{tet}} \longrightarrow \mathrm{La_{32}H_{32-o}^{oct}H_{64-t}^{tet}} + \frac{o+t}{2}\mathrm{H_2}$$

where $\mathrm{La_{32}H_{32}^{oct}H_{64}^{tet}}$ and $\mathrm{La_{32}H_{32-o}^{oct}H_{64-t}^{tet}}$ represent the supercell of $\mathrm{LaH_3}$ and the optimized model structure, respectively. This reaction is associated with the dehydrogenation energy calculated from the corresponding total energies

$$E_\mathrm{d}\left(\mathrm{La_{32}H_{32-o}^{oct}H_{64-t}^{tet}}\right) = E\left(\mathrm{La_{32}H_{32-o}^{oct}H_{64-t}^{tet}}\right) + \frac{o+t}{2}E\left(\mathrm{H_2}\right) - E\left(\mathrm{La_{32}H_{32}^{oct}H_{64}^{tet}}\right). \tag{6}$$

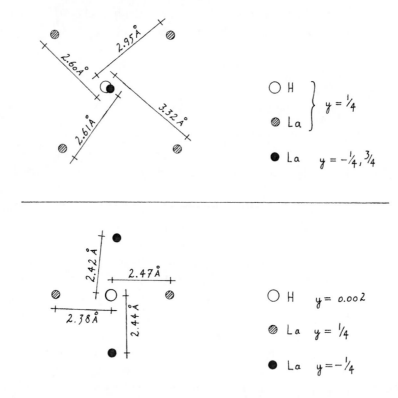

Figure 10. Projections onto the plane with $y = \frac{b}{4}$ of the positions of the H atoms and the coordinating La atoms in the La_4H_{12} structure with *Pnma* symmetry. La–H distances are indicated. The *a* axis is vertical. *y* values are given in units of the lattice parameter *b*. Top: H atom at a distorted octahedral interstitial site (H1 in table 7). The distance between the H atom and the La atoms at $y = -\frac{b}{4}$ and $y = \frac{3}{4}b$ is 2.65 Å. Bottom: H atom at a distorted tetrahedral interstitial site (H2 in table 7). Figure from reference 12.

Comparing the unrelaxed structures with a single vacancy per unit cell, $La_{32}H_{31}^{oct}H_{64}^{tet}$ and $La_{32}H_{32}^{oct}H_{63}^{tet}$, in which the H atoms retain their $D0_3$ positions, the formation of an octahedral vacancy appears to be favoured by 619 meV. The energetic effect of the structure relaxation (-104 and -681 meV) compensates for the most part of this difference. The dehydrogenation energies are $E_d(La_{32}H_{31}^{oct}H_{64}^{tet}) = 0.244$ eV and $E_d(La_{32}H_{32}^{oct}H_{63}^{tet}) = 0.287$ eV, i.e., the difference is reduced to 43 meV [19]. The H^{oct} atoms neighbouring the tetrahedral vacancy undergo drastic relaxations; they are shifted towards the vacancy by as much as 0.76 Å [19].

A plot of the dehydrogenation energies of all possible vacancy-pair structures, i.e. the structures with 2 unoccupied octahedral and/or tetrahedral interstitial sites per unit cell vs the vacancy–vacancy distance is shown in figure 12. The most stable vacancy pair is the one consisting of two vacant octahedral sites at the nearest-neighbour distance of 3.94 Å [20]. As expected from the experimentally observed insulating nature of the compound, a gap is present in the band structure of this model, which is shown in figure 13. Partial electron densities for the first two bands below the Fermi energy are displayed in figure 14. These two

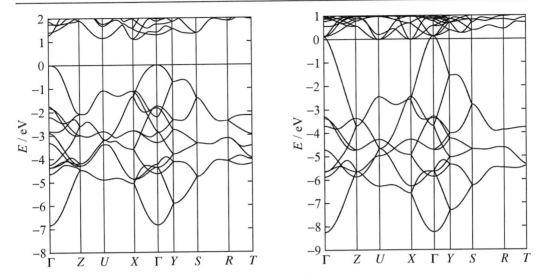

Figure 11. Electronic band structures (VASP) of LaH_3 (unit cell La_4H_{12}) along high-symmetry directions through the Brillouin zone corresponding to the orthorhombic primitive Bravais lattice [80]. Left: *Pnma* structure. Right: $D0_3$ structure with orthorhombic setup of the unit cell equivalent to the *Pnma* structure (see table 7). The energy is measured relative to the Fermi energy.

bands mainly correspond to the d states of the La atoms next to the vacant octahedral sites forming bonds across the vacancies. A band gap has been found also for the energetically less favourable $La_{32}H_{31}^{oct}H_{63}^{tet}$ structures and for some $La_{32}H_{32}^{oct}H_{62}^{tet}$ structures [20].

4. Conclusion

In this chapter, we report on results from first-principles studies of the electronic, energetic, structural, and elastic properties of the stoichiometric and non-stoichiometric fluorite-type dihydrides of the rare-earth metals R = Sc, Y, La, and Lu. Besides, the properties of stoichiometric and hypostoichiometric trihydride of La are taken into consideration.

The computed formation energies of the stoichiometric dihydrides are exothermic and lie between -2.2 eV for Y and -2.0 eV for La and Lu.

The elastic properties have been calculated for the stoichiometric dihydrides as well as for cubic $RH_{1.75}$ and $RH_{2.25}$. The bulk moduli increase with increasing H concentration and with decreasing atomic radius of R. Band structures, densities of states, and partial electron densities have been employed in order to get a better understanding of the chemical bonding in the stoichiometric dihydrides. The investigated compounds show close similarities in their electronic properties. The states making up the band crossing the Fermi energy correspond to $e_g–e_g$ interactions between second-neighbour R atoms and $t_{2g}–t_{2g}$ interactions between nearest-neighbour R atoms. H s states only contribute to the states of the two lower bands. The partial electron densities corresponding to the energy range of these bands demonstrate bonding H–H and R–H interactions. Possible ordering tendencies in the hypostoichiometric and hyperstoichiometric dihydrides and the energetics of non-stoichiometry

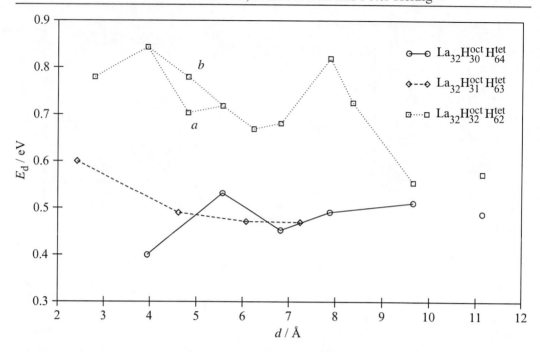

Figure 12. Dehydrogenation energies E_d for $La_{32}H^{oct}_{30}H^{tet}_{64}$, $La_{32}H^{oct}_{31}H^{tet}_{63}$, and $La_{32}H^{oct}_{32}H^{tet}_{62}$ vs the vacancy–vacancy distance d in the unrelaxed structures. For comparison, $2 \times E_d$ of $La_{32}H^{oct}_{31}H^{tet}_{64}$ (○) and $La_{32}H^{oct}_{32}H^{tet}_{63}$ (□) are added at $d = 11.14$ Å (pseudo-cubic lattice parameter). In the structures labelled as a and b, a La atom and a H^{oct} atom, respectively, lie at the center between the two tetrahedral vacancies 4.82 Å apart.

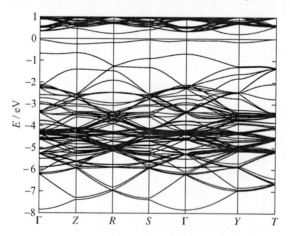

Figure 13. Electronic band structure (VASP) for $La_{32}H^{oct}_{30}H^{tet}_{64}$ with two octahedral vacancies 3.94 Å apart (space group $Cmmm$; the 126-atom unit cell is the primitive cell). The energy is measured relative to the Fermi energy. The Brillouin zone corresponds to the base-centered orthorhombic Bravais lattice, the path has been chosen according to reference 80. The band structure of this structure is plotted for a different path through the Brillouin zone in reference 20 (Bravais lattice erroneously called orthorhombic *primitive*).

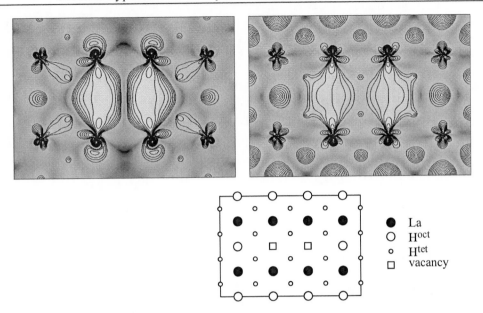

Figure 14. Contour maps of partial electron densities (FLAPW) in the (110) plane for $La_{32}H_{30}^{oct}H_{64}^{tet}$ with a vacancy–vacancy distance of 3.94 Å. Left: energy range of the first band below the Fermi energy. Right: energy range of the second band. Contour lines are shown for the densities $n_i = n_0 \times 2^{i/2}$. n_0 has been chosen so that $n_0 \times \Omega = 20\ e$, where Ω is the volume of the unit cell. The superimposed grey shadings may help to discern the areas of higher density (lighter grey areas) due to the La–La bonds across the vacancies. The positions of the atoms and the vacancies in the (110) plane are shown in the sketch below. An analogous figure appears in reference 20.

have been examined by means of numerous model structures derived from supercells of the conventional fluorite-type unit cells with up to four defect sites (additional H atoms at octahedral sites or vacant tetrahedral sites). The dehydrogenation of RH_2 is endothermic. The formation of a hydrogen vacancy leads to a destabilization by 1.2–1.4 eV. On the other hand, hydrogenation of RH_2 is exothermic. The insertion of an additional H atom is connected with reaction energies between -0.51 eV ($R = $ La) and -0.13 eV ($R = $ Sc). Defect structures with a vacant tetrahedral site and a H atom at an octahedral site are destabilized by 0.9–1.1 eV with respect to the fluorite structure. An accumulation of certain structure elements has been observed for the relatively stabilized defect clusters in the hypostoichiometric and hyperstoichiometric dihydrides. The energetic impact of defect ordering is far more pronounced in the case of LaH_{2-x} than in the case of the other investigated non-stoichiometric dihydrides. The energy of a particular LaH_{2-x} structure relative to other structures with the same hydrogen content is determined by the number of pairs of vacancies grouped around central La atoms. For stoichiometric LaH_3 an orthorhombic structure has been found that is energetically and vibrationally stable in contrast to the cubic $D0_3$-type structure. The band structure of the orthorhombically distorted structure exhibits a gap. Pairs of vacant octahedral interstitial sites at the shortest possible distance have turned out to be energetically favourable defect configurations in hypostoichiometric trihydride of La.

The presence of these vacancy pairs goes along with the occurrence of a band gap. Also various other pair configurations lead to the opening of a gap.

Acknowledgments

The authors wish to thank Walter Wolf and Peter Vajda for many stimulating discussions. The support by the Austrian Science Fund FWF (Project Nos. P19205-N19 and P22252-N19) is gratefully acknowledged. Parts of the calculations have been performed on the Vienna Scientific Cluster (VSC).

References

[1] Y. Fukai, *The Metal–Hydrogen System*, Springer, Berlin, 2nd edition, 2005.

[2] W. Wolf and P. Herzig, J. Phys.: Condens. Matter 12, 4535 (2000).

[3] H. Kohlmann and K. Yvon, J. Alloys Compd. 299, L16 (2000).

[4] B. Lebech, N. Hessel Andersen, S. Steenstrup, and A. Schrøder Pedersen, Acta Cryst. C 39, 1475 (1983).

[5] A. Pebler and W. E. Wallace, J. Phys. Chem. 66, 148 (1962).

[6] P. Vajda, *Hydrogen in Rare-Earth Metals, Including RH$_{2+x}$ Phases*, in: K. A. Gschneidner, Jr. and L. Eyring, editors, *Handbook on the Physics and Chemistry of Rare Earths*, vol. 20, ch. 137, Elsevier, Amsterdam, 1995.

[7] M. Mansmann and W. E. Wallace, J. Phys. (Paris) 25, 454 (1964).

[8] P. J. Kelly, J. P. Dekker, and R. Stumpf, Phys. Rev. Lett. 78, 1315 (1997).

[9] J. J. Balbach, M. S. Conradi, M. M. Hoffmann, T. J. Udovic, and N. L. Adolphi, Phys. Rev. B 58, 14823 (1998).

[10] H. Kierey, M. Rode, A. Jacob, A. Borgschulte, and J. Schoenes, Phys. Rev. B 63, 134109 (2001).

[11] O. J. Żogał et al., Phys. Rev. B 64, 214110 (2001).

[12] G. Schöllhammer, *First-principles Studies of the Binary Hydrogen System of Lanthanum and the Binary hydrogen Systems of Other Selected Rare-earth Metals*, Doctoral Thesis, University of Vienna, 2010.

[13] T. Palasyuk and M. Tkacz, Solid State Commun. 141, 354 (2007).

[14] A. Ohmura et al., J. Alloys Compd. 446–447, 598 (2007).

[15] A. Ohmura et al., Phys. Rev. B 73, 104105 (2006).

[16] T. Kume et al., Phys. Rev. B 76, 024107 (2007).

[17] T. Kume et al., Phys. Rev. B 84, 064132 (2011).

[18] P. Fischer, W. Hälg, L. Schlapbach, and K. Yvon, J. Less-Common Met. 60, 1 (1978).

[19] G. Renaudin, K. Yvon, W. Wolf, and P. Herzig, J. Alloys Compd. 404–406, 55 (2005).

[20] G. Schöllhammer, W. Wolf, P. Herzig, K. Yvon, and P. Vajda, J. Alloys Compd. 480, 111 (2009).

[21] R. G. Barnes, C. T. Chang, G. Majer, and U. Kaess, J. Alloys Compd. 356–357, 137 (2003).

[22] J. N. Huiberts et al., Nature (London) 380, 231 (1996).

[23] J. N. Huiberts et al., J. Alloys Compd. 239, 158 (1996).

[24] R. Griessen et al., J. Alloys Compd. 253–254, 44 (1997).

[25] D. G. Nagengast, J. W. J. Kerssemakers, A. T. M. van Gogh, B. Dam, and R. Griessen, Appl. Phys. Lett. 75, 1724 (1999).

[26] A. Remhof and A. Borgschulte, Eur. J. Chem. Phys. Phys. Chem. 9, 2440 (2008).

[27] A. Machida, T. Watanuki, D. Kawana, and K. Aoki, Phys. Rev. B 83, 054103 (2011).

[28] G. Schöllhammer, P. Herzig, W. Wolf, P. Vajda, and K. Yvon, Phys. Rev. B 84, 094122 (2011).

[29] A. C. Switendick, Solid State Commun. 8, 1463 (1970).

[30] A. C. Switendick, Int. J. Quantum Chem. 5, 459 (1971).

[31] A. T. M. van Gogh et al., Phys. Rev. B 63, 195105 (2001).

[32] M. Gupta, Solid State Commun. 27, 1355 (1978).

[33] M. Gupta and J. P. Burger, Phys. Rev. B 22, 6074 (1980).

[34] R. Sen Gupta and S. Chatterjee, J. Phys. F: Met. Phys. 13, 639 (1983).

[35] D. J. Peterman, J. H. Weaver, and D. T. Peterson, Phys. Rev. B 23, 3903 (1981).

[36] D. K. Misemer and B. N. Harmon, Phys. Rev. B 26, 5634 (1982).

[37] J. P. Dekker, J. van Ek, A. Lodder, and J. N. Huiberts, J. Phys.: Condens. Matter 5, 4805 (1993).

[38] K. K. Ng, F. C. Zhang, V. I. Anisimov, and T. M. Rice, Phys. Rev. Lett. 78, 1311 (1997).

[39] K. K. Ng, F. C. Zhang, V. I. Anisimov, and T. M. Rice, Phys. Rev. B 59, 5398 (1999).

[40] R. Eder, H. F. Pen, and G. A. Sawatzky, Phys. Rev. B 56, 10115 (1997).

[41] P. van Gelderen, P. J. Kelly, and G. Brocks, Phys. Rev. B 63, 100301 (2001).

[42] T. Miyake, F. Aryasetiawan, H. Kino, and K. Terakura, Phys. Rev. B 61, 16491 (2000).

[43] P. van Gelderen, P. A. Bobbert, P. J. Kelly, and G. Brocks, Phys. Rev. Lett. 85, 2989 (2000).

[44] P. van Gelderen, P. A. Bobbert, P. J. Kelly, G. Brocks, and R. Tolboom, Phys. Rev. B 66, 075104 (2002).

[45] W. Wolf and P. Herzig, Phys. Rev. B 66, 224112 (2002).

[46] W. Wolf and P. Herzig, J. Alloys Comp. 356–357, 73 (2003).

[47] J. A. Alford, M. Y. Chou, E. K. Chang, and S. G. Louie, Phys. Rev. B 67, 125110 (2003).

[48] E. K. Chang, X. Blase, and S. G. Louie, Phys. Rev. B 64, 155108 (2001).

[49] Z. Wu, R. E. Cohen, D. J. Singh, R. Gupta, and M. Gupta, Phys. Rev. B 69, 085104 (2004).

[50] A.-M. Racu and J. Schoenes, Phys. Rev. Lett. 96, 017401 (2006).

[51] F. Karsai, *First-principles Investigations of the Dihydrides of Scandium, Yttrium, Lanthanum, and Lutetium*, Master Thesis, University of Vienna, 2011.

[52] F. Karsai, G. Schöllhammer, W. Wolf, and P. Herzig, in preparation.

[53] G. Kresse and J. Hafner, Phys. Rev. B 47, 558 (1993).

[54] G. Kresse and J. Hafner, Phys. Rev. B 49, 14251 (1994).

[55] G. Kresse and J. Furthmüller, Phys. Rev. B 54, 11169 (1996).

[56] G. Kresse and J. Furthmüller, Comput. Mater. Sci 6, 15 (1996).

[57] P. Hohenberg and W. Kohn, Phys. Rev. 136, B864 (1964).

[58] W. Kohn and L. J. Sham, Phys. Rev. 140, A1133 (1965).

[59] P. E. Blöchl, Phys. Rev. B 50, 17953 (1994).

[60] G. Kresse and D. Joubert, Phys. Rev. B 59, 1758 (1999).

[61] J. P. Perdew et al., Phys. Rev. B 46, 6671 (1992).

[62] J. P. Perdew, K. Burke, and M. Ernzerhof, Phys. Rev. Lett. 77, 3865 (1996).

[63] H. J. Monkhorst and J. D. Pack, Phys. Rev. B 13, 5188 (1976).

[64] M. Methfessel and A. T. Paxton, Phys. Rev. B 40, 3616 (1989).

[65] D. D. Koelling and G. O. Arbman, J. Phys. F: Metal Phys. 5, 2041 (1975).

[66] E. Wimmer, H. Krakauer, M. Weinert, and A. J. Freeman, Phys. Rev. B 24, 864 (1981).

[67] H. J. F. Jansen and A. J. Freeman, Phys. Rev. B 30, 561 (1984).

[68] B. I. Min, T. Oguchi, H. J. F. Jansen, and A. J. Freeman, J. Magn. Mat. 54-57, 1091 (1986).

[69] L. Hedin and B. I. Lundqvist, J. Phys. C: Solid St. Phys. 4, 2064 (1971).

[70] L. Hedin and S. Lundqvist, J. Phys. Colloques (Paris) 33, C3–73 (1972).

[71] O. Jepsen and O. K. Andersen, Solid State Commun. 9, 1763 (1971).

[72] G. Lehmann and M. Taut, Phys. Status Solidi (b) 54, 469 (1972).

[73] I. O. Bashkin, E. G. Ponyatovskii, and M. E. Kost, Phys. Status Solidi (b) 87, 369 (1978).

[74] J. N. Daou and P. Vajda, Phys. Rev. B 45, 10907 (1992).

[75] P. Klavins, R. N. Shelton, R. G. Barnes, and B. J. Beaudry, Phys. Rev. B 29, 5349 (1984).

[76] J. E. Bonnet and J. N. Daou, J. Appl. Phys. 48, 964 (1977).

[77] P. Dantzer and O. J. Kleppa, J. Solid State Chem. 35, 34 (1980).

[78] R. Stadler et al., Phys. Rev. B 54, 1729 (1996).

[79] J. F. Nye, *Physical Properties of Crystals*, Clarendon Press, Oxford, 1957.

[80] C. J. Bradley and A. P. Cracknell, *The mathematical theory of symmetry in solids*, Clarendon Press, Oxford, 1972.

[81] A. C. Switendick, Z. Phys. Chem. Neue Folge 117, 89 (1979).

[82] T. J. Udovic, Q. Huang, J. J. Rush, J. Schefer, and I. S. Anderson, Phys. Rev. B 51, 12116 (1995).

[83] T. J. Udovic, Q. Huang, and J. J. Rush, J. Solid State Chem. 122, 151 (1996).

In: Properties of Fluorite Structure Materials
Editors: Peter Vajda and Jean-Marc Costantini

ISBN: 978-1-62417-458-2
© 2013 Nova Science Publishers, Inc.

Chapter 2

RARE EARTH (AND ACTINIDE) DIHYDRIDES: STRUCTURAL, ELECTRONIC AND MAGNETIC PROPERTIES

Peter Vajda[*]

Laboratoire des Solides Irradiés, Ecole Polytechnique,
Palaiseau, France

ABSTRACT

After the presentation of a typical R-H phase diagram, we are specifying the CaF_2-type cubic β-phase dihydride and its eventual extension into the overstoichiometric range, RH_{2+x}, with R = Sc, Y, and the lanthanides from La through Lu. Lattice parameters are given for all systems at room temperature, showing (*a*) the lanthanide contraction with increasing atomic number, Z; (*b*) the contraction with increasing overstoichiometry, x; (*c*) the decrease of the maximum β-phase range, x_{max}, with increasing Z. Significant effects upon all properties - manifest as anomalies in resistivity, lattice parameter, etc - are observed, caused by sublattice ordering of the octahedral H_o, x, atoms leading to a tetragonal distortion of the cubic lattice, with various possible ordered structures. All our systems are analyzed in the interesting temperature range and discussed as a function of x, in particular with regard to the high-T metal-semiconductor (M-S) and the low-T S-M transitions. The magnetic (FM and/or AF) properties of these 4f- systems are described in detail both as a function of x and of T. Strong influence of the order/disorder situation in the x-sublattice upon magnetism is observed. Finally, we shall also present the few data available of the cubic actinide dihydrides, AH_{2+x}, A = Np, Pu, Am...

INTRODUCTION

The fifteen elements of the 4f-group from La[57] through Lu[71] - or lanthanides - which are forming with their light analogs Sc[21] and Y[39] the family of rare earths, possess a rather strong affinity to hydrogen.

---

[*] E-mail: peter.vajda@polytechnique.edu.

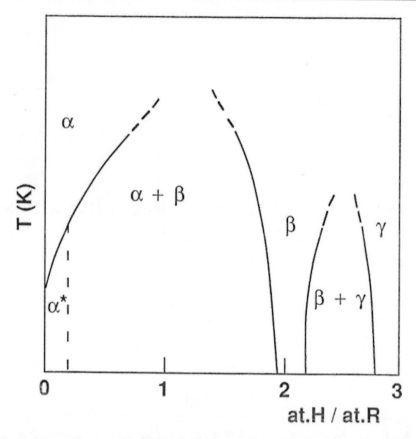

Figure 1. Typical phase diagram of a trivalent R-H system showing the principal phases and their existence ranges: α - solid solution, β - dihydride, γ - trihydride.

They absorb it easily (exothermally) under favorable (P,T) conditions and exhibit for these principally trivalent metals a phase diagram of the type presented in Figure 1. (A rather complete description of the R-H systems up to 1995 had been given by the author in the review [1].)

This phase diagram shows generally three single-phase areas: solid solution or α-RH$_x$ phase, dihydride or β-RH$_{2\pm x}$ phase, and trihydride or γ-RH$_{3-x}$ phase, with sometimes broad regions around the stoichiometric compositions. The solid solution possesses by definition the crystal structure of the metal, which is (with a few exceptions) either hexagonal or double hexagonal close packed; the β-dihydride is in most cases a cubic fluorite (with the H atoms occupying ideally all tetrahedral (t) sites; the trihydride is either again (in most cases) hexagonal close packed or an extension of the cubic β-phase where a third H atom is inserted without phase change into a free octahedral (o) site, in addition to the two t-site hydrogens. It is, therefore, the β-phase with its eventual extensions which shall concern us here as representative of a fluorite-type material. Though interesting as such and exhibiting, for example, exciting ordering phenomena, we shall avoid treating the two hexagonal phases α and γ for the sake of coherence and orient the reader towards specific rare-earth literature.

The chapter will be organized in three main parts:

1. *Structural properties*, with special consideration of the often broad non-stoichiometry, β-RH$_{2\pm x}$; also including new unexpected behavior of thin-film material;
2. *Electronic properties,* stressing the unique metallic character of these fluorites (as compared with the usually ionic compounds of the group) and the related metal-semiconductor transitions;
3. *Magnetic properties*, originating from the 4f-character of the rare earth electrons, underlining the strong influence of H non-stoichiometry upon the magnetic interactions.

Some mention will be made, in the two latter parts, of trivalent hydrides of early actinides whose 5f-electrons and metallic character yield analogies with the rare earth hydrides. (The review [2] summarizes early data on this little studied subject.)

1. STRUCTURAL PROPERTIES

The concentrational limits of the pure β-phase in the phase diagram of Figure 1 are both material- and element specific.

Thus, it was found that metallic and other impurities had a tendency to expand the phase boundaries leading to artificially broad hydride phase regions, extending e.g. between 1.8 H/R and 2.3 H/R in the case of 99.9% (3N) pure Y and Lu, while 99.99% (4N) material exhibited lower boundaries close to the stoichiometric value of 1.97 - 1.99 (the lighter lanthanides reaching often exactly 2.00 $\pm$ 1%); the upper boundary was then element specific and depended on the ionic radius reflecting i.a. the lanthanide contraction.

We have collected in Table I the lattice parameters and the upper phase boundaries at room temperature for the purest available material in well-annealed preferably bulk form.

These conditions are important to avoid uncontrolled o-site occupation, such as claiming for example RH$_{2.10}$ as a dihydride with 10% octahedral sites when, in reality, it would contain 15% occupied o-sites with a lower phase boundary at 1.95 H/R, i.e. being rather RH$_{1.95+0.15}$. (As we shall see below, the precise knowledge of the true octahedral x-concentration in RH$_{2+x}$ is essential for the correct interpretation of the electronic and magnetic behavior of the hydrides.)

The values in Table I have been taken over from ref. [1] in most cases, unless more recent reliable data have become available, where the corresponding reference is indicated. (When treating results from neutron scattering experiments we have often to deal with deuterides, not hydrides: possible isotope dependent variations are therefore mentioned.).

Table I. Lattice parameters at 300 K of β-RH(D)$_{2+x}$ hydrides at the boundaries, x = 0 and x = x$_{max}$

R	x in H(D)$_o$/R	a in Å	ref., comment
Sc	0	4.784	[1] no x on o-sites at normal pressure
	0	4.7833	[3]
	0D	4.7706	[3]
Y	0	5.2095	[1]
	0D	5.1996	[1]
	0.10	5.2056	[1]
	0.10D*	5.1954	[4] * corrected extrapol. value
La	0	5.6698	[5]
	1.0	5.616*	[1] * extrapolated
	0D	5.650*	[1] * extrapolated
	1.0D	5.6064	[1]
Ce	0	5.581	[1]
	1.0	5.535*	[6] * extrapolated
	0D	5.580*	[7] * extrapolated
	1.0D	5.531*	[1] * extrapolated
Pr	0	5.518	[1]
	1.0	5.490*	[8] * extrapolated
	0D	5.505	[1]
	1.0D	5.480*	[8] * extrapolated
Nd	0	5.4689	[5]
	0.67	5.4486	[9]
	0D	5.455	[1]
	0.67D	5.4324	[9]
Pm	0	*	* no studies on the Pm-H system with this unstable element
Sm	0	5.3773	[1]
	0.45	5.3521	[1]
	0D	5.365	[1]
	0.40D	5.3400	[1]
Eu	> 0.2 *	5.211*	[9a] * under high pressure, see text
Gd	0	5.3022	[5]
	0.3	5.290*	[10] * extrapolated
Tb	0	5.2485	[1]
	0.24	5.2380	[1]
Dy	0	5.2060	[5]
	0.23	5.199*	[5] * interpolated
	0.23D	5.1884	[4]
Ho	0	5.165	[1]
	0D	5.155	[11]
	0.12D	5.1505	[11]
Er	0	5.1290	[5]
	0D	5.116	[12]
	0.10D	5.1140*	[4] * extrapolated
Tm	0	5.0925	[5]
	0.06D	5.0808*	[4] * extrapolated
Yb	0.5*	5.192	[1] * the divalent Yb forms CaF$_2$ type
	0.7	5.178	[1] dihydrides only above x ~ 0.5;
	0.5D	5.182	[1] see text
	0.7D*	5.1697	[13]
Lu	0	5.0338	[5]
	0D	5.022	[5]
	0.03D	5.0218	[4]

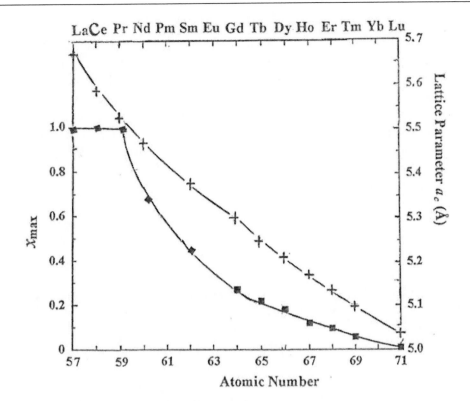

LaCe Pr Nd Pm Sm Eu Gd Tb Dy Ho Er Tm Yb Lu

Figure 2. Lattice parameters, a, of the pure dihydrides, RH_2, and the limiting concentration of the β-phase, x_{max}, in RH_{2+x}, from Table I vs atomic number Z of the metal (modified, after [4]).

From the data in Table I we can deduce several general observations:

(a) An overall trend of decreasing lattice parameter with increasing atomic number; this is the well-known phenomenon of the "lanthanide contraction" where the gradual filling of the 4f-shell (with a net break at half filled Gd) leads to a reduced nuclear repulsion and smaller ionic radius. This tendency - clearly visible in Figure 2 - is equally true for the size variation of the limiting concentration x_{max} of the β-phase.

(b) When adding octahedral hydrogens, x, into the stoichiometric dihydride, RH_2, giving RH_{2+x}, one observes another *de*crease of the lattice parameter, which seems at first somewhat surprising, in view of the presence of additional interstitial impurity material. The reason for that is mainly electronic and related to the rather ionic nature of the H_o interaction with the metal lattice. This effect as well as the trend for a decreasing extension of the pure β-phase (decreasing x_{max}) have been attributed by Renaudin et al. [8] to an increasing competition between the energy gain due to R-H bond shortening and the energy loss due to repulsive H-H interactions.

(c) Where measured one can note a weak isotope effect on the lattice parameter: the deuterides exhibit, for the same concentrations, a somewhat smaller value than the hydrides. The greater mass of the deuterium atoms results in smaller vibration amplitudes and less expansion.

(d) An interesting phenomenon is the rather general observation of a kind of "normalization" of the often strongly varying properties of the elements, when hydrided. Thus, the double hcp La, Pr, Nd and the triple hcp Sm as well as the fcc Ce and the simple hcp heavy lanthanides Gd through Lu all possess a fcc CaF_2-type structure in the dihydride phase. The same "normalization" concerns also their valence state. The tetravalent Ce, the mixed two to three- valent Sm, Tb, Tm turn fully trivalent as hydrides; the divalent Yb hesitates until ~ 2.5 H/R before normalizing and only the bcc Eu remains steadily divalent up to the end and behaves more like its alkaline earth neighbor Ba. (Very recent - see [9a] - synchrotron X-ray diffraction and Mössbauer experiments on the Eu-H system at very high pressure have finally established its simultaneous conversion into a trivalent element with an fcc fluorite-type structure of the dihydride.)

Until now, we had limited our discussion to the room-temperature properties of the RH_{2+x} hydrides, considering a full (2H/R) tetrahedral occupation with a statistical distribution of the octahedral overstoichiometric x-atoms, H_o. It was soon discovered, however, that these x-atoms had, with lowering temperature, the tendency to interact and to form superlattices of lower symmetry manifesting themselves for example as anomalies in various physical properties. In what follows, we shall present several typical examples of such superlattices from various RH_{2+x} systems describing and characterizing their interaction.

1.1: Among the earliest manifestations of a hydrogen superlattice, already at room temperature, was the tetragonal distortion of the cubic lattice observed in $CeD_{2.26}$ and $CeD_{2.43}$ through superlattice reflections in their neutron diffraction spectra [14]. They could be characterized as unit cells of the type Ce_4D (space group I4/mmm, Strukturberichte symbol $D0_{22}$) and Ce_2D ($I4_1md$), respectively.

1.2: The system Y-H has drawn much attention, during the past decade, because of its detailed investigations as precursor material for the "switchable mirrors" (SWIMs, see also later), where Huiberts and coworkers [15] had succeeded to produce stable thin films in the whole range YH_2 - YH_3 of this otherwise extremely brittle material by simultaneous deposition of a protective and H-transparent Pd layer. This offered the possibility to use various optical and spectroscopic techniques, in addition to the classical X-ray and resistivity studies. Thus, the range of the pure β-phase in the Y-H system could be extended [16] from 2.10 H/Y to nearly 3 by alloying with La, such as $La_{1-z}Y_zH_x$ and $0 < z < 0.67$, producing a kind of pseudo-yttrium trihydride in the β-phase and enabling the continuous optical observation without structural modification.

In this context, it had earlier been remarked in resistivity studies [17] of the YH_{2+x} β-phase, with $0 \leq x \leq 0.10$, that specimens with x-values from 0.05 on, $x \geq 0.05$, exhibited an anomaly near 150 - 160 K which, for increasing x, not just increased in amplitude but also developed into a more complex phenomenon, with a second anomaly above ~ 200 K. In Figure 3 are plotted the resistivity derivatives (for a better visibility) in the interesting temperature range showing clearly this evolution with x-concentration. It seemed tempting, already at that time, to interpret the resistivity anomalies as due to structural modifications of the octahedral x-sublattice, namely attributing the first peak (at lower T and for smaller x) to short-range (SRO) and the second peak (at higher T and appearing for higher x) to long-range ordering of the originally disordered phase at room temperature. (A first indication into this direction came from quench experiments across the anomaly region, which had strongly emphasized the "annealing" order-disorder process.)

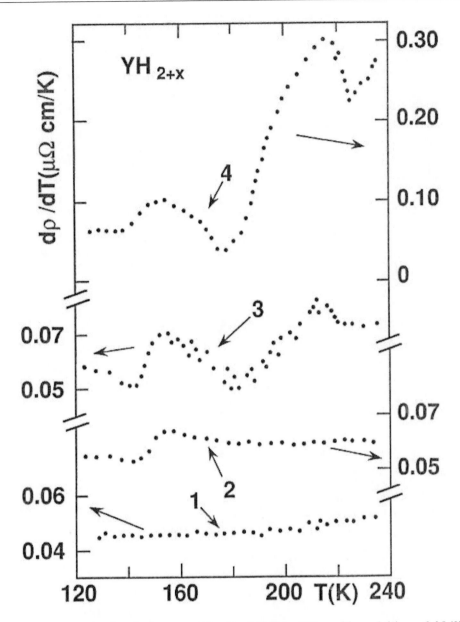

Figure 3. Resistivity derivatives in the range 120 < T < 240 K for YH_{2+x} with x = 0 (1), x = 0.05 (2), x = 0.085 (3), x = 0.095 (4), with two anomalies responsible for SRO (at 155 K) and LRO (at 215 K), respectively (from [17]).

Later Raman spectroscopic investigations [18] of $\beta YH(D)_{2+x}$ had related the splitting of an active fcc mode at 150 K to the beginning H mobility in the SRO superlattice. Further optical spectroscopy studies by the same group [19] had not only attributed the second peak to an order-disorder transformation in the LRO x-superlattice but also connected it directly to the metal-insulator transition observed for x-values close to x_{max} (see [17] and below). These and results obtained with other superstoichiometric systems had stimulated computer simulation studies [20] of possible electron diffraction patterns when applied to several ordered structures within the RH_{2+x} β-phase, with R = Y or Ho, for $0 \leq x \leq 0.25$ (Figure 4).

Name	f.c.c.	D1	D1$_a$	D0$_{22}$
(100) projection	*(atomic site diagram)*	*(atomic site diagram)*	*(atomic site diagram)*	*(atomic site diagram)*
Space group	$Fm\bar{3}m$	$Fm\bar{3}m$	$I4/m$	$I4/mmm$
x (concentration)	0	0.125	0.2	0.25

Figure 4. Calculated ordered structures in $(Y,Ho)H_{2+x}$ as considered for electron diffraction experiments. Large circles are sites on the top (100) plane, small circles are those on adjacent planes shifted by a/2; filled and empty circles are filled and empty sites (from [20]).

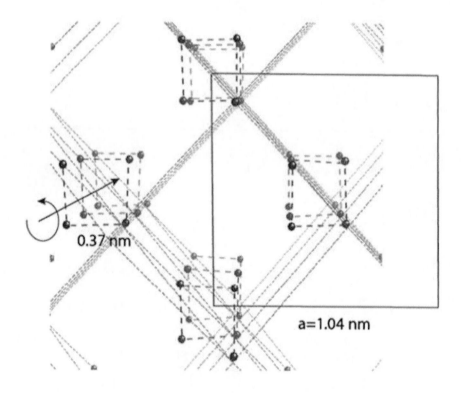

Figure 5. Schematic drawing of the 6010 triclinic (pseudo-cubic) structure as observed by TEM of $YH_{2.0625}$ (with only the H_o atoms shown) where the x-atoms form spiral chains (from [21]).

Not only they confirmed the earlier observed [14] structures of the type $D0_{22}$ in $CeD_{2.26}$ and suggested in other systems (see below) but they also proposed to assign other superlattices such as D1 for $RH_{2.125}$ (Fm-3m) and D1$_a$ for $RH_{2.2}$ (I4/m) as candidates for future discovery. It was, therefore, a quite exciting result when transmission electron microscopy experiments on βYH_{2+x} combined with first-principle calculations [21] permitted to attribute the observed diffraction patterns to either the cubic (in principle, here unstable) I-centered $YH_{2.375}$ or rather to the triclinic (ground state) of $YH_{2.0625}$ (Figure 5). The latter would not only fill the empty case in Grier's graph (Figure 4) between the "pure" dihydride $RH_{2.0}$ and $RH_{2.125}$ but would represent a strong encouragement for the understanding of all other earlier LRO manifestations.

1.3: Because of its relative stability and early availability as 4N pure material, β-$TbH(D)_{2+x}$ had been investigated rather thoroughly before many other R-H systems.

Thus, resistivity anomalies similar to those in the above described YH_{2+x} had been observed already in 1987 for $x \geq 0.2$ and related to structural ordering phenomena [22]. The temperature range and the form of the anomalies [23] (Figure 6) recalled very much those in YH_{2+x} [17] and had, therefore, inspired a specific study for its characterization.

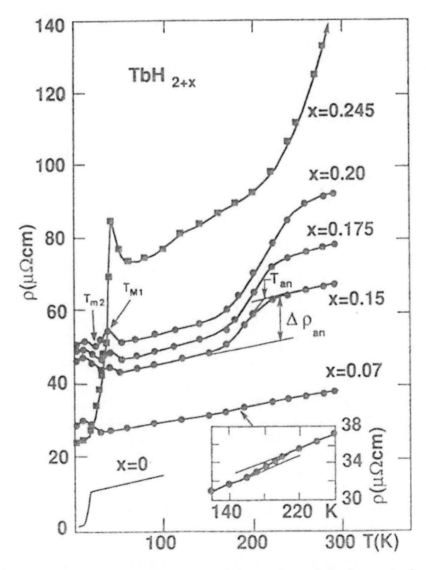

Figure 6. T-dependence of the resistivity for various TbH_{2+x} specimens, indicating structural and magnetic anomalies and their evolution with x; the inset is an enlarged view for x = 0.07 [23].

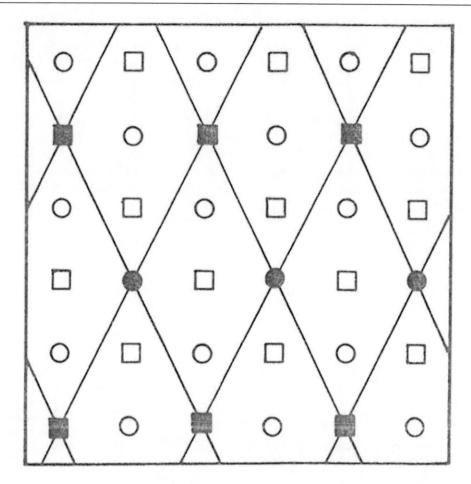

Figure 7. The $D0_{22}$ structure shown in a (200) projection as determined for TbD_{2+x} by neutron scattering; only the o-sites are shown, filled signs are occupied sites (from [24]).

A neutron scattering investigation [24] of $TbD_{2.18}$ yielded clear evidence of T-dependent deuterium ordering below ~ 250 K of the type $D0_{22}$ (Figure 7) - i.e. a $TbD_{2.25}$ stoichiometry with vacancies. A subsequent refined neutron diffraction study of $TbD_{2.25}$ at 70 K [25] had confirmed the above data and their analysis but added, as new evidence, a slight tetragonal distortion of the metal lattice, which had not been visible in the earlier experiment, accompanied by an expansion of the cubic ensemble of the t-site deuterium atoms (Figure 8).

1.4: For the sake of completeness, we wish to mention here another superlattice of the type I4/m, which was found in the $SmH(D)_{2+x}$ system by X-ray diffraction [26]. This corresponds to a composition $Sm_3H(D)_7$ or $SmH(D)_{2.33}$ which is a new symmetry situation among the rest of the R dihydrides. Later proton NMR studies [27] of SmH_{2+x} ($0 \leq x \leq 0.40$) had revealed a double-line structure of the spectra for $SmH_{2.30}$ and $SmH_{2.40}$ below 250 K, together with a small tetragonal distortion, probably indicating the mentioned H-sublattice ordering.

1.5: Thin film materials. The field of thin films within the hydride materials had experienced very rapid growth since 1995 when - as already mentioned above - the group at Amsterdam had succeeded to prepare the first solid stable films of Y hydride [15] through the whole x-range up to the trihydride.

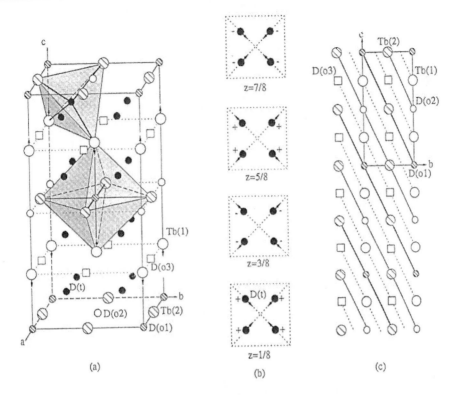

Figure 8. (a) Schematic of the $TbD_{2.25}$ structure showing c-axis displacements of some Tb atoms; (b) displacements of the tetrahedral D_t atoms from their ideal sites; (c) series of (042) planes comprising the octahedral D_o sublattice (no t-sites drawn). (From [25]).

Several reviews have been consecrated, one of the more recent ones e.g. representing a chapter of 70 pages with 250 references in a book on hydrogen energy [28].

The selection in our case will be limited to specific interesting (possibly occurring) structural phenomena and deal with properties and/or methods accessible to thin film materials, overlapping in part with the section on Electronic Properties below, where most of the metal-insulator transitions in the SWIMs will be treated.

When studying the pressure-composition deposition mechanics of Y hydride films on sapphire (Al_2O_3) or on amorphous SiO_2 Remhof and coworkers [29] noticed giant hysteresis effects between loading and unloading, which were first attributed to structural phase transitions. Adding optical transmission and electrical resistivity isotherms showed that the hysteresis effects were related to different stress states during loading and unloading between a low-concentration β-$YH_{1.9}$ and a high-concentration β-$YH_{2.1}$ phase (Figure 9).

This stress situation explained, on the one hand, the remarkable anisotropic expansion observed with the SWIMs grown on CaF_2 [30] and also enabled, on the other hand, the growth of high-quality stress-free Y films on CaF_2 by avoiding a buffer layer [31]. The optical transparency of the SWIMs in the insulating state gave soon the idea to use them for visualization of hydrogen migration [32]. When an Y layer to be hydrogenated is superimposed in part by a Pd disk and then covered with a protective oxide layer, the diffusion of hydrogen as a function of time can be followed visually under exposure to H_2 pressure: the Pd window becoming within seconds the base for a transparent trihydride gives now rise, on its own, to clearly visible lateral diffusion into the surrounding metal.

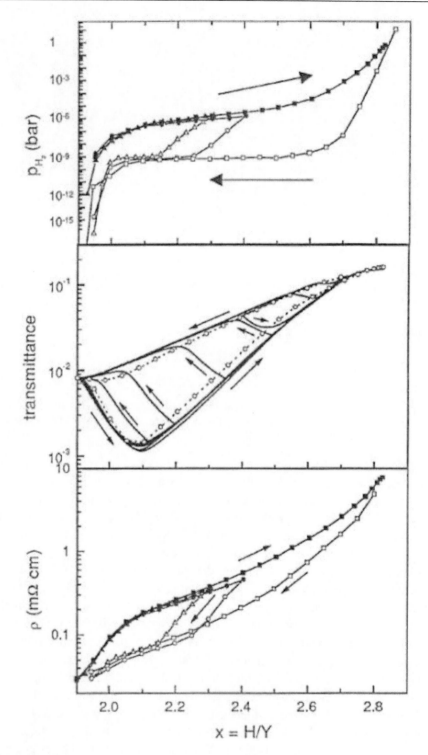

Figure 9. Hysteresis effects at room temperature in a thin film of the Y-H system: top panel - pressure-composition; middle panel - optical transmission of red light; bottom panel - electrical resistivity (from [29b]).

An electrochemical study of H diffusion in Y films has permitted to relate the time constants to effective diffusion coefficients [33] in the dihydride/trihydride concentration range, which was then the basis for the discovery of a new phenomenon: the refraction of diffusion fronts [34]. It was shown that H in a metal could be considered a model system for refraction- and reflection-like behavior of diffusion waves, with similarities to classical optics such as the applicability of Snell's law (Figure 10).

Finally, the application of high pressure to rare earth hydrides having led to a large number of data on new unexpected structural and electronic phenomena, a separate Chapter in this book seemed useful for their description.

2. ELECTRONIC PROPERTIES

As already mentioned in the Introduction, the rare earth metals, when absorbing hydrogen, transform from a trivalent metal to monovalent dihydride to insulating trihydride, the dihydride being a better metal than the elemental rare earth. This has been explained tentatively within the so-called hydridic model, where the electrons contributed by the hydrogen atoms form - together with the rare earth conduction electrons - deep lying bands below the Fermi level.Thus, in the dihydride, the two H electrons bound to two conduction electrons of the trivalent RE are forming a full band leaving us with an "ideal" single-electron Fermi surface of an "ideal" fcc crystal structure.

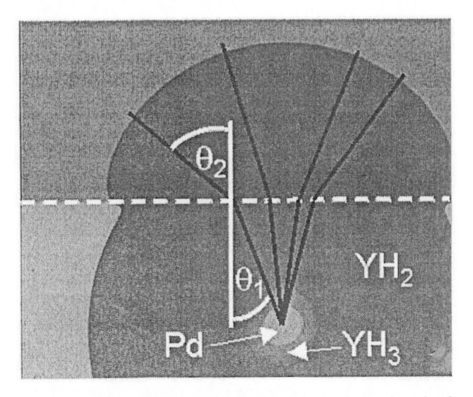

Figure 10. Evolution of the initially circular diffusion front of hydrogen when crossing an interface with different effective diffusivity (Y vs V), from [34].

(The possibilities of a theoretical treatment being rather favorable, the progress in recent years has permitted to consecrate an independent Chapter in this book to the subject.) On the other hand, the contribution of the eventual third H-atom on its octahedral interstitial site has a rather deleterious effect: its electron interacting more ionic-like with the metal lattice and reducing its carrier density makes the super-stoichiometric dihydride anew a bad conductor (worse than the pure dihydride) before turning it into an insulator (or semiconductor) with zero carrier density.

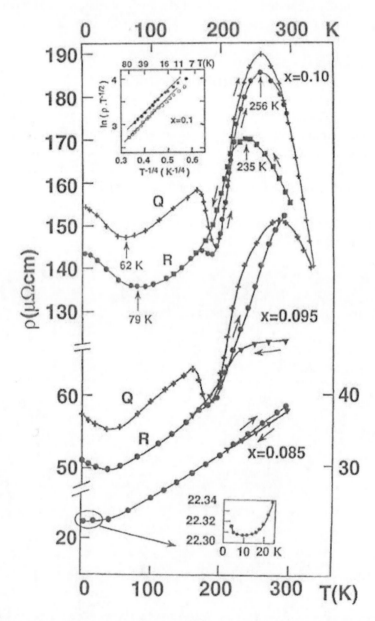

Figure 11. T-dependence of the resistivity for three YH_{2+x} samples in the relaxed (R) and in the quenched (Q) state showing the high-T M-S and the low-T S-M transitions. Upper inset: fit of the low-T part of the x = 0.10 sample in the form $\rho(T) \propto \exp(T/T_0)^{-1/4}$ (Mott mechanism) [17].

In the following, we shall present data on the electronic properties of several pure dihydrides (especially in the case of new data with regard to [1]) and their evolution with x in the super-stoichiometric RH_{2+x} compounds, specifying the interaction of an x-sublattice at lower temperatures. The eventual transition to an insulating state will be treated as a particular phenomenon.

2.1. Yttrium Hydride

It was already shown in the structural section above how the electrical resistivity data can be used (Figure 4) to observe and to characterize the order-disorder processes in YH_{2+x}. There, we had presented the temperature derivatives of measurements on a series of concentrations, x, through the whole pure β-phase range, showing the appearance of two anomalies, at 155 K and at 215 K, attributed to SRO and LRO in the octahedral H-sublattice. It is interesting to have the direct resistivities plotted up to the limiting β-phase concentration $x_{max} = 0.10$.

Figure 11 exhibits now, in addition to the already presented x = 0.085 and x = 0.095 specimens, the boundary concentration, both in the cooling and in the heating runs. A hysteresis, barely visible for x = 0.085, becomes overwhelming for x = 0.095, while the addition of just another 1/2 % of o-sites changes the whole physics. The basically unstable situation of the x-superlattice near room temperature, further destabilized by a quench across the ordering region, turns these weakly metallic samples completely semiconducting. We have here a phenomenon qualitatively different from the *concentration*-dependent M-S transformations observed e.g. in the SWIMs when, from a certain x-concentration on, the sample is semiconducting at *all temperatures*, just as a result of vanishing charge carriers. In our case, the M-S transition is *temperature* dependent and is caused by the breakdown of an ordered superlattice of octahedral x-atoms with increasing temperature.

This phenomenon reminds us of analogous processes noted earlier (Figure 12) on some understoichiometric trihydrides, RH_{3-x} (R = La, Ce), where M-S transitions were attributed to the breakdown of a superlattice of octahedral vacancies, V_o [36,37]. There, the phenomenon was interpreted through the formation, by the ordered superlattice, of a delocalized band below the Fermi energy, which, breaking down with increasing T, would create localized states in the gap losing the metallic conduction. The surprisingly low value for the critical superstoichiometry in the present case of YH_{2+x} stresses the prime role of the order-disorder mechanism as compared to the sole decreasing carrier density. The photoelectron spectra obtained by Hayoz et al. [31] showing a transparent insulating sample already for $YH_{2.3}$ could serve as a confirmation.

Finally, a few words concerning a completely unexpected phenomenon observed in Figure 11: the low-temperature S-M transition seen as flat minimum of the resistivity near 10 K for x = 0.085 and growing both in amplitude and position for the two higher concentrations. This second transition had not been noted in the earlier experiments with the H-rich light (La, Ce) rare earth hydrides because of the experimental difficulty of measuring such brittle samples at low T. After the discovery of the M-S transitions in other heavy rare earth systems (see below), this second, S-M, transition was equally well characterized and tentatively interpreted as due to a Mott mechanism of carrier scattering on atomic disorder of the excess H atoms. With the successful preparation of stable thin film specimens, the phenomenon could then be confirmed on both YH_{2+x} and other systems [38].

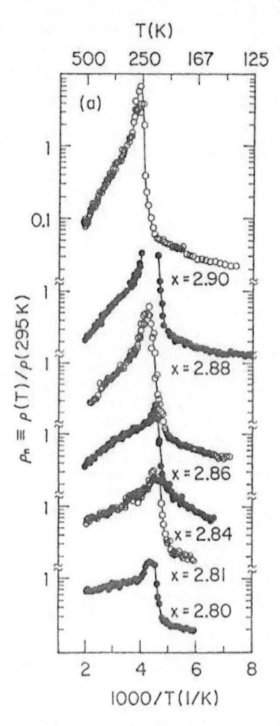

Figure 12. Normalized resistivity as a function of reciprocal temperature for various β–LaH$_x$ specimens, in the region of the metal-semiconductor transition [37].

2.2. Lanthanum Hydride

The electron density of states and the M-S transition can also be probed by magnetic resonance investigations. Thus, Barnes and coworkers [39] have studied the LaH_2 - LaH_3 system by proton and Gd^{3+} impurity ion spin-lattice relaxation as well as by ^{139}La NMR hyperfine interaction to arrive at following conclusions: (a) LaH_x is metallic at all temperatures for $x \leq 2.60$; (b) for $2.60 \leq x \leq 2.91$, LaH_x is metallic at low T and semiconducting at high T; (c) for $x \geq 2.91$, LaH_x is insulating at all T, compatible with the earlier findings (Figure 12).

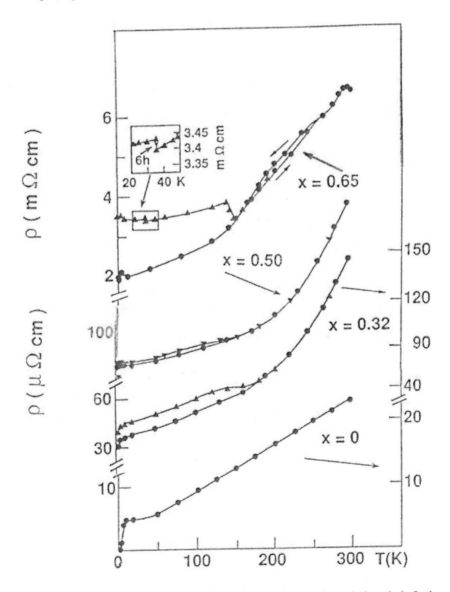

Figure 13. T-dependence of the resistivity for four NdH_{2+x} specimens, through the whole β-phase range, after slow cooling and after a quench from 300K. Note the hysteresis in the ordering region and the approach towards the M-S transition for the higher concentrations. The inset shows the effect of a 6 h anneal (the potential instability) of a quenched sample [42].

2.3. Neodymium Hydride

Recently, Renaudin et al. [40] have collected new data on a sample of $NdD_{2.27}$ and analyzed them by a joint refinement of neutron and synchrotron diffraction.

Contrary to the established belief (non-centrosymmetric space group $I4_1/md$), the structure was found centrosymmetric ($I4_1/amd$) and analogous to those of $CeD_{2.45}$ and $LaD_{2.50}$ [41] rather than to those of $LaD_{2.30}$, $CeD_{2.29}$ and $PrD_{2.37}$ (e.g. [1]). We have revisited the electrical measurements of β-NdH_{2+x} by Daou et al. [42] in the light of this new result and plotted several relevant concentrations in Figure 13.

One notes the appearance of structural ordering in the region of 150 K, strongly enhanced through the quenching procedure and the preparation of the M-S transition at 300 K for the largest concentration, x = 0.65, close to the phase boundary.

But most interesting is the plot of the $\rho(x)$ dependences in Figure 14 where one remarks, for the low-T isothermals, a clear minimum at x = 0.50, with ρ-values lower than for all other x > 0.

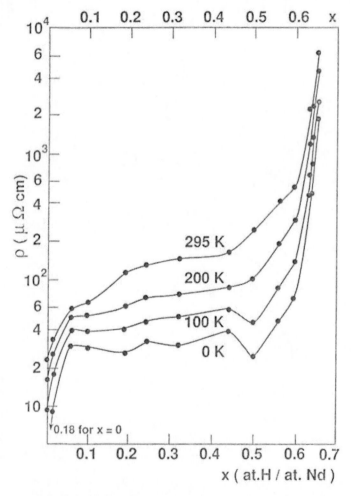

Figure 14. Resistivity isotherms (in the relaxed state) NdH_{2+x} as a function of x, for several temperatures, signaling the presence of an ordered sublattice for x = 0.5 at low T [42].

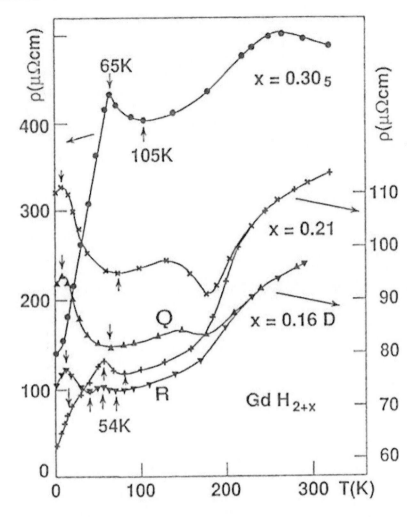

Figure 15. Resistivity of GdH(D)$_{2+x}$ for several x in the relaxed (R) and quenched (Q) state. Note the magnetic transitions at low T, the structural at 200 K, and the M-S for the highest x [1].

This seems a net indication for an energetic structural preference of the RH$_{2.5}$ superlattice.

2.4. Gadolinium Hydride

The T-dependence of the electrical resistivity of GdH$_{2+x}$ is strongly influenced by the magnetic ordering, which has to be treated separately, see next subsection. But independently, we still have the important structural H-sublattice ordering at higher x-values, which interferes with the electric properties. As an example, we are presenting here (Figure 15) the three concentrations used in ref. [1] for the demonstration of how the specimen at the phase boundary, x = 0.30$_5$, before turning semiconducting near 260 K, is being prepared for that transformation by the two others with a smaller x-value, x = 0.16D and x = 0.21, where the (SRO or LRO) order-disorder takes place visibly.

If we plot again two $\rho(x)$ isothermals, one at room temperature, the other at ~ 0 K (Figure 16), we now definitely observe the prime role of low-T ordering at the ideal x = 0.25 concentration (before diverging at the phase boundary), while nothing of this ordering effect is left at room temperature. The approach towards the insulating state can also be investigated by measuring the optical absorption of thin films. This has been done for example by Vargas et al. [43] on a specimen consisting of coexisting grains of pure GdH_2 and GdH_{2+x} through inversion of the spectro-photometric transmission measurements and applying a self-consistent effective medium treatment.

2.5. Dysprosium Hydride

The electrical resistivity of β-DyH_{2+x} has been measured through the whole β-phase range and up to 300 K (Figure 17) [44]. One notes increasing residual resistivity up to the highest x-values but, at the same time, decreasing amplitude of the structural anomaly occurring in two steps between 150 and 200 K after the x = 0.22 specimen.

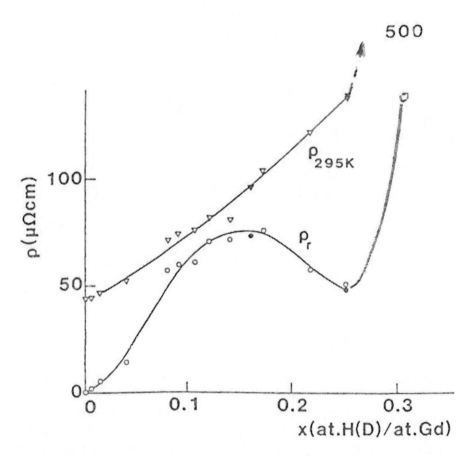

Figure 16. Resistivity isothermals at 0 K and at RT of $GdH(D)_{2+x}$. The minimum of ρ_r for x = 0.25 indicates the presence of low-T ordering (modified from [1]).

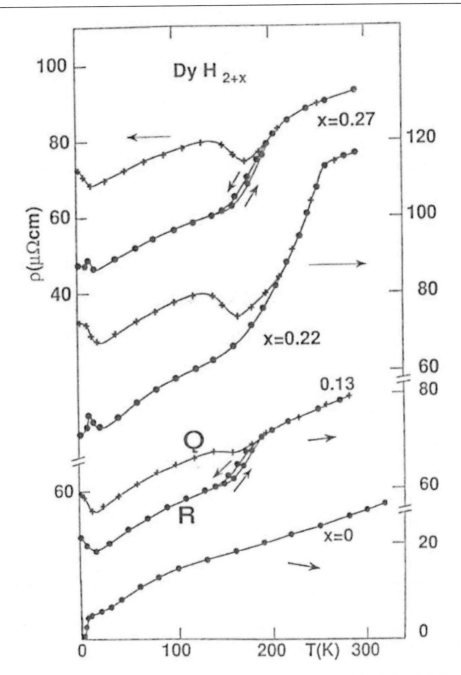

Figure 17. T-dependence of the resistivity of relaxed or quenched DyH$_{2+x}$, through the whole β-phase range, indicating magnetic and structural transitions [44].

This recalls the behavior of GdH$_{2+x}$ (Figure 16) - with a minimum ρ_{res} close to x = 0.25 - and is probably also related to a structural optimum due to ordering of D0$_{22}$ symmetry discussed above; the two steps again corresponding to SRO and LRO respectively.

Optical measurements on thin Pd-coated DyH$_{2+x}$ films have once more permitted to pursue visually the approach to semiconducting behavior with increasing hydrogen concentration [45].

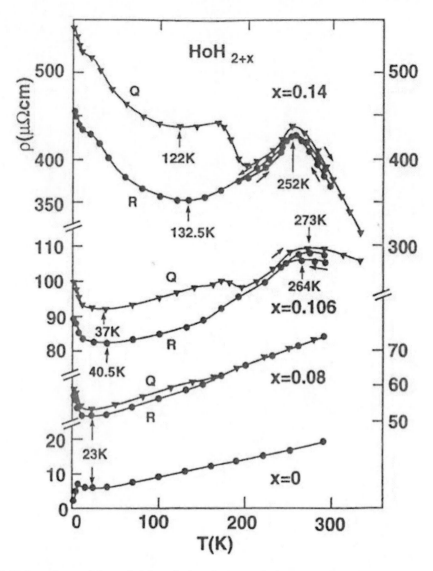

Figure 18. T-dependence of the resistivity of relaxed or quenched HoH$_{2+x}$, through the whole β-phase range, indicating magnetic, structural, M-S and S-M transitions [46].

2.6. Holmium Hydride

A detailed analysis [46] of the resistivity measurements of HoH$_{2+x}$ (a selection is given in Figure 18) was undertaken in view of the M-S transition occurring rather early within the β-phase range, its diverging growth at x_{max} reminding of analogous behavior in earlier described R hydrides. The role of SRO at 150 K for smaller x-values, $x \leq 0.08$, and of LRO near 180 K for higher concentrations was studied after a quench treatment. It permitted to determine activation energies for migration during the ordering processes of $E_m^{SRO} = 0.15(1)$ eV and $E_m^{LRO} = 0.27(2)$ eV, respectively. The resistivity data in the semiconducting regime above room temperature were tentatively fitted in an Arrhenius-type plot according to $\rho(T) \sim \exp(E_a/kT)$ to yield effective activation energies across the gap of the order of $E_a \approx 20 - 40$

meV, close to the 15 to 20 meV obtained for β-YH$_{2+x}$ earlier (Figure 11 and [17]). The group at Costa Rica had also measured optical and electrical properties of thin Ho hydride films up to the semiconducting regime [47] confirming the diverging $\rho(x)$ at and above $x \approx 2.1$.

2.7. Erbium Hydride

Erbium hydride is the heaviest of the lanthanides exhibiting a M-S transition within the β-phase range and that at similarly low concentrations as in the case of YH$_{2+x}$: for both systems, because of the relatively low β-phase boundary of H/R = 2.10 ($x_{max} \approx 0.10$).

Figure 19 shows the T-dependent resistivities up to $x = 0.091$, with strong hysteretic behavior for both the M-S transition and the structural anomaly, after the quenching treatment [48]. As before, the latter represents a mixture of two processes, with preponderance of SRO for $x \leq 0.05$ and of LRO above.

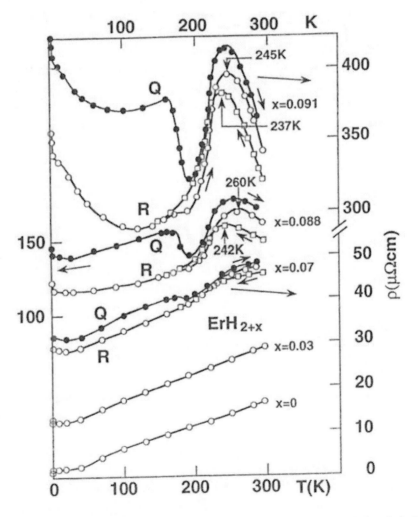

Figure 19. T-dependence of the resistivity of relaxed or quenched ErH$_{2+x}$, through the whole β-phase range, indicating magnetic, structural, M-S and S-M transitions [48].

A complementary investigation of the deuterated system, ErD_{2+x}, has shown the same qualitative behavior, with a slight shift of the ordering temperatures towards higher values, for the heavier isotope: the SRO peak shifting from 140(2) K to 147(2) K and the LRO peak remaining practically constant at 177-178 K.

An Arrhenius-type analysis of the four M-S transforming specimens resulted in effective activation energies $E_a \approx 40$ - 60 meV, in the same range as YH_{2+x} and HoH_{2+x} (see above).

On the other hand, the availability of a relatively large number of specimens to be analyzed, benefitting of the data obtained in the cooling as well as in the heating runs, permitted to relate the peak temperature of the transition, T_{MS}, with the resistivity value at this temperature, $\rho(T_{MS})$; one finds - the higher T_{MS} the lower $\rho(T_{MS})$. This indicates a sufficiently low carrier density as one necessary condition for the occurrence of the M-S transition, the second being the existence of an ordered $H_o(x)$-superlattice able to break down and to force a gap opening.

Finally, we would like to show how, apparently quite off the subject, the knowledge of structural H-sublattice ordering can be important in purely technological situations. Mixed $Er(D,T)_2$ hydride systems are being used recently as "neutron generators" where ErD_2 is bombarded by tritium or vice/versa to yield fusion neutrons and helium (e.g. [49]). Now, the helium atoms forming bubbles already at low temperatures it was important to know if and how these would interact with an eventual H_o-superlattice. It was found in $Er(D,T)_{2-x}{}^3He_x$ films that lenticular He bubbles formed as a result of tritium decay grew along the [111] direction of the fluorite lattice, leaving a "denuded" He-free zone near the surface [50].

2.8. Ytterbium Hydride

No specific resistivity data exist on cubic YbH_{2+x}, but it is possible to draw relevant conclusions from heat capacity measurements such as those made on $YbD_{2.7}$ by Drulis et al. [13].

There, a c_p singularity at 230 K was connected with a break in the T-dependence of the lattice parameter at the same temperature. The former was attributed to the M-S transition, the latter understood as indication of the structural sublattice ordering, with the expected mutual correlation.

2.9. Lutetium Hydride

The last hydride in the series, LuH_2, exhibits no structural anomaly and no M-S transition in its very limited β-phase region (cf. Table I), which seems to go conform with the above proposed model: The low enough carrier density (high ρ) at the phase boundary of $x \approx 0.03$ is not sufficient to drive the transformation, since the concentration of the available x-hydrogens is not big enough to interact and to form the required superlattice. (The inverse situation would explain why in the system TbH_{2+x} no M-S transition is observed: the large enough concentration to form a superlattice is, however, not sufficient because of a too high carrier density (too low ρ) at the phase boundary.)

2.10. Actinide Hydrides

As mentioned in the Introduction, we shall summarize here the little relevant data available on the related family of 5f - metals, the "actinides" as called from the atomic number Z = 90 on. Unfortunately for us, most of the experimental investigations were done on the early actinides Th, Pa, and U, because of evident nuclear applications. Now, their broad band-hybridized 5f-electron structure leads them to multiple valence behavior and results in phase diagrams with hydrogen quite different from those in rare earths [2]. It is only from [93]Np on - after 5f band narrowing - that the metals become "normal" trivalent, with cubic (or distorted cubic) dihydrides and comparable "A" - H phase diagrams with large overstoichiometry ranges, AH_{2+x}. In Table II, we are presenting lattice constants data obtained principally from fitted neutron diffraction and most of them cited in ref. [2].

The few generalities, which can be deduced from this limited amount of data can be summarized as:

(a) - the lattice parameters of $NpH(D)_{2+x}$ *in*crease with increasing x, in apparent contradiction with the habitual contraction of the RH_{2+x} hydrides when adding octahedral H atoms;

(b) - the parameters of both PuH_{2+x} and AmH_{2+x} contract in the usual expected way indicating similar ionic-like M-H and H-H interactions to the rare earths; very recent calculations [52a] confirm the observed lattice contraction in PuH_{2+x} attributing it to enhanced chemical bonding.

(c) - a kind of "actinide contraction" can be observed when going down from PuH_{2+x} to the heavier systems; again, NpH_{2+x} would appear too small in this plot.

Table II. Lattice parameters at 300 K of some βAḤD)$_{2+x}$ actinide hydrides

A	x in H(D)$_o$/A	a in Å	ref., comment
Np	0	5.3475	[51]
	0.15	5.3481	[51]
	0.30	5.3490	[51]
	0.50	5.3516	[51]
	0.80	5.3578	[51]
	0.13D*	5.3324	[2] * corresponds to $NpD_{1.72+0.41}$
	0.65D*	5.3361	[2] * corresponds to $NpD_{1.95+0.71}$
Pu	0	5.360	[52]
	0.15	5.358	[52]
	0.26	5.356	[52]
	0.40	5.350	[52]
	0.51	5.342	[52]
	0.70	5.340	[52]
Am	0	5.344	[53]
	0.34	5.341	[53]
	0.67	5.338	[53]
Cm	0 + x ?	5.322	[2]
Bk	0 + x ?	5.248	[2]
Cf	0 + x ?	5.285	[2]

On the other hand, it is reassuring that the few resistivity experiments on superstoichiometric AH_{2+x} reported up to now exhibit anomalies which, in addition to magnetic transitions (to be treated below), seem to indicate structural H- sublattice ordering.

Good examples [54] are shown in Figure 20 where the $AmH_{2.6}$ sample (contrary to the pure dihydride $AmH_{2.0}$) presents a break at 200 K typical for structural order-disorder processes, while the much more resistive $NpH_{2.6}$ sample has already transformed into a semiconductor at ~ 100 K.

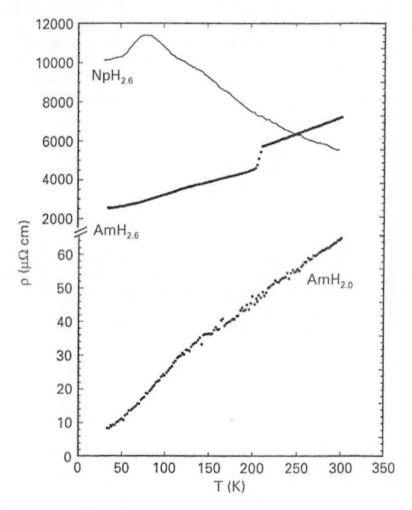

Figure 20. T-dependence of the resistivity of several AH_{2+x} specimens. Note the anomaly near 200 K for $AmH_{2.6}$, possibly due to sublattice ordering, and the M-S transition in $NpH_{2.6}$ [54].

3. MAGNETIC PROPERTIES

It is the incompletely filled 4f-shell that is responsible for the appearance of a magnetic moment in the lanthanide ions, which is then transmitted via the Ruderman-Kittel-Kasuya-Yosida (RKKY) polarization of the conduction electrons to the lattice to create long-range ordered ferromagnetic (FM) and/or antiferromagnetic (AF) structures. This mechanism remains valid in the case of dihydrides with their monovalent metallic character and it is interesting to follow its evolution with added octahedral hydrogen concentration, x, both in view of the simultaneously decreasing carrier density and also because of the expected eventual H-sublattice ordering.

Table III. Characteristic FM/AF transition temperatures, $T_{C,N}$, special points, $T_{M,m}$, and the propagation vectors, τ_m, of their configurations, in $RH(D)_{2+x}$ systems

R	x H(D)$_o$/R	$T_{C,N}$ /K	T_M /K	T_m /K	τ_m	ref.
Ce	0	4.2; 6.9	14.5	42.5	1/2[111] + 1/5[1-10]	[1]
	0D	5.0; 6.2				[1]
	0.05	-	17.5	42	not obs. to 1.3K	[1]
	0.05D	-	-	-	not obs. to 0.35 K	[1]
	0.60	3.3			FM, $\tau_m = 0$	[1]
	0.67D	3.1			FM, $\tau_m = 0$	[1]
	0.82D	-	-	-	not obs. to 1.8 K	[1]
	0.96D	4.1			1/2[111]	[1]
Pr	0	3.35		28	1/2[111] - 1/8[1-12]	[1]
	0D	3.3				[1]
	0.15	2.5	5.5	12.5		[1]
	0.23	-			not obs. to 1.5 K	[1]
	0.76	-			not obs. to 1.5 K	[1]
Nd	0	6.6			FM, $\tau_m = 0$	[1]
	0.32	5.3			FM, $\tau_m = 0$	[1]
	0.56	2.9; 4.5			AF spin glass	[1]
	0.65	2.25	4.3	12.2	AF spin glass	[1]
	0	~ 34 (SRO)			AF^{ic}, $\tau_m \sim$ 1/2[113]	[55]
Sm	0	9.6			AF_c, 1/2[111]	[1]
	0.16	8.0	10.8	12.6		[1]
	0.17	7.1	10.8	15.9	c_p peaks	[56]
	0.26	-			not obs. to 1.5 K	[1]
Gd	0	18.3			AF_c, 1/2[111]	[1]
	0.08	~ 13	~ 15	60		[1]
	0.17		14.5;54.3	36.6; 74		[1]
	0.30$_5$		65	105		[1]
Tb	0D	16; 19			1/4[113]; ~1/8[116]	[1]
	0.18D		32.5	42	1/4[114]; ~[1/4,1/6,1]	[23]
	0	18; 21				[23]
	0.07		12.5	30.5		[23]
	0.20		12; 25	38; 52.5		[23]
	0.24$_5$		36	42		[23]
Dy	0D	3.0; 5..0			~ 1/4[113]	[58]
	0.13$_5$D	n.o. to 1.6			SRO, ~ 1/4[113]	[58]
	0	3.7; 5.0				[1]
	0.13		1.8; (10)	(10.5);16		[1]
	0.22		10.7	20.5		[1]
	0.27		2.55; 8.6	10.7;18.7		[1]

Table III. Characteristic FM/AF transition temperatures, $T_{C,N}$, special points, $T_{M,m}$, and the propagation vectors, τ_m, of their configurations, in RH(D)$_{2+x}$ systems (continued)

R	x H(D)$_o$/R	$T_{C,N}$ /K	T_M /K	T_m /K	τ_m	ref.
Ho	0D	4.0; 6.3			1/4[113]; ~ 1/4[113]	[11]
	0.12D	(7)				[11]
	0	3.5; 4.7	6.3	24		[11]
	0.12		6.3	(15); 25		[11]
Er	0D	2.23			~ 1/4[113]; ~1/8[116]	[12]
	0	2.30	7.2	14.0		[48]
	0.03	1.85		8.6		[48]
	0.07	1.75	(2.1)	18.5		[48]
	0.09$_1$		(2.2);(~5)	30		[48]
Tm	0				not obs. to 1.5 K	[1]
	0.08D				not obs. to 1.8 K	[59]
Yb	0.25 -0.7				not obs. to 1.9 K	[13]
A						
Pu	0	65			FM	[2]
	0.45	65			FM	[2]
	0.65	70	100	(150)		[2]

Table III assembles the characteristic magnetic transition temperatures as observed by different techniques (mainly resistivity) and specified by neutron diffraction (where possible) in various RH$_{2+x}$ systems. (The data are mostly taken over from [1] unless more recent ones available.) A more detailed discussion will be presented below in interesting specific cases and supported by graphics.

3.1. Cerium Hydride

The magnetism of the Ce-H system has been studied as one of the earliest ones and a rather complete magnetic phase diagram could be established (Figure 21 and [1]): one notes a broad FM region for ~ 0.05 < x < 0.75 delimited by two AF regions adjoining the pure dihydride and trihydride compositions (both of them of the fluorite type!). Figure 22 shows these two AF structures as determined by neutron diffraction and represents a beautiful example of the role played by the RKKY polarization mechanism for the long-range transmission of the magnetic moments. Thus, in Figure 22a is presented the magnetic structure of pure CeH$_2$, with AF-coupled (111) planes modulated along [1-10], which can be expressed by a propagation vector commensurate with the lattice, $\tau_m^c = 1/2$ [111] + 1/5 [1-10].

The trihydride, shown in Figure 22b, having lost its last conduction electron has also lost its modulation (cf. also Table III). It is now solely controlled by dipole interaction.

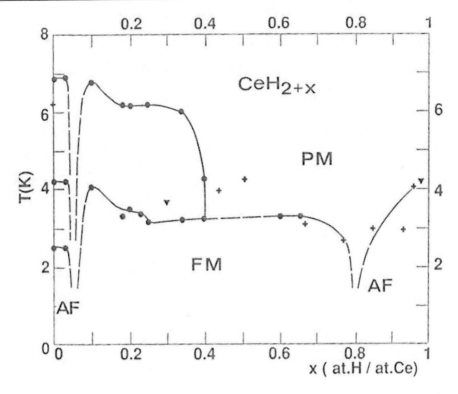

Figure 21. Magnetic phase diagram for CeH_{2+x} constructed from susceptibility, resistivity, and neutron scattering data [1].

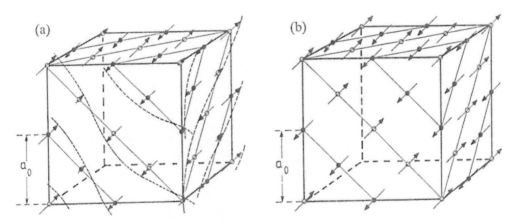

Figure 22. Magnetic structure of the pure dihydride, CeD_2 (*a*) and of the trihydride, CeD_3 (*b*), both in the β-phase. The modulation present in CeD_2 has disappeared in CeD_3. [1]

3.2. Praseodymium Hydride

The magnetic structure of the Pr-H system resembles very much that of Ce-H and not much new has been added since the last review [1]. Its AF can be described by a commensurate $\tau_m^c = 1/2$ [111] - 1/8[1-12], up to a composition of $PrH_{2+0.15}$; for higher concentrations, no magnetic ordering was observed down to 1.5 K.

3.3. Neodymium Hydride

$NdH_{2.0}$ is the only pure fluorite-type R dihydride ordering FM (below 6.5 K) and remains so up to $x \approx 0.5$. For higher x and up to the phase boundary of H/R ~ 2.7 it is an AF spin glass, with a strong sensitivity to H-sublattice ordering [1] (see Figure 23 for the quench effect on the magnetic transitions of $NdH_{2.65}$). More recently, it was reported (but not confirmed) [55] that neutron scattering on single crystal NdH_2 films has revealed a broad incommensurate SRO magnetic peak below 34 K at the position (0.532, 0.532, 1.532) which would correspond roughly to $\tau_m^{ic} \approx 1/2[113]$.

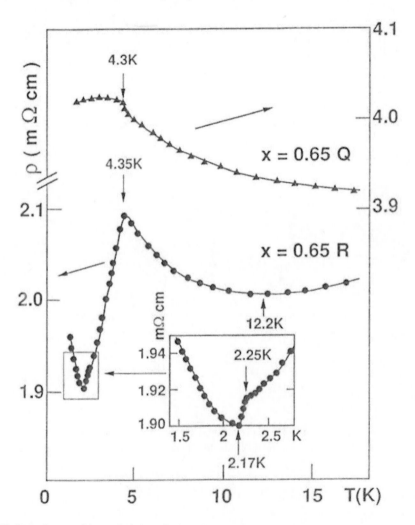

Figure 23. T-dependence of the resistivity of relaxed (R) and quenched (Q) $NdH_{2.65}$ in the magnetic range [42].

3.4. Samarium Hydride

The AF structure of SmH_{2+x} is similar to that of CeH_2 and PrH_2, with a propagation vector $\tau_m{}^c = 1/2[111]$ and a transition temperature $T_N = 9.6$ K, slightly decreasing with increasing x and disappearing above x ~ 0.2. Interestingly, the suppression of H-sublattice ordering by a quench leads to a reappearing of magnetism in the $SmH_{2.26}$ sample (Figure 24), which was interpreted [1], at that time, as a possible interaction with the crystal field. Very recently, new specific heat measurements [56] on $SmH_{2.16}$ have not only confirmed the three special points of the resistivity data (cf. Table III) but, in addition, revealed heavy-fermion behavior, explained by a non-negligible contribution of Sm^{2+} ions.

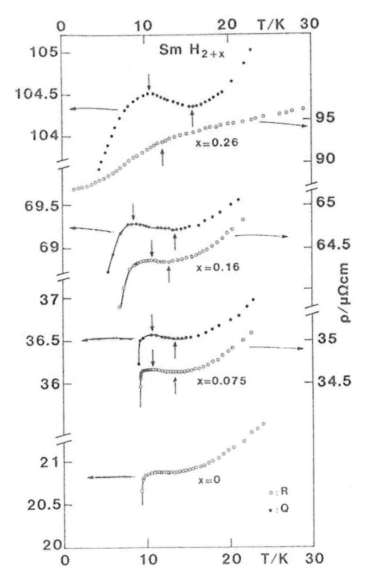

Figure 24. T-dependence of the resistivity of several relaxed (R) and quenched (Q) SmH_{2+x} specimens in the magnetic range. Note the reappearance of magnetism after a quench for x = 0.26 [1].

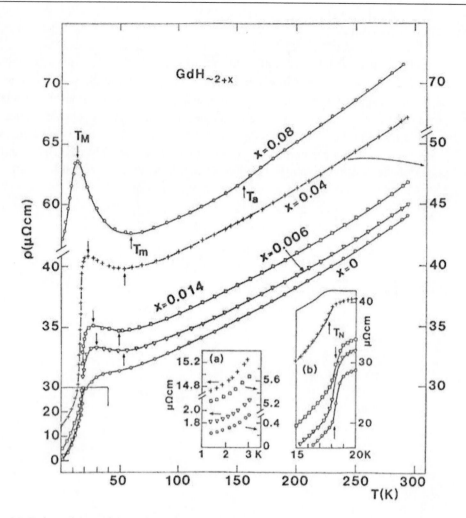

Figure 25. T-dependence of the resistivity of GdH$_{2+x}$, for small x-values, showing the evolution at the lowest temperatures and around the magnetic transition [1].

3.5. Gadolinium Hydride

In Figure 15 above, we had already shown the influence of H-sublattice ordering upon the electrical resistivity of GdH(D)$_{2+x}$ at high x-values, $0.16 \leq x \leq 0.30$, preparing the M-S transition.

We had also noted the simultaneous modification and near suppression of the magnetic transitions after a quench. Now it is interesting to see how this evolution is being initiated through the lower concentrations, beginning with the pure dihydride GdH$_2$, with its commensurate AF and a $\tau_m^c = 1/2[111]$, just like in most earlier R-H systems. Figure 25 shows, for the specimens with $0 \leq x \leq 0.08$, not only the expected decrease of T_N, due to decreasing carrier density, but also a growing resistivity peak in the region of T_N leading to a minimum around 50 K.

This latter effect is probably caused by strong spin-disorder scattering in this mid-group 4f material with a half-filled shell (S = 7/2).

3.6. Terbium Hydride

The pure dihydride, TbD_2, exhibits two partially overlapping AF configurations below T $\approx$ 19 - 20 K as shown in Figure 26. The structure stable at lower T (Figure 26a) is commensurate, modulated with a propagation vector τ_m^c = 1/4[113], *different* from the commensurate phases of the light R dihydrides (including the mid-series GdH_2), thus initiating a different magnetic behavior.

The higher-temperature structure (Figure 26b) is incommensurate, with a propagation vector τ_m^{ic} = [0.12, 0.14, 0.76], close to the [116] direction.

As to the higher super-stoichiometric compositions, for example $TbD_{2.18}$, one observes now a favorable influence of the ordered H-superlattice of the $D0_{22}$ -type (cf. Figure 7) existing here at low T and maintaining magnetic order to a T_N twice as high, up to 42 K! Its role is immediately clear when quenching the sample across the ordering range at ~ 200 K (cf. Figure 6), exemplified in Figure 27.

Here, the clean neutron diffraction spectrum with narrow lines of the magnetic structure observed at 1.5 K becomes strongly perturbed after the quench, yielding broadened magnetic and superstructure lines to indicate an evolution towards SRO.

The two magnetic phases present in this specimen have now, moreover, changed their structure to τ_m^c = 1/4[114] below 32.5 K, and τ_m^{ic} = [0.24, 0.18, 1] or ~ 1/4[1, 2/3, 4] below 42 K.

A potentially interesting application of the TbH_{2+x} dihydrides was recently suggested by Drulis et al [57] who performed heat-capacity and magnetization measurements in applied fields. The observed strong magnetic entropy changes indicated a possibility for their use as magneto-caloric materials for adiabatic cooling.

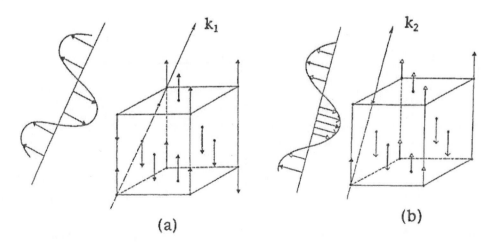

Figure 26. Magnetic structures of pure TbD_2 together with the projections of the moments upon their propagation vectors: (*a*) commensurate phase observed below 16 K; (*b*) incommensurate phase present in the range 14.8K $\leq$ T $\leq$ 19K [23].

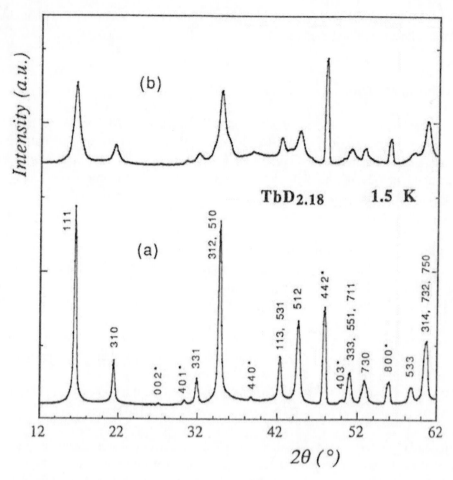

Figure 27. Neutron diffraction spectrum of $TbD_{2.18}$ in the commensurate phase at 1.5 K in the relaxed (a) and in the quenched (b) state. Note the general broadening of the magnetic and superstructure lines (marked by an asterisk) after the quench [23].

3.7. Dysprosium Hydride

New cold-neutron measurements [58] have been undertaken on this rather unfavorable material (because of the high neutron absorption cross section of Dy), which yielded more precise results, as a supplement to the data and in part different from the earlier review [1]. Thus, the "intermediate" structure observed below 5 K and overlapping with the low-T phase (Figure 28) has now been specified as AF incommensurate, modulated with a propagation vector $\tau_{m2}^{ic} = [0.275, 0.275, 0.750]$, not far from 1/4[113]. The low-T phase, however, is no longer commensurate but locks in into another slightly incommensurate one, even closer to 1/4[113], namely $\tau_{m1}^{ic} = [0.258, 0.273, 0.750]$.

The overstoichiometric compound $DyD_{2.135}$ exhibited only magnetic SRO below ~ 6 K, in agreement with the detailed resistivity measurements (Figure 29, cf. also Figure 17).

μSR spectroscopy, where the implanted positive muon is assumed to occupy one of the free octahedral interstices, used as a specific probe for magnetic SRO confirmed the above findings [60].

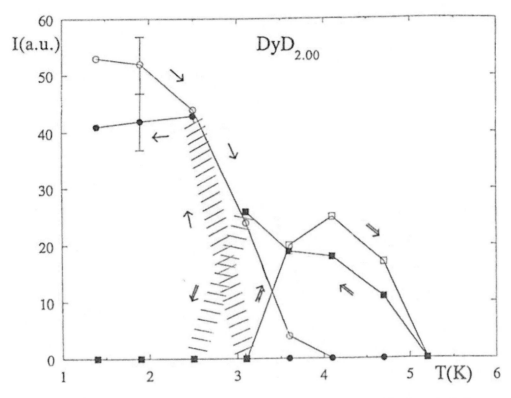

Figure 28. T-dependence of the intensities for the two incommensurate magnetic phases in DyD$_2$ showing the hysteresis in the overlap region [58].

3.8. Holmium Hydride

Like in the case of DyD$_2$ above, new neutron diffraction measurements [11] have permitted to determine the "intermediate" structure below T$_N$ = 6.3 K (Figure 30).

It turned out to be no longer intermediate but locked in below ~ 3.5 K and, with a strong hysteresis, coexisted with the low-T phase down to the lowest temperatures measured.

It is AF incommensurate with a propagation vector τ_m^{ic} = [0.273, 0.273, 0.748] which is close but still significantly different from the commensurate low-T phase with τ_m^c = 1/4[113]; this seems to be the general picture for the heavy R dihydrides from TbD$_2$ on. In addition to the two long-range structures of Figure 30, magnetic fluctuations (SRO) are observed to rather high temperatures, ~ 40 K. On the other hand, overstoichiometric HoD$_{2.12}$ exhibits (like DyD$_{2.13}$ but much stronger) only magnetic SRO up to ~ 7 K; compare also Figure 18 and ref. [46] for the resistivity as well as ref. [60] for the μSR data.

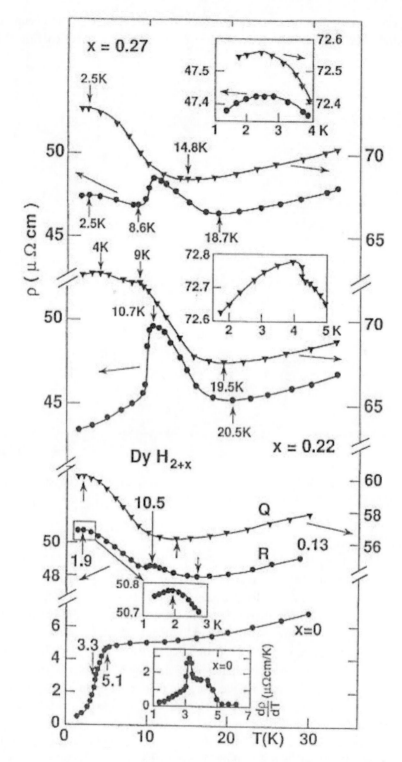

Figure 29. T-dependence of the resistivity of DyH$_{2+x}$ in the magnetic region in the relaxed (R) and in the quenched (Q) state. Note the quasi-disappearance of magnetism for the x-rich samples after a quench [44].

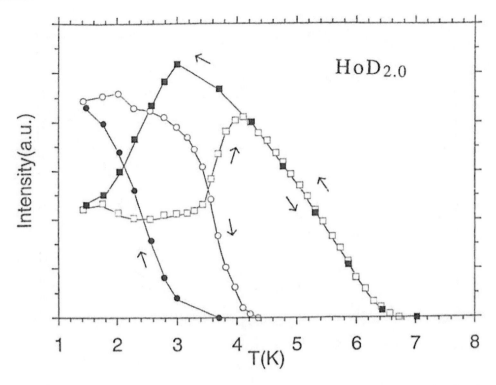

Figure 30. T-dependence of the intensities for the two magnetic phases present in HoD$_2$ showing the blocking of the intermediate phase below 4 K and the strong hysteresis for both phases in the overlap region [11].

3.9. Erbium Hydride

ErH(D)$_2$ - the heaviest of the "normal" magnetic R-dihydrides - has also lacked, until recently, a determination of its eventually existing phases. A careful neutron diffraction experiment combined from different laboratories [12] yielded no commensurate magnetism down to 0.12 K but, instead, two coexisting *in*commensurate phases below T = 2.3 K, one close to 1/4[113] with τ_{m1}^{ic} = [0.275, 0.275, 0.750], the other close to 1/8[116] with τ_{m2}^{ic} = [0.120,0.120,0.750].

Again, magnetic SRO is observed superimposed upon the LRO phases, in agreement with and in addition to the earlier data [48]. A modified tentative magnetic phase diagram is proposed in Figure 31.

3.10. Thulium Hydride

No magnetic transitions have been observed down to 1.5 K in TmH(D)$_{2+x}$, both for x = 0 [1] and x = 0.08 [59]; a fact which was explained by a non-magnetic ground state sufficiently far below the first excited magnetic state - a paramagnetic Van Vleck compound.

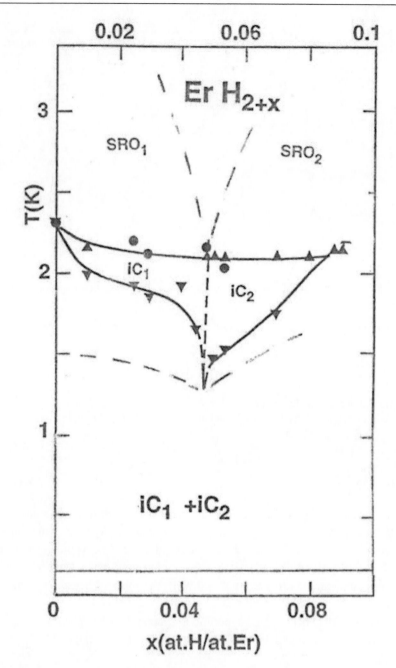

Figure 31. Tentative magnetic phase diagram for ErH(D)$_{2+x}$ constructed from susceptibility, resistivity, and neutron diffraction data, after [1, 12, 48]. The broken lines delimit possible coexisting (and overlapping) SRO phases.

3.11. Ytterbium Hydride

The superstoichiometric fluorite-type dihydride YbH$_{2+x}$ is not magnetically ordered; eventually observed anomalies in specific heat or resistivity are attributed to Kondo-lattice (heavy fermion) behavior [13].

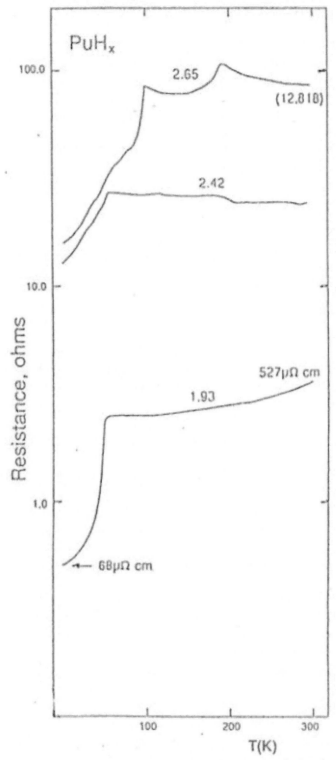

Figure 32. T-dependence of the electrical resistance of several PuH_{2+x} specimens showing the evolution with x of magnetic and possibly structural as well as M-S transitions [2].

3.12. Actinide Hydrides

The only existing reliable data on magnetic order in actinide hydrides of the fluorite type concern the plutonium-hydrogen system and have been discussed in [2]. Figure 32 presents the T-dependence of the resistivity of three PuH_{2+x} samples within the cubic β-phase range, with a clear indication of magnetic and other anomalies. The very sharp break at 65 K both in the pure PuH_2 and in $PuH_{2.42}$ is attributed by Ward [2] to a FM transition; it seems still present in the $PuH_{2.65}$ sample but masked and only as a shoulder around 70 K. The "puzzling" sharp peak at 100 K followed by the M-S transition at 190 K remained unexplained, but reminds *us* strongly of the resistive behavior observed in many overstoichiometric R dihydrides above (cf. for example Figures 15, 18, 19, 23). There, we had to consider possible combined action of an order/disorder situation in the octahedral H-sublattice, of the related high-T electronic M-S transformation and of the low-T S-M transition, in addition to the eventual magnetic SRO and/or LRO. In view of the complexity of the phenomena and the temperature ranges in question, it is not absurd to relate the observed peaks and minima to a similar mechanism.

CONCLUSION

The fluorite-type β-phase rare earth dihydrides and in particular their overstoichiometric compounds, RH_{2+x}, represent an excellent playground for the observation of various often coexisting and interacting phenomena:

- the decreasing carrier density with increasing x leading to an x-dependent M-S transition;
- the H-H interaction at low T and high enough x leading to a superlattice of low symmetry;
- the ordered superlattice forming a delocalized band in the gap and giving - when breaking down - a T-dependent M-S transition and, at the same time, a Mott type S-M transition;
- the 4f magnetism eventually superimposed upon all the phenomena above.

All these order/ disorder effects result in structural and electronic anomalies well observable by XR and neutron diffraction, by optical and other spectroscopies (especially with thin films) but, in particular, by electrical resistivity (where most of them were first described). The great number of existing R-H systems (15 lanthanides plus Sc and Y) permits, in addition to the fine analysis of the described effects, to try to compare and relate with each other and draw possible general rules for the mechanisms in question.

The actinide hydrides seem to behave similarly, especially those with 5f-band narrowing (Np, Pu, Am etc), form cubic dihydrides and exhibit indications for H_o sublattice ordering, M-S transitions and magnetic phases: worth of continuing studies by resistivity, neutrons...

REFERENCES

[1]   P. Vajda, "Hydrogen in rare earth metals" in Gschneidner K.A. (ed.), Handbook on the physics and chemistry of rare earths, vol. 20, North Holl. (Amsterdam), p. 207, 1995.

[2]   J.W. Ward, J.M. Haschke, "Comparison of 4f and 5f element hydride properties" in Gschneidner K.A. (ed.), Handbook on the physics and chemistry of rare earths, vol. 18, North Holl. (Amsterdam), p. 293, 1994.

[3]   A.V. Galakhov, L.D. Finkelstein, E.Z. Kurmaev, R.G. Wilks, A. Moewes, V.K. Fedotov, *J. Phys. Cond. Matter.* 20, 335224, 2008.

[4]   T.J. Udovic, Q. Huang, J.J. Rush, *J. All. Comp.* 356/7, 41, 2003.

[5]   J.E. Bonnet, J.N. Daou, *J. Appl. Phys.* 48, 964, 1977.

[6]   V.A. Shaburov, A.E. Sovestnov, G.P.Smirnov, A.V. Tyunis, H. Drulis, M. Drulis, *Phys. of the Solid State.* 40, 1393, 1998.

[7]   F.D. Manchester, J.M. Pitre, *J. Phase Equil.* 18, 63, 1997.

[8]   G. Renaudin, P. Fischer, K. Yvon, *J. All. Comp.* 330/2, 175, 2002.

[9]   G. Renaudin, P. Fischer, K. Yvon, *J. All. Comp.* 313, L 10, 2000.

[9a] T. Matsuoka et al., *Phys. Rev. Lett.* 107, 025501, 2011.

[10] M. Chiheb, J.N. Daou, P. Vajda, *Z. Phys. Chem.* 179, 255, 1993.

[11] P. Vajda, G. André, O.J. Zogal, *Phys. Rev.* B 57, 5830, 1998.

[12] P. Vajda, G. André, T.J. Udovic, R.W. Erwin, Q. Huang, *Phys. Rev.* B 71, 054419, 2005.

[13] M. Drulis, W. Iwasieczko, M. Wolcyrz, H. Drulis, *J. All. Comp.* 337, 64, 2002, *and ibid.* 366, 9, 2004.

[14] V.K. Fedotov, V.G. Fedotov, M.E. Kost, E.G. Ponyatovskii, *Sov. Phys. Solid State.* 24, 1252, 1982.

[15] J.N. Huiberts, PhD thesis, Free Univ. of Amsterdam, 1995.

[16] A.M. van Gogh et al., *Phys. Rev.* B 63, 195105, 2001.

[17] P. Vajda, J.N. Daou, Phys. Rev. Lett. 66, 3176, 1991; *and* J.N. Daou, P. Vajda, *Phys. Rev.* B 45, 10907, 1992.

[18] A.M. Carsteanu et al., *Phys. Rev.* B 69, 134102, 2004.

[19] J. Schoenes, M. Rode, H. Schröter, D. Zur, A. Borgschulte, *J. All. Comp.* 404, 453, 2005.

[20] E.J. Grier, A.K. Petford-Long, R.C.C. Ward, *J. Appl. Cryst.* 33, 1246, 2000.

[21] L.A. Bendersky, B. Burton, K. Wang, *Phys. Rev.* B 82, 144111, 2010.

[22] P. Vajda, J.N. Daou, J.P. Burger, *Phys. Rev.* B 36, 8669, 1987.

[23] P. Vajda, J.N. Daou, G. André, *Phys. Rev.* B 48, 6116, 1993.

[24] G. André, O. Blaschko, W. Schwarz, J.N. Daou, P. Vajda, *Phys. Rev.*B 46, R8644, 1992.

[25] Q. Huang, T.J. Udovic, J.J. Rush, J. Schefer, I.S. Anderson, *J. All. Comp.* 231, 95, 1995.

[26] O. Greis, P. Knappe, H. Mueller, *J. Solid State Chem.* 39, 49, 1981.

[27] O.J. Zogal, P. L'Heritier, *J. All. Comp.* 177, 83, 1991.

[28] "Hydrogen functionalized materials" in A. Zuettel (ed.) Hydrogen as a future energy carrier, Wiley-VCH, p.265 , 2008.

[29] (a)A. Remhof et al., Phys. Rev. B 62, 2164, 2000 *and* (b)*Phys. Rev.* B 65, 054110, 2002.

[30] E.S. Kooij et al., *Thin Solid Films* 402, 131, 2002.

[31] J. Hayoz, J. Schoenes, L. Schlapbach, P. Aebi, *J. Appl. Phys.* 90, 3925, 2001.

[32] F.J.A. den Broeder et al., *Nature* 394, 656, 1998.

[33] M. Di Vece, J.J. Kelly, *J. All. Comp.* 356/7, 156, 2003.

[34] A. Remhof, R.J. Wijngaarden, R. Griessen, *J. All. Comp.* 356/7, 300, 2003.

[35] F. DiMeo, M.F. King, Patent N° US6.897.960 B2, May 24, 2005.

[36] G.G. Libowitz, *Ber. Bunsenges. Phys. Chem.* 76, 837, 1972.

[37] J. Shinar, B. Dehner, R.G. Barnes, B.J. Beaudry, *Phys. Rev. Lett.* 64, 563, 1990.

[38] S. Enache et al., *J. All. Comp.* 397, 9, 2005.

[39] R.G. Barnes, C.T. Chang, G. Majer, U. Kaess, J. All. Comp. 356/7, 137, 2003 *and* S.Leyer, S. Heck, A. Kaiser, E. Dormann, R.G. Barnes, *Phys. Rev.* B 72, 125115, 2005.

[40] G. Renaudin, P. Fischer, K. Yvon, *J. All. Comp.* 329, L 9, 2001.

[41] T.J. Udovic, Q. Huang, J.J. Rush, *J. Solid State Chem.* 122, 151, 1996.

[42] J.N. Daou, J.P. Burger, P. Vajda, *Phil. Mag.* 65, 127, 1992.

[43] W.E. Vargas, D.E. Azofeifa, N. Clark, *J. Phys. D: Appl. Phys.* 42, 015416, 2009.

[44] P. Vajda, J.N. Daou, *Phys. Rev.* B 45, 9749, 1992.

[45] W.E. Vargas, A.Amador, D.E. Azofeifa, N. Clark, *Thin Solid Films* 515, 8087, 2007.

[46] J.N. Daou, P. Vajda, *Phys. Rev.* B 50, 12635, 1994.

[47] D.E. Azofeifa, W.E. Vargas, N. Clark, H. Solis, *J. All. Comp.* 446/7, 522, 2007.

[48] P. Vajda, J.N. Daou, *Phys. Rev.* B 49, 3275, 1994.

[49] H.T. Bach, F.J. Steinkruger, W.S. Chamberlin, C.R. Walthers, *J. Vac. Sci. Techn.* B 22, 1738, 2004.

[50] C.S. Snow et al., *J. Nucl. Mat.* 374, 147, 2008.

[51] J.W. Ward, W. Bartscher, J. Rebizant, *J. All. Comp.* 130, 431, 1987.

[52] T. Muromura, T. Yakata, K. Ouchi, M. Iseki, *J. Inorg. Nucl. Chem.* 34, 171, 1972.

[52a] B.Y. Ao, X.L. Wang, P. Shi, P.H. Chen, X.Q. Ye, X.C. Lai, T. Gao, *J. Nucl. Mat.* 424, 183, 2012.

[53] J.W. Roddy, *J. Inorg. Nucl. Chem.* 35, 4141, 1973.

[54] B. Cort, J.W. Ward, F.A. Vigil, R.G. Haire, *J. All. Comp.* 224, 237, 1995.

[55] S. Hemon, et al., *J. Phys. Cond. Matter.* 12, 5011, 2000.

[56] O. Nakamura et al., *J. Magn. Magn. Mat.* 310, e 65, 2007.

[57] H. Drulis, A. Hackemer, L. Folcik, *Sol. State Comm.* 149, 1266, 2009; 150, 164, 2010.

[58] P. Vajda, G. André, J. Hammann, *Phys. Rev.* B 55, 3028, 1997.

[59] J.Weizenecker, H.Winter, H.J.Mattausch, E.Dormann, *J. Mag. Mag. Mat.* 152, 183,1996.

[60] F.N.Gygax, P.Vajda, D.Andreica, M.Pinkpank, A.Schenck, *J. All. Comp.* 330, 376,2002.

In: Properties of Fluorite Structure Materials
Editors: Peter Vajda and Jean-Marc Costantini

ISBN: 978-1-62417-458-2
© 2013 Nova Science Publishers, Inc.

Chapter 3

HIGH-PRESSURE STUDIES OF RARE EARTH HYDRIDES

Taras Palasyuk and Marek Tkacz[*]

Institute of Physical Chemistry,
PAS, Warsaw, Poland

ABSTRACT

Systems of rare earth metals and hydrogen (RE - H) provide a good research platform for studying the interplay between structural and electronic transformations. Beside solid solution phase (α-REH$_x$ (x<<2)), hydrogenation of the rare earth metals leads to the formation of at least two structurally distinct hydride phases ($\beta - REH_2$ and γ-REH$_3$, cubic (CaF$_2$- type) and hexagonal (HoD$_3$ – type) respectively). Along with different crystal structure at ambient conditions the hydride phases exhibit distinguishable electrical transport and optical properties ranging from that of metallic to insulating ones which in the 90's of the last century have attracted lots of interest for both the academic research and possible industrial applications.

The last decade has been marked by the growing interest in the high-pressure behavior of the rare earth hydrides. The experimental observation of the hexagonal to cubic phase transition in the series of REH$_3$ and the theoretically predicted metallization and superconductivity under high-pressure conditions have been the main driving motivation for research.

Here a comprehensive overview of the progress in high-pressure studies of the rare earth hydrides using various experimental techniques is presented. The chapter encloses 4 sections: 1. "Introduction", 2. "Experimental Studies", 3. "Theoretical Studies" and 4. "Concluding Section". In the Section 2 along with presenting the main results of experimental studies, a particular emphasis has been put on the description of the role of interactions between hydrogen species and the host metal in driving the observed structural and electronic transformations as well.

---

[*] Email: mtkacz@ichf.edu.pl

1. INTRODUCTION

Systems of rare earth metals (RE) with hydrogen (H) provide a unique opportunity for studying physical properties which depend on hydrogen content. Pure RE metals show high reactivity with respect to hydrogen resulting in a set of similar phase diagrams where the hydrogen concentration ranges from 0 to 3 in atomic ratio. Beside solid solutions, two hydride phases with a nominal composition REH_2 and REH_3 can be formed if corresponding hydrogen amount is available.

Hydrogenation causes strong structural changes in RE metals. In general, heavy RE (such as Gd, Tb, Dy, Ho, Er, Tm and Lu) upon hydrogenation changes their structure from initially hcp-type to fcc-type of the respective REH_2 hydride phase and another hcp-type crystal structure is acquired when hydrogen stoichiometry close to 3, i.e. REH_3, is reached. A characteristic feature for hydride phases is a relatively narrow composition range in which they are stable.

Unlike heavy RE, hydrides of light rare earth elements (La, Ce, Pr and Nd) crystallize in fcc-type structure in most of the composition range.

In this respect, Y and Sc behave like heavy RE metals and their hydrogenation results in a similar structural sequence.

Such modifications of structure with hydrogen content exert a strong influence on many physical properties of RE- H systems.

Up to date, at least three main experimental observations can be pointed out, which have been exciting the interest of both experimentalists and theoreticians for REH_x hydrides.

First of all, this is the reversible composition-dependent "switching" of electrical and optical properties of REH_x, for the first time observed during the process of hydrogen absorption/desorption in Y and La metals at ambient temperature by Stalinski [1] and lateron spectacularly demonstrated by the Dutch group [2].

$REH_{2\pm x}$ exhibits metallic properties such as good electrical conductivity and surface reflectivity for almost the entire wavelength range of light. $REH_{3-\delta}$ hydrides have an optical gap generally near the visible light range which makes them insulators. It is worth noting that a metal–insulator type transition (MI) was detected for cubic as well as for hexagonal trihydrides ($REH_{3-\delta}$) [2] and the transition was shown to be reversible during hydrogen desorption. Such a behavior of RE systems during hydrogenation opens the way for a wide application in optoelectronics and some research has already been performed in that direction [3,4]. A comprehensive review, including in particular the electric and magnetic properties of the REH_2 - systems has been given by Vajda [5].

The next two areas of scientific interest concern the properties of RE trihydrides under high-pressure conditions.

Recently, a number of experimental papers presenting results of studies under high-pressure have appeared reporting the observation of the hcp to fcc structural phase transition in $REH_{3-\delta}$ [6–24] previously predicted by theoretical calculations [25,26].

The most intriguing and so far unanswered issue is the metallization and the possible superconducting properties of the high-pressure cubic phase.

In the following we will review the general progress of experimental and theoretical research on RE-H systems under high pressure.

2. EXPERIMENTAL STUDIES

2.1. X-Ray Diffraction Studies

The interest in the high-pressure behavior of rare earth trihydrides was renewed after the experimental observation of the hcp to fcc phase transition of ErH_3 under high pressure in 2004 [18]. Later on, in the period from 2005 to 2007, Palasyuk and Tkacz [19 - 24] reported on similar phase transitions from hexagonal to cubic in the series of lanthanide hydrides (SmH_3, GdH_3, HoH_3, LuH_3) and YH_3 under high pressure using the energy dispersive X-ray diffraction method in a diamond anvil cell (DAC), and predicted similar behavior for TbH_3, DyH_3 and TmH_3.

As an example of results obtained, the energy dispersive X-ray diffraction (EDXRD) spectra of holmium trihydride collected over 24 hours, each for different pressures are shown in Figure 1. At lower pressures, all trihydrides investigated exhibit a hexagonal structure with all diffraction lines available at a given diffraction angle.

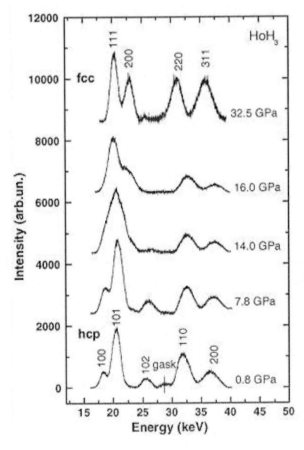

Figure 1. EDXRD spectra of HoH_3 for different pressures indexed for both the initial hexagonal and high pressure phases. Index {200} in the initial hexagonal structure represents the strongest diffraction line in the quadruple set of peaks (Ref. [20]).

When pressure was increased, new lines appeared in the spectra and they grew in intensity with growing pressure, eventually sweeping out the initial hexagonal structure. The new lines have been identified as belonging to the cubic fcc structure.

When releasing the pressure the samples remained cubic well below the transition point exhibiting a relatively wide hysteresis, eventually reaching the structure of the initial hexagonal phase. The only difference in the behaviour of these hydrides is the value of transition pressures.

All phase transformations observed are reversible with respect to the pressure, with however significant hysteresis between increase and decrease of pressure. This behavior reflects theoretical calculations that have shown only small differences in Gibbs free energies between the two phases taking part in the transformation. The results clearly show that the stability of the fcc phases is decreasing with the decrease of molar volume of the hcp phases and, correspondingly, transformation pressure is rising to its highest value for the lutetium trihydride.

X-ray diffraction studies of RH_x have revealed some systematics about the hcp – fcc transition and the compressibility of RE trihydrides. It has been clearly shown that the transition pressure of the respective hydride depends on its initial molar volume.

As can be seen in Figure 2 this tendency includes all trihydrides investigated and the relation can be used for predicting transition pressures for other, not yet studied rare earth trihydrides as indicated for Tb, Dy and Tm.

Since other properties of lanthanides are closely linked to their molar volume such as ionic radius, electronegativity or atomic number similar dependences can be expected for the hydrides.

An interesting feature of these transitions is the fact that the molar volume of the hexagonal hydrides after pressure induced phase transformation, extrapolated to ambient pressure, approaches the values expected from simple extrapolation of the volume of the hydrides that are cubic at normal pressure.

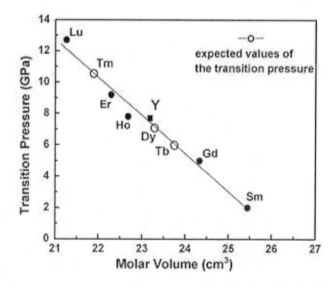

Figure 2. Transition pressure as a function of the molar volume of the initial trihydride hexagonal phase (Ref. [23]).

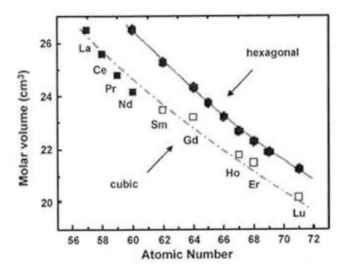

Figure 3. Molar volume of different forms of lanthanide trihydrides as a function of atomic number. Solid and dotted lines are eye-guides only (Ref. [24]).

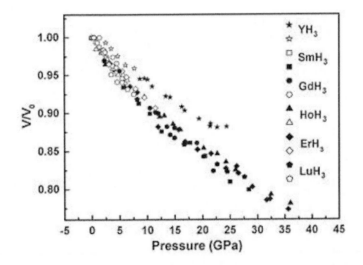

Figure 4. Change of the reduced molar volume of yttrium and lanthanide trihydrides with pressure (Ref. [21]).

This behavior is presented in Figure 3 which shows that the molar volumes of high pressure cubic phases of lanthanide hydrides nicely follow the trend initiated by cubic lanthanide hydrides which are stable at ambient pressure, such as LaH_3, CeH_3 and PrH_3.

Regarding a possible mechanism for the observed phase transformation it was assumed [25] that the repulsive interaction between hydrogen species in the metal lattice could be the main contribution to the Gibbs free energy responsible for the instability of the system under specific pressure. For the quantitative analyses the shortest H–H distances in both structures were chosen. The shortest H–H distance before (for hexagonal structure) and after (for cubic structure) the transition has been analyzed as a function of pressure. Though the change of minimal H–H is almost the same (~0.22Å) for all the hydrides, the relative change of this distance increases with the atomic number of the lanthanide element. That can partly account for the tendency of the transition pressure to increase within the trihydrides. Another observation is that the value of the H–H distance before the transition varies around 2Å. This value was shown to be critical for many stable hydrides of d-elements by Switendick [27] and is believed to represent the minimal distance between two positively charged hydrogen particles in a stable hydride lattice. Thus, repulsive interactions increase dramatically if this distance is less than the critical one for either positively or negatively charged hydrogen particles. However, its exact value may vary and it is logical to assume that it may depend on the radius of the hydrogen particles: smaller hydrogen particles can come closer to each other reaching the same repulsive effect.

Compressibilities and parameters of Equation of State (EOS) of a number of lanthanide trihydrides are presented in Figure 4, 5 and Table 1 along with that for the yttrium, scandium compound and corresponding pristine rare earth metals. The data have been fit to Murnaghan's equation of state (EOS) and the assumption of a constant first pressure derivative of bulk modulus ($B'_0 = 4$) was made.

Table 1. Structural parameters and parameters of Equation of State of the investigated rare earth trihydrides

Sample		Lattice parameters at atmospheric pressure		Molar Volume cm³/mol	hcp-fcc transition pressure (GPa)	EOS parameters		References
		a (Å)	c (Å)			B_0 (GPa)	B_0'	
Sm	rhomb.	3.611	26.22	19.8		33	2.9	Ref. 28
SmH₃	hcp	3.77	6.77	25.1	2.0	70	4 fixed	Ref. 21
	fcc	5.37		23.3		80		
Gd	hcp	3.636	5.783	19.9		35	2.9	Ref. 28
GdH₃	hcp	3.75	6.69	24.5	5.0	80	4 fixed	Ref. 20
	fcc	5.36		23.2		78		
Ho	hcp	3.577	5.6158	18.7		42	2.9	Ref.28
HoH₃	hcp	3.64	6.69	22.7	7.8	87	4 fixed	Ref. 20
	fcc	5.25		21.8		90		
Er	hcp	3.559	5.587	18.4		44	2.9	Ref. 28
ErH₃	hcp	3.62	6.53	22.3	8.0	70	4 fixed	Ref. 18
	fcc	5.23		21.5		81		
Lu	hcp	3.503	5.551	17.8		50	2.9	Ref.28
LuH₃	hcp	3.57	6.41	21.3	12.0	90	4 fixed	Ref. 20
	fcc	5.12		20.2		89		
Y	hcp	3.64	5.744	19.91		40	3.6	Ref.28
YH₃	hcp	3.65	6.544	23.29	11	71.9	5.0	Ref. 11
		3.67	6.62	23.3	7.7	142	4 fixed	Ref. 19
	fcc	5.28		22.2		145	4 fixed	
Sc	hcp	3.309	5.268	15.03		53	3.6	Ref.28
ScH₃	hcp	3.39	6.10(3)	18.16	30	103	2.6±0.5	Ref. 9 and Ref. therein
	fcc							

Moreover, it was assumed that B'_0 did not change after structural transition. While some reservations should be kept for the absolute values of the bulk modulus, they generally change little with the atomic number of the corresponding element. There is also an evident tendency of the bulk modulus to increase after the transition. Generally, a significant hardening of the hydride metal lattice has been observed in comparison to the pristine metal.

Murnaghan model of EOS:

$$\frac{V(P)}{V_0} = \left(1 + \frac{B'_0}{B_0} P\right)^{-1\,B'_0}$$

Birch-Murnaghan model of EOS:

$$P = \frac{3}{2} B_0 \left[\left(\frac{V}{V_0}\right)^{-7/3} - \left(\frac{V}{V_0}\right)^{-5/3}\right] \times \left\{1 + \frac{3}{4}\left(B'_0 - 4\right)\left[\left(\frac{V}{V_0}\right)^{-2/3} - 1\right]\right\}$$

Therein, B_0, bulk modulus [GPa]; B'_0, the first pressure derivative of bulk modulus; V_0 molar volume at ambient pressure.

Though the values of bulk moduli for particular lanthanide trihydrides are different, the difference is almost negligible when we compare them with the bulk modulus of YH_3 (see Figure 5).

Note that YH_3 definitely does not follow the tendency of other lanthanide trihydrides. Its compressibility resembles the compressibility of d-metal hydrides. The authors [21] explained this difference by the difference in electronic structure of Y, that formally belongs to the d-metal family and unlike lanthanide elements, does not possess a shell of f-electrons.

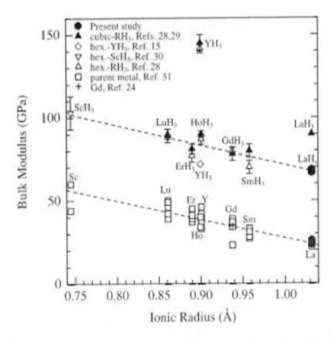

Figure 5. B_0 values of rare-earth metal hydrides and their parent metals against effective ionic radius of the rare-earth metals. Dashed lines are to guide the eye (by the courtesy of Machida A. (Ref. [17])).

Recent measurements [11, 12] carried out in hydrogen environment have shown however that the compressibility of yttrium trihydride seems more like that of other rare earth hydrides. Whether it results from non-hydrostatic conditions in the measurements done by the Polish group or from problems with the sample composition in the Japanese studies is not clear. Following the first structural study of the Polish group, several research groups from Japan have conducted extensive studies of YH$_3$ using various experimental techniques and detailed data analysis significantly contributing to the understanding of high-pressure behavior of REH$_3$.

Pressure induced structural transition of yttrium hydride has been investigated using synchrotron radiation X-ray diffraction measurement up to 24 GPa at room temperature. A reversible hexagonal–fcc transition with a wide intermediate region from 11 to 20 GPa has been confirmed.

Furthermore, the XRD measurements using a synchrotron radiation source have revealed another aspect for the hexagonal-cubic transition of YH$_3$ [11,12] The highly resolved XRD patterns of YH$_3$ under a good hydrostatic condition have allowed more detailed structural investigations on the coexisting state. Instead of a two-phase region, the existence of an intermediate state has been experimentally demonstrated.

The intermediate state is interpreted in terms of a long-period polytype that undergoes a successive conversion from the hexagonal to the fcc arrangement of the metal layers as the pressure increases from 10 to 20 GPa (Figure 6). This is a type of structural transition specific to metal trihydrides. The authors focused on the pressure shift of one reflection peak which showed a continuous change in 2θ position with the hexagonal-cubic transition.

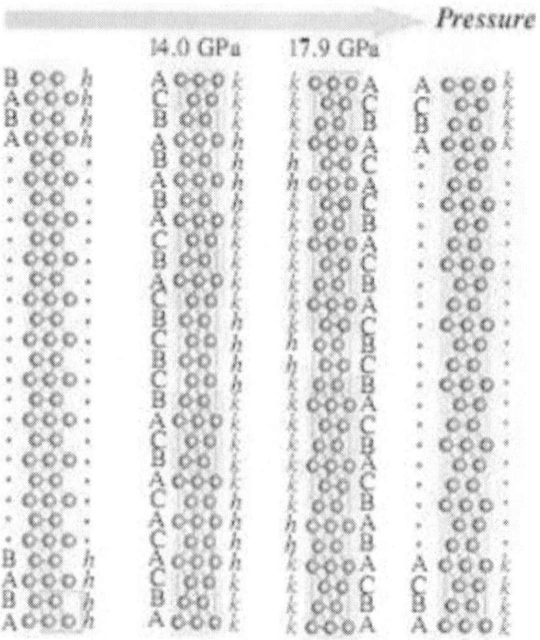

Figure 6. Schematic illustrations of the 27 R polytypes presented for intermediate stage of YH$_3$ at 14 and 17.9 GPa. Spheres indicate the Y atoms. H atoms are omitted. ABC and Jagodzinski (h-k representing hexagonal and cubic layer respectively) notations are also shown (by the courtesy of Machida A. (SPring-8 press release; for another presentation the reader is kindly advised to refer Ref. [12])).

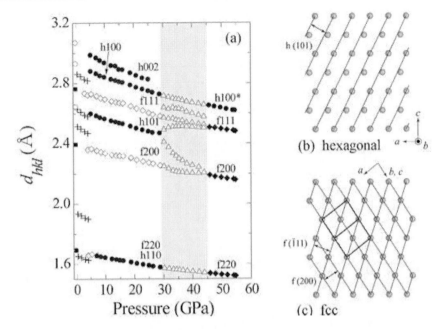

Figure 7. (a) Interplanar spacings, d_{hkl}, plotted as a function of pressure: solid solution ScH_x (+), fcc-ScH_2 (◊), hexagonal-Sc-H_3 (●), intermediate phase (□), and the fcc phase (♦). Open circles (○) and solid squares (■) indicate those of fcc-ScH_2 and hexagonal-ScH_3 respectively. The spacing shown as an asterisk (*) in the fcc phase is most likely the (1 0 0) plane of hexagonal-ScH_3. Hatched area shows the region of the intermediate state. (b) and (c) The (1 0 $\bar{1}$) planes in the hexagonal lattice and the (-1 1 1) and (2 0 0) planes in the fcc lattice, respectively (by the courtesy of Machida A. (Ref. [9])).

The 110 reflection peak of the hexagonal structure was continuously converted into the 220 reflection peak of the cubic structure with pressure across the intermediate region (see for instance the Figure 7 (Ref. [9]) where the similar transformation is shown for ScH_3). Because the ($2\bar{0}2$) plane of the fcc lattice corresponds to the (110) plane of the hexagonal lattice, the smooth and continuous peak conversion implies that the Y metal planes maintained their planar shape during the hexagonal-cubic transition. In addition, the peak widths did not show significant broadening in the intermediate pressure region of 13–22 GPa.

These features lead to an initial model in searching a candidate structure for the intermediate state. The gradual change in the XRD profile could be interpreted as a reconstruction process of the stacking sequence of the metal layers.

Then a series of candidate structures were calculated by sequentially varying the numbers of hexagonal-type and fcc-type layers contained within a unit cell to attain the best fit to the experimental XRD pattern (In profile simulation, the lattice of the Y metal was considered alone). The primitive cell is assumed to be rhombohedral or hexagonal depending on the stacking sequence. The lattice constant in the metal plane and the interplanar spacing were fixed to be 3.5 and 3 Å, respectively.

It has been found that the $27R$ $(HHHHKKKKK)_3$ polytype structure reproduces well the overall experimental profiles and therefore was chosen as a model for further refining of the structural parameters (Figure 8). The authors have shown that, during the transition, the number of cubic layer domains increases and introduced $\eta = \eta_K / (\eta_K + \eta_H)$, where η_H is the number of H layers and η_K that of K layers to describe the intermediate structure of the hexagonal-fcc transition process (Figure 9).

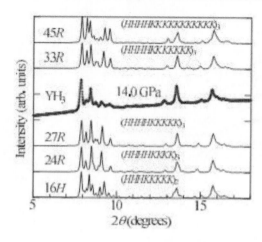

Figure 8. Simulated patterns of the polytypes with a long periodicity (solid curves). Middle pattern is the experimental one measured at 14.0 GPa for YH$_3$. Symbols *nR* and *nH* represent the primitive rhombohedral and hexagonal lattices with *n* metal layers, respectively (by the courtesy of Machida A. (Ref. [12])).

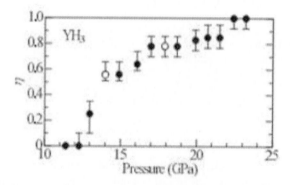

Figure 9. Pressure variation of the ratio of $\eta=\eta_K/(\eta_K + \eta_H)$, where η_H is the number of *H* layers and η_K is that of the *K* layers. Data points at 14.0 and 17.9 GPa (open circles) are those used for the Rietveld refinements of YH$_3$. Other values (solid circles) are obtained by comparing the experimental and simulated XRD patterns (by the courtesy of Machida A. (Ref. [12]).

Basing on the refined analysis of highly resolved XRD patterns the pressure-induced hexagonal-cubic transition can be interpreted as the gradual *H-K* layer conversion, without keeping periodicity.

2.1.1. Mechanism of Structural Transformation during the hcp to fcc Transition

As early as in their first reports, basing on approximate models of crystal structure, Polish researchers have pointed out the repulsive interaction between hydrogen species as the most probable driving force for structural transformation. Later on Japanese researchers having gained much more detailed knowledge of structure behavior under pressure from XRD and IR absorption measurements (see further in the next section) and it became possible to thoroughly follow the role of H – H and RE – H interactions during phase transformation.

It was found that the process of conversion from hexagonal to cubic phase can be conditionally separated into two stages (Figure 9):

1. The first stage of rapid conversion is caused by the increased H-H repulsive interactions of neighboring H atoms between the face shared *T* sites in *H* (hexagonal) - layers.

Their study revealed that when approaching the closest H species towards the empirical minimal H-H spacing of ~ 2 Å and thus to increasing repulsive interactions, from a certain pressure on, the *H*-layer arrangement became unfavorable and should collapse to transform into the *K*-layer arrangement.

2. The second stage exhibits a much more sluggish rate of conversion and is due to a reduced hexagonal layer fraction and increased metal-hydrogen interaction in cubic layers which suppresses the slip of the metal plane.

The reduction in the repulsive energy between hydrogen atoms due to the *H-K* layer conversion should become smaller as the *H*-layer fraction decreases and likely results in a gradual conversion into the cubic lattice. On the other hand, the contribution of the covalent like H–*M* bonding at the *O* site of *K* layers increases with further compression. This H–*M* bonding suppresses the slip of the metal plane. Consequently, the hexagonal-cubic transition does not occur by a one-step process but via successive change of long-period polytypes.

2.2. Spectroscopic Studies

2.2.1. IR and Visible Absorption Measurements

The experimental observation of hcp-fcc phase transitions reinforced the scientific interest in the electronic properties of the high-pressure cubic phase. As it was theoretically predicted by calculations of Ahuja et al. [26] the cubic form of YH_3 should exhibit metallic properties. In order to investigate this issue various spectroscopic techniques were employed for the study.

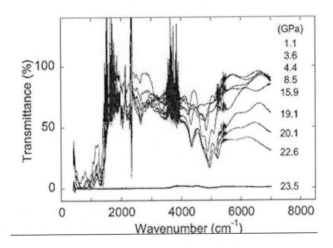

Figure 10. The infrared transmission spectra measured for the entire wave-number region, 400-7000 cm^{-1}. The transmission spectrum collapses at 23.5 GPa and the sample becomes opaque in the infrared region (by the courtesy of Machida A. (Ref. [10])).

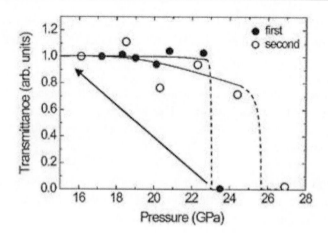

Figure 11. Pressure variation of transmission intensity at a fixed wavenumber of 2800 cm^{-1}. The transmission intensity abruptly drops to zero near 23 GPa and recovers when the pressure decreases to 16 GPa. The abrupt intensity drop is reproduced near 26 GPa upon the second compression. Solid and dashed lines are to guide the eye (by the courtesy of Machida A. (Ref. [10])).

The first experimental investigations on YH$_3$ have been conducted in 2000 by Wijngaarden et al. [29] who measured optical transmission and X-ray diffraction at pressures up to 25 GPa. An optical gap of 1.4 eV still existed at 25 GPa and was tentatively extrapolated to reach zero near 55 GPa. In 2006, Japanese researchers published results of infrared vibrational and transmission spectra for YH$_3$ at pressures up to 30 GPa [10]. In contrast to the previous visible absorption measurements of Wijngaarden et al, the gap closure was observed to occur at 23-26 GPa (Figures 10, 11).

This discrepancy could be probably explained by the sample conditions. In the visible absorption measurements of the Dutch group the hydride was prepared by evaporating a 0.5 μm thick film of yttrium metal on the top surface of a diamond anvil and hydriding it with hydrogen fluid under pressure.

Thus, the evaporated thin film on the diamond may have suffered from non-hydrostatic stress during compression due to significant mismatch in the compressibility between the hydride and diamond. On the other hand, the IR absorption measurements were conducted on a self-supporting metal foil.

Soon afterwards, a visible absorption study was carried out for YH$_3$ at room temperature up to 20 GPa to clarify the phase transition and the insulator-metal transition [13] (Figure 12). The results of the absorption measurements provided new experimental evidence for the band gap closure.

It was clearly shown that the band gap starts to close on transition from the hexagonal to the intermediate phase and was predicted to be complete in the cubic phase.

The authors initiated a discussion on the possible mechanism of the band gap closing observed for the fcc YH$_3$. One of the scenarios interprets the observed insulator to metal transition in terms of band overlap similarly to the case of CsI [30]. Although this mechanism predicts a continuous closing of the energy gap, which was inconsistent with the experimental observations, a very recent theoretical investigation [31] seems to corroborate the assumed model.

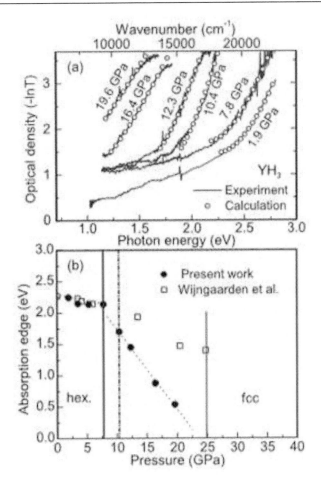

Figure 12. Pressure dependence of (a) absorption spectra and (b) energy gap of YH_3. In (a), the measured spectra and fitted absorption edges are shown by solid lines and open circles, respectively. In (b), the optical gap energies obtained by fitting the data are plotted. The solid circles and open squares correspond to the results from [13] and from [26], respectively. The region between the solid lines corresponds to the intermediate phase (by the courtesy Machida A. (Ref. [13])).

According to the calculations, hydrogen atoms at O sites play a key role in tuning metallic properties under pressure due to hybridization changes of its s state with the d state of Y. Once the minimum in the s-state density at the Fermi level reached, the s state transformed from a narrow atomic band to a much broader band, thus giving rise to a metallic state which has been observed in this pressure region (around 25 GPa), in excellent agreement with experimental findings.

Along with the detection of crucial electronic changes (like band gap closure) spectroscopic measurements provided much valuable experimental data giving deeper insight into the subtle structural changes during the hcp-fcc transformation helping to understand its mechanism. In the IR vibrational spectra collected for YH_3 in the pressure range up to 23 GPa, the Japanese scientists managed to detect tiny features reflecting the behavior of hydrogen atoms during structural transformation (Figures 13, 14).

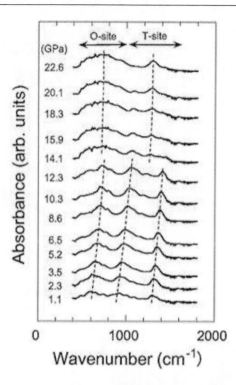

Figure 13. Infrared vibrational spectra measured for YH$_3$ at pressures up to 23 GPa. The spectral features gradually change as the pressure increases above 12 GPa, which is where the metal lattice begins to transform from hcp to fcc (by the courtesy of Machida A. (Ref. [10])).

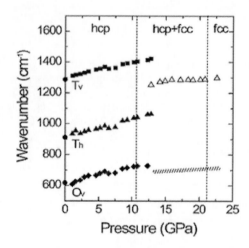

Figure 14. Variations in the peak frequencies with pressure measured for the infrared-active hydrogen vibrations of YH$_3$. The frequencies of the dominant peaks in the hcp structure, one O-site, and two T-site modes, are represented with solid symbols. Solid circles represent the frequencies at atmospheric pressure (by the courtesy of Machida A. (Ref. [10])).

A strong site-dependent behavior in the peak shift of the hydrogen vibrations with pressure has been observed. In the hcp phase, the O-site peak shifted to higher frequencies with pressure somewhat faster than the T-site ones, especially in the low-pressure region.

The Grüneisen parameter (calculated via the bulk modulus, B_0, from the compressibility study) showed significant differences for the O-site and the T-site modes:

$$\gamma (Ov) = 1.91 \pm 0.03,\ \gamma (Th) = 0.61 \pm 0.01,\ and\ \gamma (Tv) = 0.72 \pm 0.01.$$

It was assumed that such a behavior could probably reflect the different bonding nature at the two interstitial sites: the ionic-like bonds at the T site and the hybridized bonds at the O site. According to a band calculation [32] the hydrogen at the T site likely interacts as an anion with the surrounding metal atoms, whereas hydrogen at the O site forms s-d hybridization with a covalent-like bonding nature. Comparison of the Grüneisen parameters with those reported for representative covalent and ionic compounds though intuitive seemed to corroborate the assumption. The determined value of 1.91 for the O-site vibrations is comparable to those of the optical phonons of III-V compounds such as BN and GaAs, which range from 1.0 to 1.6 [33], while the γ -values of 0.61 and 0.72 for the T-site vibrations are comparable to those obtained for the optical phonons of LiH, an ionic compound, 0.7–1.2 [34].

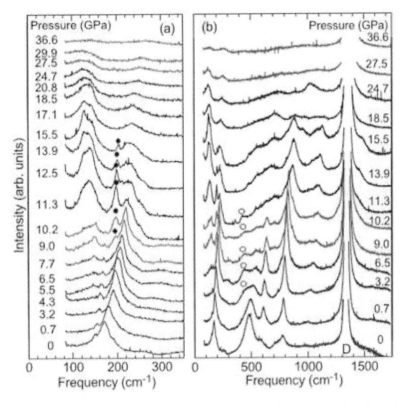

Figure 15. Pressure dependence of Raman spectra of YH_3. (a) and (b) correspond to the regions expanded in low frequencies (0-350 cm^{-1}) and covering whole of spectra (0-1750 cm^{-1}), respectively. The spectrum of 1 atm (0 GPa) was obtained after the high pressure experiments. The spectra characterics of the hexagonal, intermediate and fcc phases were observed at P<8 GPa, 11 GPa<P<25 GPa, and P>25 GPa, respectively. The spectra at 9 GPa<P<11 GPa can be explained by the coexistence of hexagonal and intermediate phases (closed and open circles.) The strong signal around 1330 cm^{-1} corresponds to the signal from diamond anvil (by the courtesy of Machida A. (Ref. [13])).

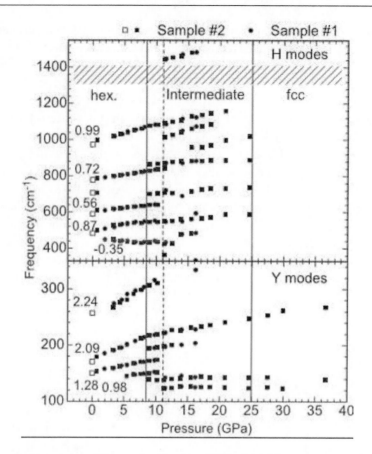

Figure 16. Pressure dependence of Raman frequencies of YH₃ obtained upon compression. The results obtained for two different samples are indicated. The data of 1 atm shown by open squares were obtained after releasing the pressure. For the hexagonal phase, the mode Grüneisen parameters are shown in this figure. The region between the two solid lines corresponds to the intermediate phase. At the pressure drawn by dashed line, a drastic spectral change was observed. The hatched area corresponds to the strong diamond signals (by the courtesy of Machida A. (Ref. [13])).

Thorough analysis of IR vibrational spectra and available literature data on neutron vibrational spectroscopy measurements [35] for YH₃ (hexagonal) and LaH₃ (cubic) allowed concluding on tendencies in the position of hydrogen atoms. It was suggested that the doublet-singlet conversion of the *T*-site vibrational peak in the hcp-fcc transition could be explained by the accompanying rearrangement of the *T* sites from the face-shared to the edge-shared configuration. The hydrogen vibrations, which originally split into doublet peaks in the face-shared configuration of the hcp structure, return to a degenerate singlet peak in the high-symmetry fcc structure, in accordance with the similar doublet and singlet structures observed for YH₃ (hexagonal) and LaH₃ (cubic) in neutron measurements [35]. Though hydrogen vibrations at T sites of the fcc phase are degenerate its measured frequency is a mean value of the T site vibrations of the hcp phase. Hence, it was concluded that the strength of the hydrogen-metal interactions did not change at the *T* site during the hcp-fcc transition.

Another spectral feature - peak broadening of the signal from hydrogen vibrations at O sites (Figure 13)– was proposed to reflect the rearrangement of the hydrogens located either on the metal plane or at the off planar positions above or below the metal plane in the hcp phase towards the symmetric center positions of the O sites in the cubic phase.

2.2.2. Raman Measurements

Raman studies performed on YH_3 and HoH_3 also revealed drastic changes (Figures 15, 16) in the pressure region of the hcp-fcc transition [13, 22]. Detailed analysis of the spectral features assigned to the vibrations of Y and H allowed a better understanding of the process of metal atomic layer transformation and of H atom movement during transformation.

The softening behavior of the Ov band (open circles in Figure 15) is possibly a precursor of the centering of H_O atoms in octahedral sites. Simultaneous occurrence of the H_O atom movement and of the stacking change of Y planes implies that the removal of H_O atoms from Y plane triggers the sliding of Y planes. Raman spectra peculiar to the new phase intermediate between the low-pressure hexagonal and high-pressure fcc phase were observed providing new experimental evidence for successive changes in the stacking sequence and corroborating a long-period stacking structure model.

2.3. Electrical Properties Study

Despite tremendous progress in understanding the hcp-fcc transition which has been achieved in structural and spectroscopic studies, a direct observation of metallization is still waiting to be confirmed. The only reported experimental research indeed revealed significant changes of electrical resistance corresponding to the hcp-fcc transition (Figure 17).

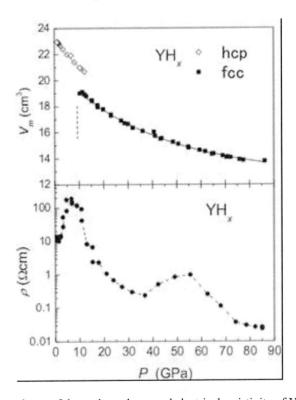

Figure 17. Pressure dependence of the molar volume and electrical resistivity of YH_x at room temperature. The solid and dashed lines passing through the dots are guide for eyes. The phase boundary between hcp and fcc is represented by the vertical dashed line at 8 GPa (by the courtesy of Matsuoka T. (Ref. [14])).

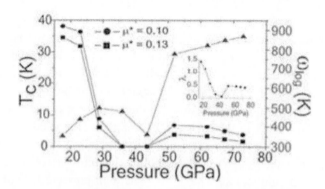

Figure 18. Pressure dependency of calculated T_c and phonon momentum ω_{log} The inset shows the evolution of the electron-phonon coupling constant λ with pressure (by the courtesy of Ahuja R. Ref. [31])).

However, the electronic transition itself was not confirmed up to 85 GPa. Measurement of the temperature dependence of the electrical resistance under pressure is required to obtain a convincing proof of the insulator to metal transition.

An interesting anomaly was observed in the relatively large pressure range 40-60 GPa, which according to XRD measurements seemed not to correspond with any structural changes.

In the light of recent theoretical calculations, this anomaly might reflect the strong alteration of electronic structure on the way to the superconducting state [31] (Figure 18).

2.4. Cases of Eu and Yb Hydrides

Eu and Yb represent rare-earth elements whose valence states may be changed. The ground valence state of most lanthanides is $4f^n$ $(5d6s)^3$ while Eu and Yb exhibit an electronic configuration $4f^{n+1}$ $(5d6s)^2$ of the ground valence state, which may have effect on the chemical bonding and therefore the structural properties of the corresponding hydrides. At ambient conditions, the rare-earth dihydrides EuH_2 and YbH_2 resemble the divalent alkaline-earth dihydrides crystallizing in the orthorhombic CaH_2 type structure (space group Pnma $(PbCl_2)$), which is in contrast to the "normal" trivalent rare-earth dihydrides crystallizing in the fcc fluorite (CaF_2) structure. Up to date only a few experimental reports can be found in the literature concerning the high pressure behavior of the Eu and Yb hydrides. They were for a long time considered irregular members of the rare earth hydride family, until a very recent report of Matsuoka et al. [6] the XRD and Moessbauer effect studies of which significantly pushed forward our knowledge and understanding of the effect of pressure on the structure and valence state of the Eu − H system. Taking into account the high-pressure XRD study of YbH_2 reported much earlier by Olsen et al. [36], the systems of Eu-H and Yb-H with hydrogen are no longer considered as irregular members of the rare-earth metal hydrides.

2.4.1. EuH_x

Once hydrided in normal conditions, europium hydride EuH_2 when exposed to further high-pressure H_2, has been found to exhibit the following structural, composition and valence changes (Figures 19, 20):

Ambient pressure Phase EuH$_x$ I: Pnma (x= 2; divalent) –> Phase EuH$_x$ II: P6$_3$/mmc (x= 2; 7.2–8.7 GPa) –> Phase EuH$_x$ III: I4/m (x >2; 8.7–9.7 GPa) –> Phase EuH$_x$ IV I4/mmm (x> 2; 9.7 GPa; trivalent).

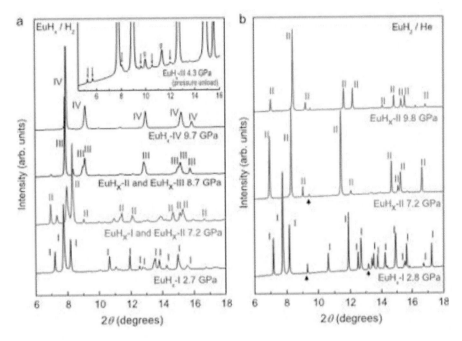

Figure 19. Integrated XRD profiles of (a) the EuH$_x$/H$_2$ and (b) the EuH$_2$/He. The inset graph in (a) indicates the XRD profile of EuH$_x$ -III at 4.3 GPa when pressure is unloaded. The downward arrows in the inset graph show the satellite peaks of EuH$_x$ –III phase. The "g" labels and upward arrows in (b) show the diffraction peaks of Re-metal gasket and EuO, respectively (by the courtesy of Machida A. Ref. [6])).

On the basis of results from Mössbauer-effect measurements, the EuH$_x$-IV may be considered as EuH$_3$ since the charge transfer from Eu to H is thought to drive the valence changes.

Therefore, the hydrogen compositions of EuH$_x$-III and EuH$_x$-IV are assumed to lie between 2.2 and 3. The chemically driven nature of valence change has been confirmed in the same report by compressing EuH$_2$ in a He environment.

Compression of EuH$_2$ in an inert environment has led only to the transformation to the phase EuH$_x$ II (P6$_3$/mmc) – a characteristic structure for high-pressure phase divalent alkaline-earth hydrides (Figure 19).

2.4.2. YbH$_x$

Similarly to Eu, ytterbium metal reacts with hydrogen gas to form a dihydride, α-YbH$_2$, a phase with an Pnma orthorhombic structure. Magnetic susceptibility studies [37] have indicated a divalent, Yb^{2+} , non-magnetic 4f state of the ytterbium ions in this compound. When the hydride composition is higher than H/Yb ~ 2.2 the system undergoes a phase transition from α-orthorhombic to the two β and β$^{/}$- cubic crystallographic structures which differ from each other in the lattice constant only [38].

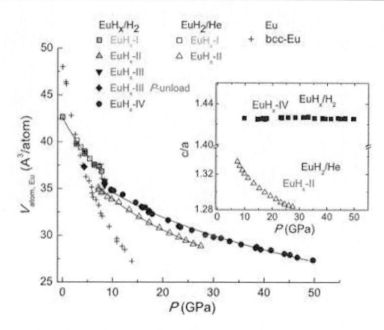

Figure 20. Pressure dependence of $V_{atom, Eu}$. The solid lines represent the Birch-Murnaghan equation of state (BM-EOS). The fitting to BM-EOS gives the following results: $B_0=10.17(3)$ GPa and $V_0=42.52(8)$ $Å^3$ for EuH_x –I, $B_0=11.2(2)$ GPa and $V_0=39.8(1)$ $Å^3$ for EuH_x –II, $B_0=14.33(7)$ GPa and $V_0=32.82(3)$ $Å^3$ for EuH_x –IV. The inset graph shows the pressure dependence of the c/a ratio for EuH_x –II, EuH_x –III and EuH_x –IV. EuH_x –IV is stable up to the highest pressure of 50 GPa (by the courtesy of Machida A. Ref. [6])).

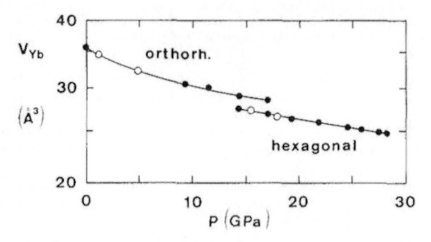

Figure 21. Pressure dependence of the volume per Yb atom in the unit cell. Open circles denote measurements for decreasing pressure. The curve for the orthorhombic phase has been calculated from Murnaghan's equation of state using $B_0=40,2$ GPa and $B_0'=4,75$. The curve for the hexagonal phase has been calculated using $B_0=138$ GPa and $B_0'=0$ (by the courtesy of Gerward L. (Ref. [36])).

The β' phase is metastable and exists only in the high temperature range [39]. It was shown that the α to β phase transformation is accompanied by an Yb^{2+}- Yb^{3+} valence transition. Investigations of the electronic structure of YbH_x hydride ($2.2 \leq x \leq 2.71$) samples performed by the X-ray line shift (XLS) method and magnetization measurements have shown that ytterbium changes its valence from 2 in YbH_2 to an average non-integer valence value of 2.72 in the β-cubic phase [40, 41].

Similarly to europium dihydride, compression of YbH_2 leads to a phase transition from the initially orthorhombic (Pnma) phase to hcp ($P6_3/mmc$) phase at a pressure of ~ 15 GPa (Figure 21).

Although the observed transition is common to EuH_2 and similar to divalent alkaline-earth hydrides (e.g., CaH_2 [42]) the authors expressed some reservations about drawing definite conclusions on the valence change. They linked the observed c/a = 1.34 and a significant hardening of the high-pressure phase to non-integral valence or to the fact that the hexagonal structure is typical for the Ln-dihydrides under high pressure.

2.5. Differences in High-Pressure Behavior of the Hexagonal and Cubic (LaH_3) Trihydrides

Hydrides of light rare-earth elements represent a special case in their response to hydrogenation and high-pressure application. Overall, light rare-earth hydrides are much less studied under high pressure and most of the studies reported in the literature are focused on La – H system.

First of all, in contrast to heavy rare-earth metals, light rare earths upon hydrogenation form hydride phases (LaH_x) crystallizing in cubic form in the whole hydrogen composition range (2 <x< 3).

Table 2. Overview of high-pressure and low-temperature studies of different samples of LaH_x

	High pressure		Low temperature
	Pressure range studied/ pressure medium	Observations/ methods used	
$LaH_{3.00}$ [3, 53]	A.P. – 25 GPa/ mineral oil	no structural change/ XRD (energy dispersive mode) [23]; IR + Raman [3]	
$LaH_{2.85}$[7, 53]	A.P. – 22.7 GPa/ mineral oil	unidentified structural change (most probably tetragonal distortion + disproportionation reaction)/ XRD (energy dispersive mode)	not studied
$LaH_{2.46}$[17]	A.P. – 14 GPa/He	no structural change/ XRD	not studied
$LaH_{2.3}$ [16]	A.P. – 20.3 GPa/He	tetragonal distortion + phase separation due to the disproportionation reaction (Figures)/XRD	not studied
LaH_x, x = 2.6, 2.75, 2.9 [45, 46]	not studied		tetragonal distortion
LaH_2 [17]	A.P. ~ 10 GPa/He	no structural change	
LaH_2 [7]	A.P ~ 30 GPa/He	disproportionation reaction / IR + Raman	

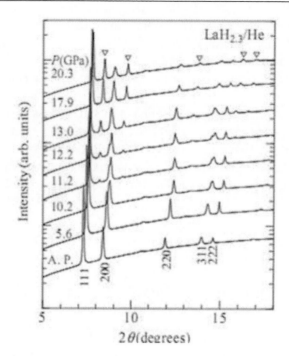

Figure 22. X-ray diffraction patterns measured for $LaH_{2.3}$ in a He medium upon compression (by the courtesy of Machida A. (Ref. [16])).

Upon hydrogen absorption, the double hexagonal close-packed (dhcp) lattice of La transforms into a face-centered cubic (fcc) one, where the H atoms selectively occupy the tetrahedral interstitial sites (T-sites) of the dihydride LaH_2. The hydrogenation reaction at this stage causes a relatively large volume expansion ($\sim$20%) which is interpreted in terms of the T-site hydrogens being negatively charged due to charge transfer from the surrounding metal atoms.

Further hydrogen uptake leads to occupation of the less energetically favorable octahedral interstitial sites (O-sites) up to maximum LaH_3 stoichiometry. This results in a slight contraction of the metal lattice ($\sim$3%) [43-46]).

In other words, the behavior of the metal lattice upon hydrogenation strongly depends on the site occupation. A qualitative insight on the site dependent bonding nature for rare-earth metal hydrides has been presented in several theoretical articles [32, 47, 48].

The possibility of continuous composition variation of hydrogen within the same crystallographic arrangement of the metal lattice makes La – H a convenient model system for studying phenomena (like structural and electronic transitions) associated with hydrogen transfer between the tetrahedral and octahedral interstitial sites as a response to external forces (such as pressure and temperature).

A concise overview of the high-pressure low-temperature studies of different samples of LaH_x is given in the Table 2.

One notes that most samples with either occupied or unoccupied octahedral interstitial sites, exhibit instabilities with respect to the initial phase under pressure. In general, two major structural changes were observed: a tetragonal distortion of the fluorite type cubic structure and phase separation.

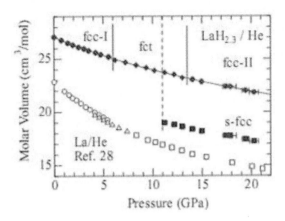

Figure 23. Pressure variations of the molar volume for $LaH_{2.3}$ pressurized in a He medium. Closed circles, diamonds, and squares represent the parameters of the fcc-I (fcc-II), fct, and s-fcc phases, respectively. Open symbols indicate the volume of La metal pressurized in a He medium. Solid curve is a fit of the compression curves with the equations of state (by the courtesy of Machida A. (Ref. [16])).

In the case of $LaH_{2.3}$, which is the most representative composition (Figures 22, 23) it has been shown that a tetragonally distorted cubic structure is more favorable in the pressure range from ~ 6 to ~ 14 GPa. Further pressure increase induced phase separation, due to the disproportionation reaction resulting in a solid solution phase LaH_x (x<1) and a hydrogen rich phase close to $LaH_{x~3}$.

2.5.1. Mechanism of the Structural Changes in $LaH_{2÷3}$ Under Pressure: Tetragonal Distortion

Hydrogen ordering at the O- sites is the most likely process driving the tetragonal distortion of the cubic phase. At low temperatures, LaH_x exhibits a characteristic tetragonality in a hydrogen concentration between 2.6 <x< 2.9 [45, 46]. Moreover, the change from an one-line spectrum to a more complicated one was reported for 2D-NMR in LaD_{2+x} deuterides, with 2.28 <x < 2.48, [49] below 240 K possibly indicating structural deformation. In fact, it resembles the hydrogen ordering described for some non-stoichiometric dihydrides of heavy rare-earth metals (e.g.TbD_{2+x} [49], SmH_{2+x} [51] and in the review article [5]). A close relation between hydrogen excess (x) and the degree of tetragonal distortion has been also revealed: for low x-values – no distortion observed [51]. The only high-pressure study on super-stoichiometric $ErH_{2.091}$ did not show tetragonal distortion either [52].

2.5.2. Mechanism of the Structural Changes in $LaH_{2÷3}$ Under Pressure: Phase Separation

Hydrogen transfer from the T-sites to the O- sites is the most likely process associated with phase separation. The molar volume increases upon hydrogenation to LaH_2, but decreases with further hydrogenation from LaH_2 into LaH_3:

$$V_0(LaH_2) > V_0(LaH_3) + V_0(LaH_x \text{ (solid solution)})$$

In ideal LaH_2, the hydrogen atoms occupy only the T-sites, while occupying both T- and O-sites in LaH_3. Additional hydrogen occupation of the O-sites in LaH_{2+x} leads to the formation of LaH_3, with contraction of the metal lattice, while the introduction of T-site vacancies causes the LaH_2 lattice to shrink, forming a solid solution LaH_x. Because phase separation is accompanied by a volume reduction (Figure 24), it is favorable at high pressure.

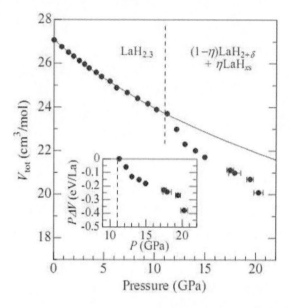

Figure 24. Pressure variations for the total volume of the system. Inset shows the $P\Delta V$ ($\Delta V = V_{tot} - V_{EOS}$) against pressure. Solid line: computed fit with EOS (by the courtesy of Machida A. (Ref. [16])).

3. THEORETICAL STUDIES: PROSPECTS OF HIGH TC IN RARE EARTH HYDRIDES UNDER PRESSURE

Beside the high-pressure hcp-fcc transitions revealing an intricate role of metal – hydrogen interactions which drive structural transformations, quite recently several predictions of metallization and of the superconducting state in hydrogen-rich materials have enormously boosted the interest in the lanthanide hydrides in particular [31, 54, 55, 56]. According to recent theoretical reports, along with the hydrides of general stoichiometry MH_4 (e. g., GeH_4 [57], SnH_4 [58], SiH_4 [59]), metal hydrides with 3 hydrogen atoms (MH_3) may exhibit significant superconductive properties as well [31, 56, 60].

The result of this study is presented in the Figure 25. Two tendencies become noticeable in the picture:

- MH_4-type systems exhibit relatively higher critical temperatures (T_c) of the superconducting state in comparison to MH_3-type compounds;
- the pressure at which superconductivity sets in (10–20GPa) is nearly an order of magnitude lower than that for the MH_4 compounds.

The latter finding gives experimentalists an exciting opportunity to verify theoretical predictions and gain better insight onto the origin of superconductivity as well as to approach the verification of a long-standing prediction about hydrogen acquiring a metallic state under high pressure.

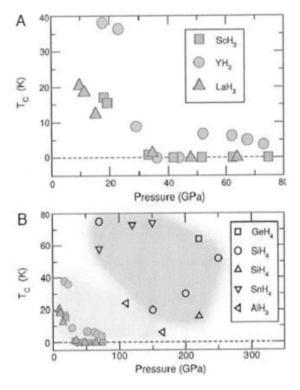

Figure 25. Calculated critical temperature of superconductivity (T_c) as a function of pressure. (A) predictions for ScH_3, YH_3, and LaH_3. (B) The data for GeH_4, SiH_4, SnH_4, and AlH_3 (*Hollow Symbols*), as predicted by various groups, compared with the data for the three RE-trihydride systems (*Filled Symbols*). The approximate grouping of the MH_3 and MH_4 T_c-P data pairs is highlighted by the shaded areas (by the courtesy of Ahuja R (Ref. [56])).

4. Concluding Remarks

Rare-earth hydrides revealed intricate structural and electronic behavior under high-pressure conditions. In the following a brief summary of the observed phenomena is presented.

4.1. Structural Transformations

In general, hexagonal hydrides (REH_3) of heavier Ln-elements (Sm, Gd, Er, Ho, Lu) and ScH_3, YH_3 transform to cubic form via a complex intermediate state featured by a successive change of hexagonal for cubic structural motif with pressure increase. The overall transformation has been shown to occur in two stages: rapid and sluggish conversion stage, where the H-H repulsive interactions play the dominant role.

Hydrides of Eu and Yb, featuring ground valence state $(4f^{n+1}(5d6s)^2)$ of constituting metal, have long been considered irregular members of Ln-hydride family resembling the alkaline earth metal hydrides in their behavior under pressure. Once the valence state changes towards $4f^n(5d6s)$ [3] (chemically driven by interactioin with hydrogen under high pressure) EuH_x has been shown to follow the structural transformations similar to the heavier trivalent rare-earth dihydrides.

Finally, hydrides of $LaH_{2 \leq x < 3}$ (representative of the light rare-earth metal hydrides) have revealed instability of the initial cubic phase under pressure transforming via tetragonally distorted cubic phase to the mixture of hydrogen-rich ($LaH_{\sim 3}$) and solid solution ($LaH_{< 2}$) phases as a result of the disproportionation reaction. A relatively large mobility of hydrogen species between tetrahedral and octahedral sites is associated in the observed structural changes. On the other hand, the $LaH_{\sim 3}$ hydride with fully occupied interstices has been shown to retain the initial cubic structure in the whole pressure range studied.

4.2. Electronic Transformations

The observed structural changes in hexagonal hydrides (REH_3) of heavier Ln-elements are accompanied by dramatic electronic changes manifesting with optical gap closure (IR and visible absorption studies), significantly changed Raman scattering spectra and electrical transport measurements. Although lacking direct clear evidence, so far collected experimental findings strongly support the possibility of metallization of these hydrides under pressure predicted by several theoretical research groups.

Summarizing the state of art, a tremendous progress has been achieved in understanding the effect of high pressure on the crystal structure of Ln-hydrides and the role of hydrogen species involved in the observed transformations. The next goal is an experimental exploration of the predicted metallization and superconducting properties under pressure.

REFERENCES

[1]   Stalinski, B. *Bull. Acad. Pol. Sci. Class III* 1957, 5, 1001.

[2]   Huiberts, J.N.; Griessen, R.; Rector, H.H.; Wijngaarden, R.J.; Decker, J.P.; De Groot, D.G.; Koeman, N.J. *Nature* 1996, 380, 231.

[3]   Armitage, R.; Rubin, M.; Richardson, T.; O'Brien, N.; Chen, Y. *Appl. Phys. Lett.* 1999, 75, 1724.

[4]   Kerssemakers, J.W.J.; Van der Molen, S.J.; Koeman, N.J.; Günther, R.; Griessen, R. *Nature* 2000, 406, 489.

[5]   P. Vajda, Hydrogen in rare earth metals including RH_{2+x} phases, in: K.A. Gschneidner (Ed.), Handbook on the Physics and Chemistry of Rare Earths vol. 20, North-Holland, Amsterdam, 1995, p. 207.

[6]   Matsuoka, T.; Fujihisa, H.; Hirao, N.; Ohishi, Y.; Mitsui, T.; Masuda, R.; Seto, M.; Yoda, Y.; Shimizu, K.; Machida, A.; Aoki K. *Phys. Rev. Lett.* 2011, 107, 025501.

[7]   Sakurai, Y.; Machida, A.; Aoki, K. *Solid State Commun.* 2011, 151, 815–817.

[8] Ohmura, A.; Machida, A.; Watanuki, T.; Aoki, K.; Nakano, S.; Takemura, K. *Appl. Phys. Lett.* 2007, 91, 151904.

[9] Ohmura, A.; Machida, A.; Watanuki, T.; Aoki, K.; Nakano, S.; Takemura, K. *J. Alloys Compd.* 2007, 446–447, 598–602.

[10] Ohmura, A.; Machida, A.; Watanuki, T.; Aoki, K.; Nakano, S.; Takemura, K. *Phys. Rev. B* 2006, 73, 104105.

[11] Machida, A.; Ohmura, A.; Watanuki, T.; Ikeda, T.; Aoki, K.; Nakano, S.; Takemura, K. *Solid State Commun.* 2006, 138, 436–440.

[12] Machida, A.; Ohmura, A.; Watanuki, T.; Aoki, K.; Takemura, K. *Phys. Rev. B* 2007, 76, 052101.

[13] Kume, K.; Ohura, H.; Sasaki, S.; Shimizu, H.; Ohmura, A.; Machida, A.; Watanuki, T.; Aoki, K.; Takemura, K. *Phys. Rev. B* 2007, 76, 024107.

[14] Matsuoka,T.; Kitayama,T.; Shimizu, K.; Nakamoto,Y.; Kagayama,T.; Aoki, K.; Ohishi, Y.; Takemura, K. *High Pressure Res.* 2006, 26, 391–394.

[15] Kume, K.; Ohura, H.; Takeichi, T.; Ohmura, A.; Machida, A.; Watanuki, T.; Aoki, K.; Sasaki, S.; Shimizu, H.; Takemura, K. *Phys. Rev. B* 2011, 84, 064132.

[16] Machida, A.; Watanuki, T.; Kawana, D.; Aoki, K. *Phys. Rev. B* 2011, 83, 054103.

[17] Machida, A.; Watanuki, T.; Ohmura, A.; Ikeda, T.; Aoki, K.; Nakano, S.; Takemura, K. *Solid State Commun.* 2011, 151, 341-345.

[18] Palasyuk, T.; Tkacz, M. *Solid State Commun.* 2004, 130, 219–221.

[19] Palasyuk, T.; Tkacz, M. *Solid State Commun.* 2005, 133, 477–480.

[20] Palasyuk, T.; Tkacz, M. *Solid State Commun.* 2005, 133, 481–486.

[21] Palasyuk, T.; Tkacz, M. *Solid State Commun.* 2007, 141, 302–305.

[22] Palasyuk, T.; Tkacz, M.; Dubrovinsky, L. *Solid State Commun.* 2007, 142, 337–341.

[23] Palasyuk, T.; Tkacz, M. *Solid State Commun.* 2007, 141, 354–358.

[24] Tkacz, M.; Palasyuk, T. *J. Alloys Compd.* 2007, 446–447, 593–597.

[25] Kelly, P.J.; Dekker, J.P.; Stumpf, R. *Phys. Rev. Lett.* 1997, 78, 1315.

[26] Ahuja, R.; Johansson, B.; Wills, J.M.; Eriksson, O. Appl. Phys. Lett. 1997, 71,3497.

[27] Switendick, A.C. *Zeitschrift für Phys. Chem.*, Neue Folge 1979, 117, 89.

[28] Grosshans, W. A.; Holzapfel, W. B. Phys. Rev. B 1992, 45, 5171-5178.

[29] Wijngaarden, R.J.; Huiberts, J.N.; Nagengast, D.; Rector, J.H.; Griessen, R.; Hanfland, M.; Zontone, F. *J. Alloys Compd.* 2000, 308, 44.

[30] Williams, Q.; Jeanloz, R. *Phys. Rev. Lett.* 1986, 56, 163-164.

[31] Kim, D. Y.; Scheicher, R. H.; Ahuja, R. *Phys. Rev. Lett.* 2009, 103, 077002.

[32] Fujimori, A.; Minami, F.; Tsuda, N. *Phys. Rev. B* 1980, 22, 3573.

[33] Aoki, K.; Anastassakis, E.; Cardona, M. *Phys. Rev. B* 1984, 30, 681.

[34] Ho, A. C.; Hanson, R. C.; Chizmeshya, A. *Phys. Rev. B* 1997, 55, 14818-14829.

[35] Udovic, T. J.; Rush, J. J.; Huang, Q.; Anderson, I. S. *J. Alloys Compd.* 1997, 253–254, 241–247.

[36] Olsen, J. S.; Buras, B.; Gerward, L.; Johansson, B.; Lebech, B.; Skriver, H. L.; Steenstrup, S. *Phys. Scr.* 1984, 29, 503-507.

[37] Warf, J. C.; Hardcastle, K. J. *Inorg. Chem.* 1966, 5, 1736.

[38] Hardcastle, K. J.; Warf, J. C. *Inorg. Chem.* 1966, 5, 1728.

[39] Drulis, H.; Drulis, M.; Iwasieczko, W.; Suleimanov, N. M. *J. Less-Common Met.* 1988, 141,201.

[40] Shaburov, V.A.; Sovestnov, A.E.; Smirnov, Yu. L.; Tyunis, A.W.; Drulis, H.; Drulis, M. Phys. of the Solid State 1998, 40, 1265.

[41] Iwasieczko, W.; Drulis, M.; Drulis, H. *J. Alloys Compd.* 2001,327, 11-16.

[42] Tse, J. S.; Klug, D. D.; Desgreniers, S.; Smith, J. S.; Flacau, R.; Liu, Z.; Hu, J.; Chen, N.; Jiang D. T. *Phys. Rev. B* 2007, 75, 134108.

[43] Bashkin, I. O.; Ponyatovskii, E. G.; Kost, M. E. *Phys. Stat. Sol.* 1977, 83, 517.

[44] Goon, E.J. *J. Phys. Chem.* 1959, 63, 2018.

[45] Klavins, P.; Shelton, R.N.; Barnes, R.G.; Beaudry, B.J. *Phys. Rev. B* 1984, 29, 5349.

[46] Boroch, E.; Conder, K.; Xiu, C.R.; Kaldis, E. *J. Less-Common. Met.* 1989, 156, 259.

[47] Ng, K. K.; Zhang, F. C.; Anisimov, V. I.; Rice, T. M. *Phys. Rev. B* 1999, 59, 5398.

[48] Miyake, T.; Aryasetiawan, F.; Kino, H.; Terakura, K. *Phys. Rev. B* 2000, 61, 16491.

[49] De Groot, D. G.; Barnes, R. G.; Beaudry, B. J.; Torgeson, D. R. *J. Less-Common Met.* 1980, 73, 233.

[50] André, G.; Blaschko, O.; Schwarz, W., Daou, J.N., Vajda, P. *Phys. Rev. B* 1992, 46, 86448.

[51] Zogal, J.; L'Heritier, Ph. *J. Alloys Compd.* 1991, 177, 83.

[52] Palasyuk, T.; Tkacz, M. ; Vajda, P. *Solid State Commun.* 2005, 135, 226–231.

[53] Palasyuk, T.; Tkacz, M. *J. Alloys Compd.* 2009, 468, 191–194.

[54] Ashcroft, N.W. *Phys. Rev. Lett.* 2004, 92, 187002.

[55] Araújo, C. M.; Da Silva A. F.; Ahuja, R. *Phys. Stat. Sol.* 2004, 241, 3219–3223.

[56] Kim, D. Y.; Scheicher, R. H.; Mao, H.kwang; Kang, T. W.; Ahuja, R. *Proc. Nat. Acad. Sci.* 2010, 107, 2793.

[57] Gao, G.; Oganov, A.R.; Bergara, A.; Martinez-Canales, M.; Cui, T.; Iitaka, T.; Ma, Y.; Zou, G. *Phys. Rev. Lett.* 2008, 101, 107002.

[58] Tse, J.S.; Yao, Y.; Tanaka, K. *Phys. Rev. Lett.* 2007, 98, 117004.

[59] Chen, X.-J.; Wang, J.-L.; Struzhkin, V.V.; Mao, H.kwang; Hemley, R. J.; Lin, H.-Q. *Phys. Rev. Lett.* 2008, 101,077002.

[60] Goncharenko, I.; Eremets, M. I.; Hanfland, M.; Tse, J. S.; Amboage, M.; Yao, Y.; Trojan, I. A. *Phys. Rev. Lett.* 2008, 100, 045504.

In: Properties of Fluorite Structure Materials
Editors: Peter Vajda and Jean-Marc Costantini

ISBN: 978-1-62417-458-2
© 2013 Nova Science Publishers, Inc.

Chapter 4

POINT DEFECTS IN LITHIUM OXIDE

François Beuneu[*]

Laboratoire des solides irradiés, Ecole polytechnique,
CNRS-CEA, Palaiseau, France

ABSTRACT

The present chapter is devoted to the study of the properties of point defects and their agglomerates in a ionic simple oxide of antifluorite structure, lithium oxide (Li_2O). This lithium compound is regarded as a serious candidate for tritium breeding material for the future fusion reactors. In this context, a detailed study of point defects and their agglomerates is highly desirable, as well as the creation of these defects under irradiation and their annealing properties. The main point defect detectable in irradiated lithium oxide is the so-called F^+ center, corresponding to an oxygen vacancy with an electron trapped. It is easily detected by electron paramagnetic resonance (EPR) or by optical techniques. Depending on the irradiation or annealing conditions, agglomerates of F^+ centers can also be observed. We describe the conditions when this agglomeration gives rise to lithium precipitates with clear metallic properties. Again, EPR is a good technique for that, because lithium gives with this method an intense and easily recognizable signal. These colloids are studied not only by EPR but also by dielectric constant measurements, optical microscopy, NMR, differential calorimetry and neutron scattering; magnetization measurements on O_2 bubbles are also presented. Finally, some extensions of these observations are discussed, such as similar measurements on lithium imide (another antifluorite type compound), but also bistable conduction electron spin resonance and molecular-dynamics studies of the superionic phase of Li_2O.

1. INTRODUCTION

Lithium oxide (Li_2O) is a transparent colorless solid, highly ionic and quite hygroscopic, forming lithium hydroxide with air moisture. The somewhat recent interest for this compound is due to its high lithium content, which gives it a high tritium breeding potential under

---

[*] E-mail: francois.beuneu@polytechnique.edu.

neutron irradiation, making it a good candidate as solid breeder material of a deuterium-tritium fusion power plant.

The molar mass of Li_2O is 29.88 g/mol and its density is 2.013 g/cm^3. This density corresponds to a partial Li density of 0.935 g/cm^3, to be compared with the Li density of 0.53 g/cm^3 for bulk metallic bcc lithium.

The melting point of Li_2O is 1570 C, its refractive index is 1.644. It crystalizes in the antifluorite structure - i.e. CaF_2 structure with the cation and anion positions exchanged – with a lattice parameter 0.461 nm (space group $Fm\overline{3}m$).

Lithium oxide has a relatively high thermal conductivity [1]. It is known as a superionic conductor, being of interest in the context of solid state batteries [2]. It is of high importance to know how Li_2O behaves under irradiation, specially for its uses as tritium breeder in future fusion reactors. In this chapter, we shall present results concerning irradiation defects in Li_2O, obtained mainly by the group of Noda in Japan and by our own group in Palaiseau. In a recent short review paper, Popov et al [3] discuss the "basic properties of the F-type centers in halides, oxides and perovskites". They treat, in particular, the optical properties of F and F^+ centers in several types of insulators, including oxides with the fluorite or antifluorite structure.

2. THE WORK OF NODA AND COWORKERS

Noda and his coworkers have published, from 1980 to 1998, an important set of papers on irradiation effects in lithium oxide [4-14]. In the first of these papers [4], the authors irradiated polycrystalline (sintered) Li_2O samples with thermal neutrons to fluences between 1.5 x 10^{20} and 9.8 x 10^{21} thermal neutrons/m^2, around room temperature. They observed the irradiated samples with electron paramagnetic resonance (EPR) and obtained spectra with well-resolved hyperfine structure centered on a g value near 2.002 ± 0.001 (Figure 1). This spectrum was attributed to F^+ centers i.e. oxygen vacancies with one electron trapped.

Increasing the neutron fluence up to 5 x 10^{23} thermal neutrons/m^2, the authors got a different lineshape, see Figure 1, with a narrower (2.4 G) and higher central component, with g = 2.003 ± 0.001.

They interpreted this narrow line as being due to metallic lithium colloids. We note already here that such an attribution is questionable: the g value measurement is not precise enough to prove that the line comes from metallic Li, the line is narrow but not very narrow, and, which is more annoying, no intensity versus temperature tests were made to show a possible Pauli law dependence of the line intensity. Later on, we shall discuss this point and suggest that the present line is linked to small agregates of F centers, without any metallic character.

Subsequent papers from Noda's group concerned poly- and monocrystalline samples irradiated with neutrons on which optical absorption was measured [5] – several absorption bands were observed, one of which was attributed to F^+ centers –, single crystals irradiated with neutrons and measured by EPR [6] – only F^+ centers were detected, no colloids, and annealing treatments were conducted –, and poly and single crystals irradiated with neutrons and oxygen ions, giving again only F^+ centers [7]. As an example, we show in Figure 2 the variation of the F^+ center concentration versus the neutron fluence [7].

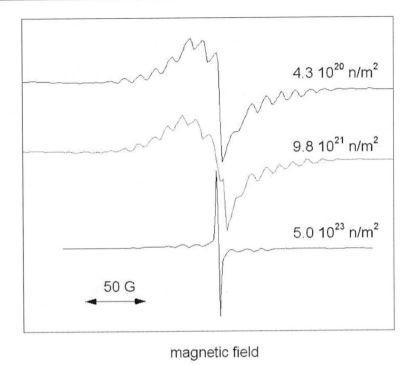

Figure 1. EPR spectra of lithium oxide pellets irradiated with thermal neutrons up to 5.0×10^{23} neutrons/m^2 (data from [4]).

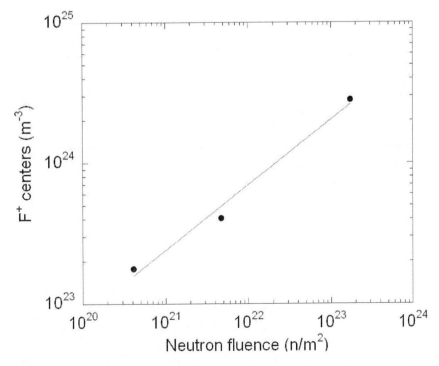

Figure 2. Variation of the F$^+$ center concentration versus the neutron fluence (data from ref [7]).

In the following papers [8-12], they continued their study with neutron and oxygen irradiation, using optical measurements, EPR, isothermal and isochronal annealing and ionic conductivity. In ref [12], they measured the electrical conductivity of Li_2O single crystals between 413 and 673 K under and after irradiation using 24 and 60 MeV Li-ion irradiations. Finally, in some single crystals, they varied the relative ^6Li content [13].

For instance, in this last reference, they give an optical absorption spectrum of an irradiated sample with a low ^6Li content. The spectrum is deconvoluted into five gaussian peaks: in these samples, they claimed again − but in our opinion without proving it − that colloidal lithium metal was found in neutron irradiated Li_2O; they also concluded that in a fusion reactor with a Li_2O blanket "the colloidal Li metals will remain in Li_2O in the lower temperature part of the blanket, since colloidal Li metals are not completely recovered up to 870 K": this assertion is of great practical importance and will be discussed in the following sections.

3. THE WORK FROM PALAISEAU ON IRRADIATED LI₂O POLYCRYSTALS

Our own work on irradiated Li_2O began in 1996 [15-16]. Its main purpose was to detect colloids of metallic lithium, as they were detected long time ago in neutron-irradiated LiF [17-20] or LiH [21-23].

Just before this study on Li_2O, we studied the fluorite itself, CaF_2, under electronic irradiation [24]. CaF_2 single crystals were irradiated at T=21 K and at 0°C with electrons of 0.5 and 1 MeV energy. While the low temperature irradiated samples exhibit EPR spectra due to F-centers, the room temperature irradiated ones present EPR spectra due to V_F and U centers. A line would be possibly attributable to metallic colloid (g=2.003) centers, although it does not depart from the Curie law for the magnetic susceptibilty, indicating that these supposed colloids must be of very small size. A thermal annealing treatment up to 900°C gave a complex recovery behavior, which could be interpreted as a competition between growth and annihilation processes of metallic Ca clusters estimated to have initially a radius of 200 Å. The appearance of a new ESR line near g=2.000 after an anneal at 200°C indicated the possible transformation of colloids to larger units before vanishing: a non-Curie contribution was detected in the T behavior of its susceptibility (see Figure 9 in [24]).

We used first 99.5% pure polycrystalline Li_2O grains from which platelets were cut and irradiated with our Van de Graaff electron accelerator, using a beam energy of 1 MeV [16]. The samples were irradiated in the gas atmosphere of a liquid-hydrogen cryostat, and the irradiation temperature was controlled by adjusting the beam current. We used the following irradiation temperatures: T_{irr} = 21(1)K, 90(5)K, 150(3)K, 200(2)K, and 275(3)K. X-band EPR experiments were performed between 4 and 300 K. Furthermore, microwave conductivity measurements were done on the same specimens, using a cavity perturbation technique. A thermal annealing treatment was applied to the specimens by heating them in a dynamic vacuum in steps of 50 degrees, for one hour each.

On Figure 3 we show the room temperature EPR spectra of a sample irradiated at 21 K. The upper line is typical of a F^+ center, the same that Noda and coworkers observed in neutron irradiated samples: it exhibits the 25 lines of an hyperfine structure coming from the cubic environment of an oxygen vacancy surrounded by eight ^{7}Li first neighbors, with I=3/2. The lower signal corresponds to the same sample after an annealing at 400°C; we get a central line at g=2.0030, corresponding to agregates of F$^+$ centers, clearly non-metallic as proved by the Curie-like behavior of the line intensity with temperature. It is most probable that this last line is the same as the one observed by Noda et al. after high neutron fluence ([4] and Figure 1).

For T_{irr} = 90 K and 150 K, a similar behavior was observed.

But for T_{irr} = 200 K, together with a more complex F$^+$ type EPR signal, we observed an additional very narrow line ($\Delta H \sim 0.05$ mT) at g = 2.00232 to 2.00235, close to the free-electron value (Figure 4). Unlike all the other signals present, this line exhibits no Curie like temperature dependence and could be a first manifestation of small metallic colloids.

At last, for T_{irr} = 275 K, we got a completely different situation, depicted in Figure 5. No more hyperfine structure linked to F$^+$ centers was detected, but instead we got a very narrow EPR line ($\Delta H \leq 0.01$ mT) line, with all characteristics of a signal due to metallic lithium: it is positioned at a g value of 2.00234 to 2.00238, very close to the free-electrons g value, which is in coherence with the fact that Li being the lightest metal has virtualy no spin-orbit interaction [25]; its intensity follows a Pauli law - the T-independence is shown in the inset of Figure 5 -, with an equally T-independent linewidth. The line is somewhat broad at the wings and a good fit requires at least two lorentzians, indicating the probable presence of colloids of various sizes. The lineshape is definitely not dysonian, which is coherent with a colloid size below the micron range.

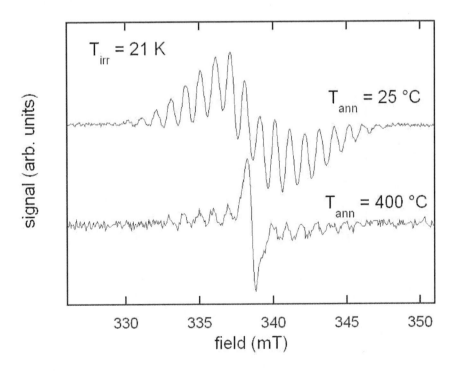

Figure 3. Room-temperature EPR-spectra of Li$_2$O irradiated at 21 K by 1-MeV electrons to a dose of 0.8×10^{20} e$^-$/cm^2. Upper spectrum: after irradiation; lower spectrum: after an anneal at T_{ann} = 400°C [16].

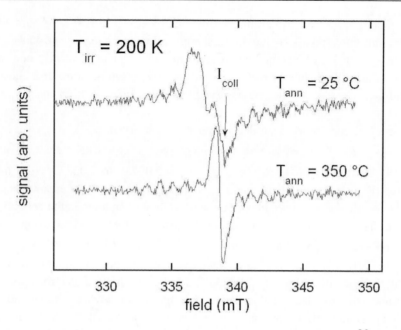

Figure 4. Room-temperature EPR-spectra of Li_2O irradiated at 200 K with 0.6 x 10^{20} e⁻/cm². Upper spectrum: after irradiation. Lower spectrum: after an anneal at T_{ann} = 350°C. Note the presence of a narrow colloid line at g = 2.0023, after irradiation [16].

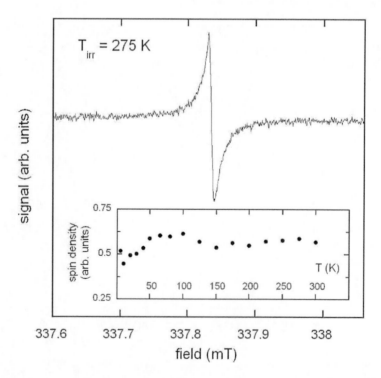

Figure 5. Upper part: room-temperature EPR-spectrum of Li_2O irradiated with 1.1 x 10^{20} e⁻/cm² at 275 K. Inset: T-dependence of the signal, showing Pauli behavior of its intensity [16].

Simultaneously, we measured the complex dielectric constant of the same samples, before and after electron irradiation, in the microwave range betweeen 7 and 15 GHz. For these experiments, we used a TE_{10n} multimode cavity, measuring the frequency and width of 8 resonance modes before and after sample introduction by means of a HP8510C network analyzer. For the Li_2O sample irradiated at 275 K, we observed an important increase of the dielectric constant, $\varepsilon'_{irr} = 27$ and $\varepsilon''_{irr} = 7$ - before irradiation, $\varepsilon' = 6$ and ε'' was very close to zero - , suggesting in a convincing manner the presence of metallic particles.

Isochronal annealings were performed on the same samples. Whereas, for the lower irradiation temperatures, the EPR signal disappears in the 350-400°C range, for $T_{irr} = 275$ K the signal disappears much earlier, in the 200-300°C range.

The annealing is shown in Figure 6, indicating that the radiation-induced $\Delta\varepsilon'$, $\Delta\varepsilon''$ recover more or less simultaneously with the disappearance of the colloid line, at $T_{ann} = 350°C$ (623 K). It seems to be clear that in the temperature conditions which are expected to prevail in fusion reactors, there is no risk that metallic colloids should be stable, in contradiction with the assertion cited at the end of section 2.

Grishmanov and coworkers [26] presented an interesting work with Li_2O, both polycrystalline and single crystalline, on the so-called "excess luminescence". They irradiated samples with light ions (H^+, He^+) and with 5 MeV electrons.

After electron irradiation of polycristalline Li_2O, they obtained an EPR behavior very close to ours [15]: a rather narrow lorentzian line close to g = 2.0023, a Pauli-type temperature law for the signal intensity, and an isochronal annealing behavior similar to ours.

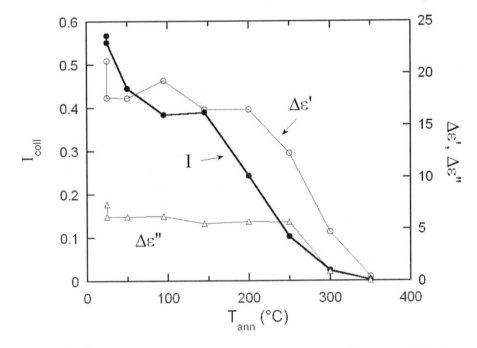

Figure 6. Annealing of the intensity of the colloid line of Figure 5, together with the evolution of the radiation-induced changes in the real and in the imaginary parts of the dielectric constant, $\Delta\varepsilon'$ and $\Delta\varepsilon''$ ($\varepsilon'_0 = 6.0(3)$, $\varepsilon''_0 = 0.01(1)$, before irradiation) [16].

These data indicate the presence of metallic Li precipitates, with a Li metal concentration of about 10^{-4}. They also presented thermoluminescence glow curves of various samples, irradiated with γ-rays (wich create F^+ and F^0 centers due to the capture of electrons by oxygen vacancies), with 5 MeV electrons or with both. The results are analyzed in terms of thermo-dissociation of colloidal Li into Li sublattice ions, F^+ and F^0 centers, and oxygen vacancies.

4. THE WORK FROM PALAISEAU ON IRRADIATED LI$_2$O SINGLE CRYSTALS

Analogous experiments were done in lithium oxide single crystals. Single crystals of Li$_2$O were grown, using a floating zone method [27] on sintered powder rods prepared from 99.5 % pure lithium oxide grains. The obtained cylindrical bars were 80 mm long with an average diameter of 5 mm. Two crystals had been grown in this manner, and were sliced without cutting fluid with a diamond blade saw, and the final samples were obtained by cleavage, or were cut by means of a tungsten wire saw, with SiC-powder suspension in glycerol as medium, allowing thinner (down to 100 μm) platelets. As far as possible, the slices were kept under vacuum to prevent pollution by air moisture.

We have irradiated such platelets of lithium oxide near 0°C with 1 MeV electrons [28-30]. The striking feature is the observation of an EPR line composed of two different signals (see Figure 7). These two signals correspond unambiguously to two kinds of metallic colloids manifesting themselves as two EPR metallic lines. The two lines are centered at g = 2.0023; the narrow line, with a peak-to-peak width around 10^{-2} mT, is lorentzian in shape and has saturation properties compatible with a $T_1 = T_2$ behavior, while the broader line is not saturated with full microwave power (250 mW) and has a lineshape looking like the "metallic" shape described by Feher and Kip after a model by Dyson [31]. The narrow line corresponds to small metallic clusters (size <1 μm), and the broad and asymmetric one is associated with larger metallic colloids, whose size is much larger than the skin depth of microwaves in the metal, which is in the micrometer range: this is known to correspond to a ratio A/B between the left and the right lobe heights of 2.55.

The definitive proof of the metallic character of the colloids responsible for the two lines of Figure 7 is given in Figure 8. In this figure, we show the variation of the two line intensities with the EPR measuring temperature. Both strongly differ from the typical Curie law obtained with isolated F^+ centers or clusters of these centers.

The narrow line follows a strict Pauli (T-independent) law, confirming the fully metallic character of these small colloids, while the broad dysonian line has a more complex behavior, which is however easy to understand [29]: for these large metallic colloids, only a surface layer is seen by EPR, due to the skin effect, and the skin depth decreases with decreasing T, because the Li metal resistivity also decreases with T. Spin concentrations corresponding to the two types of colloids are estimated in the 10^{-4} range for the small ones, in the percent range for the large ones.

In [28] and [29], we also discussed the somewhat unusual EPR properties of the large metallic colloids.

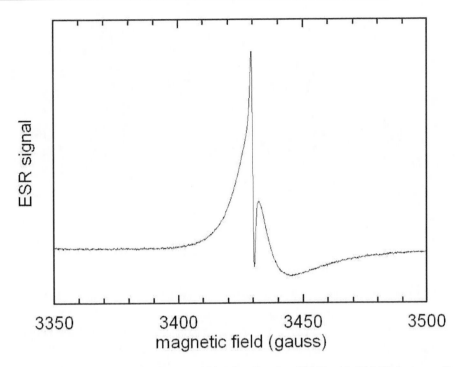

Figure 7. Room-temperature EPR-spectrum of Li_2O irradiated at 280 K with 1 MeV electrons. Two colloid lines at g = 2.0023 are detected. Here, the narrow line is much saturated and over-modulated [33].

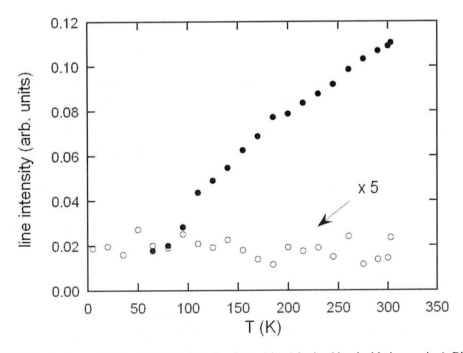

Figure 8. Temperature variation of the two EPR line intensities (obtained by double integration). Black circles: broad line – white circles: narrow line [28].

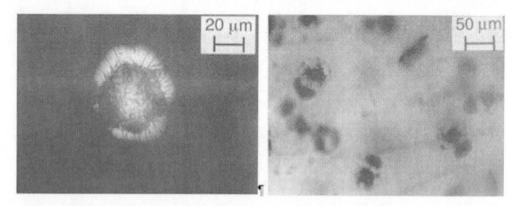

Figure 9. Optical micrographs of a 95 μm thick Li$_2$O crystal cleaved parallel to (111), after electron irradiation (1 MeV, 5 x10^{19} e$^-$/cm^2) at 275 K. Left: in reflection, showing the hexagonal cavity surrounded by metallic lithium; right: in transmission, showing the various {111} oriented colloids [30].

First, the linewidth is quite broad for metallic Li particles of micronic size, and second, a detailed discussion on the parameters giving rise to the dysonian lineshape showed that the metallic Li must have unusual transport properties. We deduced from these considerations that the structure of our large Li colloids is possibly not the same as that of bulk bcc metallic Li; see also Section 7 later.

The large Li colloids are visible by optical microscopy, through a sample particularly thin and thus partially transparent.

Images taken in reflection or in transmission are shown on Figure 9. The metallic colloids appear in reflection as brilliant zones of typical size around 20 μm, surrounding an hexagonal flat box in a (111) plane; such boxes are quite probably filled with oxygen gas. These observations confirm the existence of large lithium colloids and show that they are non-spherical and anisotropically distributed.

The ^{7}Li NMR signal, taken at a frequency of 140 MHz and at room temperature, is given in Figure 10. Two lines are seen: a broad one near 0 ppm – the only one measured in a non irradiated sample – and a narrower one near 250 ppm. This NMR signal clearly shows the existence of metallic regions: the main line is related to the unaffected Li$^+$ ions, while the position of the smaller line corresponds exactly to the published value for the Knight shift in metallic lithium. More details on subsequent NMR experiments will be given in section 6.

A further indication for the presence of colloids of different types is the distinct recovery behavior of the two EPR lines in an annealing treatment (Figure 11). The small (<1 μm) colloids, responsible for the narrow lorentzian line, anneal near 300°C like the ones observed in irradiated polycrystals (section 3), while the large (»1 μm) colloids, giving rise to the dysonian signal, recover only at 400°C, when the crystal decomposes. Again, this is in contradiction with the assertion cited in the end of section 2, which supposed that Li colloids could still be present up to 870 K (about 600°C).

Dielectric-constant measurements [29] in the microwave frequency range reveal a substantial increase of both real and imaginary parts of ε, corroborating the metal colloid formation. An effective medium analysis of the ε variation after irradiation suggests non-spherical shapes for the metal colloids.

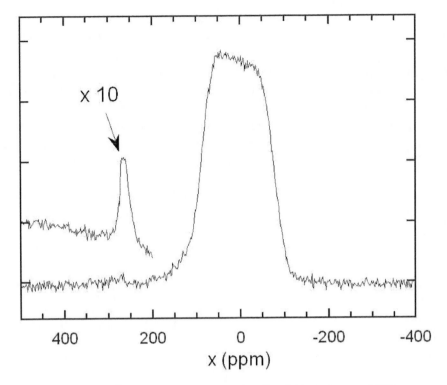

Figure 10. Room-temperature ^{7}Li NMR-spectrum in an irradiated Li single crystal [28].

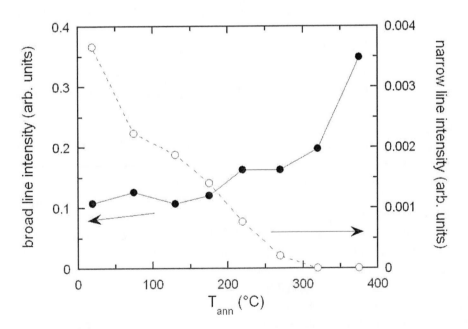

Figure 11. Isochronal annealing behavior of the EPR line intensities, in a Li$_2$O crystal irradiated with 3.9 x10^{19} e$^-$/cm^2; the EPR spectra are taken at room temperature. Black symbols - broad line; open symbols - narrow line. The data are given in the same arbitrary units [29].

The recovery of the irradiation-induced ε-increase occurs in the same range as that of the colloid lines, with a strong peak of Δε" near 400°C, probably indicating a colloid shape redistribution before decomposition.

Experiments were done at temperatures higher than room temperature, in order to detect the Li metal melting of the colloids. Bulk Li metal melts at 453.7 K, i.e 180.5°C. On Figure 12, we give the results of an EPR experiment on a crystal from 150 to 320 °C [32]: both signal intensity and linewidth show a clear discontinuity at the melting point. We present also the results of a differential scanning calorimetry (DSC) run. In both experiments, the melting of Li metallic colloids is clearly seen at the nominal Li metal melting temperature.

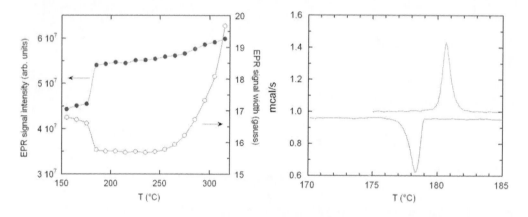

Figure 12. High temperature behavior of an irradiated Li_2O crystal. Left: behavior of the CESR broad line (dysonian); the melting of the colloids is clearly detected both on the linewidth (open symbols) and on the line intensity (full symbols), near 180°C. Right: differential scanning calorimetry with increasing (above) or decreasing (below) temperature; variation rate 4°C/min; sample mass 10.6 mg [32].

5. DETECTION OF MOLECULAR OXYGEN

In the preceding section, we demonstrated by a set of different techniques that high-fluence electron irradiation can generate the nucleation of Li metal colloids in lithium oxide single crystals. It is clear that the radiolysis responsible for the nucleation of Li metal must also generate a corresponding concentration of oxygen, possibly in the form of molecular O_2. It is very tempting to suggest that the hexagonal flat cavities observed by optical microscopy (Figure 9) are filled with this molecular oxygen.

In order to detect it, we have measured [33, 34] the temperature-dependent magnetisation of electron-irradiated Li_2O crystals exhibiting metallic lithium colloids as detected by EPR. Magnetisation measurements were then performed between 1.8 and 300 K using a SQUID susceptometer, with an applied external field of 4.7 T.

Figure 13 shows the susceptibilities of a non-irradiated and an irradiated Li_2O crystal as a function of temperature. The irradiated sample was submited to a fluence about $5x10^{19}$ e⁻/cm², at 275 K and at an electron energy of 1 MeV; EPR shows the presence of the two kind of colloids, the small ones corresponding to a Li metal content of $3x10^{-5}$, the large ones to at least $8x10^{-4}$, an underestimated value due to the strong skin effect.

As expected, the virgin crystal is weakly diamagnetic, the slight upturn at low temperature being probably related to some paramagnetic impurities. After irradiation, the sample has turned paramagnetic and exhibits an ordering transition at $T_N = 38$ K; the high-T part of the susceptibility curve can be fitted with a Curie-Weiss law with a Curie temperature of -58 K, which shows that this ordering transition is an anti-ferromagnetic one. This magnetism is attributed to close to 1 mol.% of molecular oxygen produced together with the Li colloids, a value higher (by a factor near 10) than the estimated concentration of Li by EPR, which we considered above as underestimated, and in good quantitative agreement with the Li concentration obtained in DSC experiments. The antiferromagnetic transition at T_N can be related to the $\beta-\gamma$ transformation in solid oxygen. Furthermore, a closer look at the region around T_N (Figure 14) shows a break at 50 K.

We attribute this break at 50 K to the melting point of oxygen and the transition at 38 K to the $\beta-\gamma$ transformation of solid oxygen, whereas bulk oxygen exhibits ([36]) a $T_m = 54.4$ K and a $T_N = 43.8$ K, about 5 to 6 degrees above the values we measured. This difference could be attributed to the fact that, in our irradiated samples, oxygen is not free but is contained in bubble form in a host lattice, with possibly unusual environmental, for example, pressure conditions.

We recall that Meier et al. [36] had observed that, in bulk oxygen, T_N shifted under pressure towards higher values by about 6 K per 10^8 Pa; on the other hand, the melting curve of oxygen [37] indicates a corresponding shift of T_m by 10 K per 10^8 Pa.

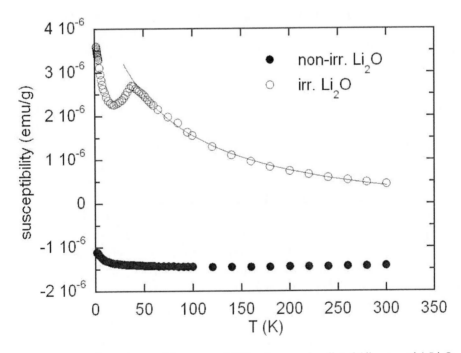

Figure 13. Temperature dependence of the susceptibilities for an unirradiated (diamagnetic) Li_2O crystal and for an irradiated crystal, showing a Curie-Weiss fit at higher temperatures, with a paramagnetic T =-58 K for the latter [33].

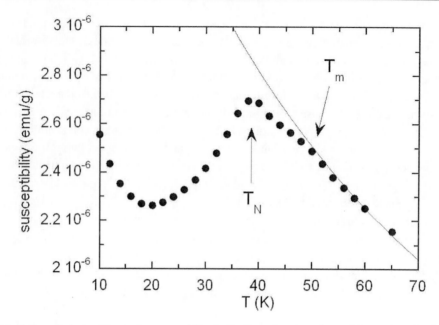

Figure 14. Enlarged view of the region around T_N, indicating a break at the melting point of solid oxygen [33].

It is then tempting to suggest that our negative T-shifts mean "negative" pressures. Such a situation could be envisaged for cases where a liquid was filling a cavity surrounded by material with a much lower expansion coefficient than the liquid in its solid phase. This is just what is encountered here: γ-oxygen, with a volume expansion coefficient of 2.3 x10^{-3}/K at 50 K - sometimes called "plastic phase" - contracts 30 times more than the surrounding Li_2O crystal, with a d/dT($\Delta V/V$) ≈ 8 x10^{-5}/K as extrapolated from room-temperature data. Since, at the same time, the oxygen compressibility in the γ-phase is also nearly two orders of magnitude higher than that of Li_2O, we are tempted to consider the possibility of "negative" pressures existing inside the cavities.

6. NUCLEAR MAGNETIC RESONANCE

More precise experiments with Li NMR were conducted after the study described in section 4 [35, 38]. First, in standard ^{7}Li room-temperature NMR on electron-irradiated Li_2O crystals, it was discovered that for most samples the metallic NMR line consists of two components, one at K = 265(3) ppm and the other at K = 246(3) ppm, as seen for instance for the upper spectrum shown in Figure 15. In the literature, the accepted value for the Knight shift in bulk lithium is about 260 ppm [39,40]. It is tempting to attribute the 265 ppm peak to "normal" b.c.c. lithium corresponding to the dysonian line in CESR and the other peak to another metallic phase of Li, corresponding to the lorentzian line.

The problem with this interpretation is that the two NMR peaks seem to have comparable intensities, in strong contrast with the behavior of the two CESR lines. Another possible interpretation for the double NMR peak could be in terms of the strong anisotropy of the large colloids (the small colloids giving a too small NMR line to be observed).

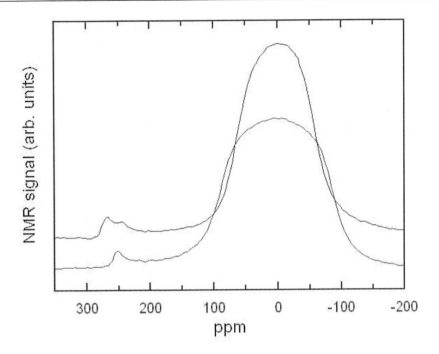

Figure 15. Room-temperature ^{7}Li NMR-spectra of Li$_2$O irradiated at 280 K. The upper spectrum corresponds to a sample annealed at 125°C and the lower one to a sample annealed at 475°C. In both cases, the main signal near 0 ppm is due to Li$^+$ ions while the smaller signal near 250 ppm comes from metallic lithium. For the low annealing temperature, this Knight-shifted signal is split [38].

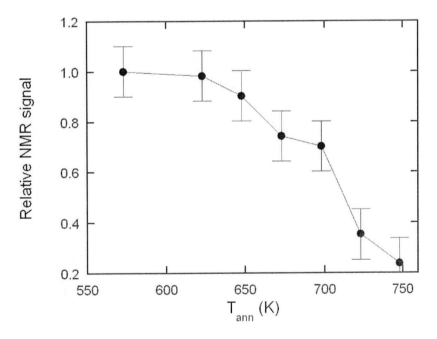

Figure 16. Room-temperature ^{7}Li NMR intensity of the metallic line versus annealing temperature [38].

This model is developed in [34] where we discuss the effect of the anisotropy in terms of different values of the demagnetizing factor, giving a small shift in the value of the magnetic field in the colloid. Further in this section, we shall propose still another interpretation for these two lines.

In Figure 16, we give the annealing behavior of the intensity of the Knight-shifted NMR signal, which anneals in the same temperature range as the large colloids observed in EPR. We showed also that the temperature dependence of the Knight shifted line taken in the interval 230 to 400 K shows diffusion narrowing occuring near 270 K, some 15 K above that observed in bulk Li metal [39], probably a sign of stress-induced retardation.

We also took a series of NMR spectra on the same irradiated sample at different temperatures [34], as shown in Figure 17. The magnetic field was parallel to a (111) crystallographic axis. When plotting the line position of the two NMR lines versus temperature, we observed a shift for both lines just at the melting temperature of bulk metal lithium, meaning that the two NMR lines correspond most probably to bcc lithium.

It is worth mentioning here that, a few years later, we made similar experiments on electron-irradiated LiF [41]. Metallic Li colloids were also generated in these samples. We observed a similar behavior of the NMR signal, with two Knight-shifted lines, collapsing in only one line after annealing at a sufficiently high temperature.

The position of the line near 264 ppm is very close of that of bulk bcc Li, so that we may identify this signal as originating from lithium in an environment close to normal bulk. The second line, near 271 ppm, is attributed to some high pressure Li phase, as observed by Bertani et al. [40] in NMR measurements of bulk lithium under pressure.

These authors report a displacement of the ^{7}Li Knight-shift signal toward higher values and inhibition of translational diffusion with increasing pressure, at room temperature. Rough estimates of the changes, for pressures of the order of 2 GPa, yield a shift by 6 ppm upwards with respect to ambient pressure and a lower value of the self-diffusion coefficient and, consequently, a lower value of the correlation time and a broader absorption line, by a factor of 3. So this kind of change could account for the observed features of the broader component of the ^{7}Li signal located at 271 ppm.

7. NEUTRON SCATTERING

It seems interesting to know the microscopic structure of the Li colloids and, if possible, their position in the antifluorite-type host matrix. Earlier investigations of metallic Li colloids in ionic material concerned the NaCl-type LiF [20] and LiH [42], but attempts to determine their configurations were limited to X-ray structural analysis, with all the difficulties due to the low Z of this element.

In view of the low concentration of the available metal (10^{-3} to 10^{-2} per Li_2O unit), and in the hope to circumvent the problems inherent to X-ray and electron-microscope studies, we decided, therefore, to undertake a neutron-spectroscopic investigation both on a triple-axis spectrometer and a small angle scattering instrument.

We were able, for the first time, to observe metallic (and, in particular, lithium) colloids in ionic crystals by neutron scattering and to determine their structure as well as the orientation relationships within the Li_2O matrix.

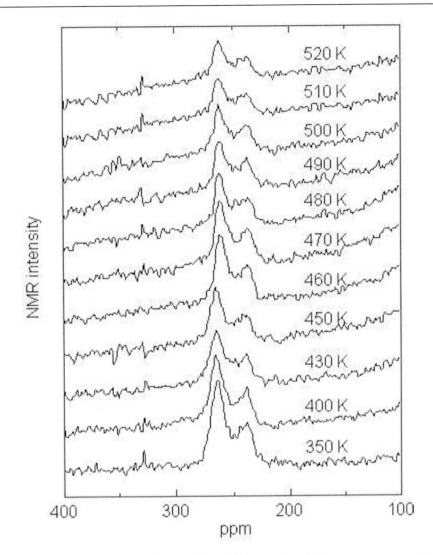

Figure 17. NMR spectra taken on the same irradiated Li$_2$O sample at different temperatures. The magnetic field is perpendicular to the sample, i.e. parallel to a (111) crystallographic axis. Bulk b.c.c. Li metal melting temperature is 453 K [34].

On an oriented single crystal, electron irradiations were done at 1 MeV and 300 K to a dose of 15 C/cm^2 [43]. Neutron investigations were performed in the wide-angle range on the triple-axis spectrometer VALSE and for the small-angle neutron scattering (SANS) measurements on the instrument PAXE, both at the Laboratoire Léon Brillouin at Saclay; the measurements were done at room temperature.

In Figure 18, we show a comparison of radial scans through the [111] reflections of the irradiated crystal and an unirradiated one. One can notice a slight broadening of the (111) reflection of the Li$_2$O matrix (at the position Q = 1.00) due to the introduced defects; the presence of largely symmetric shoulders on both sides of the Bragg peak suggesting an interpretation in terms of Huang-type diffuse scattering; the presence of a small peak (at Q ~ 1.07) corresponding to the (110) reflection of bulk bcc lithium precipitates, the intensity of which is compatible with a concentration of some 10^{-3} of the matrix. The orientational relations found are in agreement with the earlier observation of quasi two-dimensional (disk-shaped) precipitates situated on (111) planes of the anti-fluorite type host lattice though no detailed information on the shape and aspect ratio of the precipitates can be derived from the data. The lithium precipitates are aligned according to the orientational relation [110]Li // [111]Li$_2$O and may correspond to the large (>1μm) Li colloids observed earlier by conduction electron spin resonance (CESR) and by optical microscopy.

We also compared the scattering intensity between irradiated and non-irradiated samples for different orientations [44], namely the (111) and (200) peaks. The study of the radial part of the scattering intensity (Huang scattering - Figure 19) gives typical diameters of the defect clusters yielding an averaged Guinier radius about 2.5 nm corresponding to a mean geometrical diameter of about 6.5 nm and leading to $n_{cl} \sim 10000$ for the number of atoms in one cluster.

The SANS experiments performed on the same irradiated crystal [43] give information on small precipates in contrast with the preceding triple axis experiments. They show the presence of a distribution of non-spherical precipitates likewise aligned along specific crystallographic directions which may correspond to the small (lorentzian) colloids («1μm) observed by CESR.

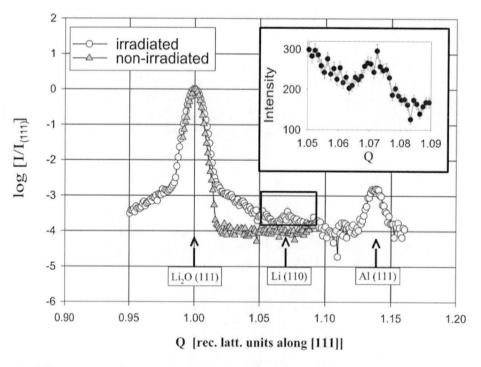

Figure 18. Radial scans along the [111] axis of an irradiated and a non-irradiated Li$_2$O crystal, respectively. Intensities are normalised to the intensity of the (111) Bragg peak and shown on a logarithmic scale. The values on the abscissa are given in units of $(2\pi\sqrt{3}/a)$, i.e. reciprocal lattice units along the [111] direction. The (111) reflection of the irradiated crystal is slightly broadened and for values of $Q \leq 0.98$ and $Q \geq 1.02$ broad shoulders due to distortion scattering are visible which extend far into the Brillouin zone. The inset shows a more accurate determination of the position of the (110) peak of metallic lithium displayed on a linear scale. The aluminium (111) peak is due to the sample wrapping [43].

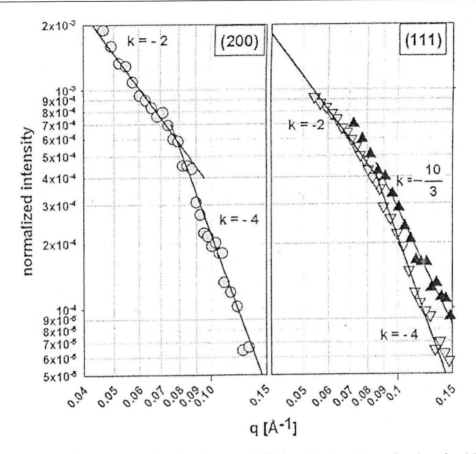

Figure 19. Radial part of the scattering intensity on a doubly logarithmic scale as a function of $q = |\, Q —$ H $\,|$, where H stands for the reciprocal lattice vectors [200] and [111] ([44]).

In a subsequent work [45], we extended the investigation of the two colloid distributions down to low temperatures close to 30K. Radial and transverse scans through (111), (200) and (022) Bragg peaks were done at several temperatures between 290 and 20K in order to monitor the possible changes in the distortion scattering.

Practically no variations were observed over the entire temperature range. It is beyond doubt that oxygen occurring in clusters, whose size lies in the range of several nanometers, will be found in a condensed (and even solid) state at temperatures as low as 30K.

We therefore conclude that the concentration of oxygen nanoclusters, if they are present at all, must be very low in comparison with the small lithium colloids.

8. THEORY

It is interesting to describe here briefly a theoretical study of defects in lithium oxide. Hayoun et al [46] made a molecular-dynamics (MD) investigation on the complex atomic-diffusion mechanism in Li_2O, which is an ionic superconductor. The high-temperature superionic phase of lithium oxide is characterized by a high concentration of Frenkel defects and a diffusion mechanism involving several types of atomic jumps.

In the study performed in the superionic phase of Li_2O, the authors investigated the fast-diffusion process. They found the calculated concentration of cationic Frenkel-pairs to be in good agreement with the experimental data. A few of these defects are dissociated and contribute to diffusion, whereas the major part quickly recombines. By analysing the cation trajectories, they could identify three types of discrete jumps characterised by their length (Figure 20). They correspond to the migration towards the Li sites that are nearest neighbours (type 1), second neighbours (type 2) and third neighbours (type 3), respectively.

The nearest-neighbour jumps are dominant and follow two different migration paths: a direct one, D1, and another one through the cube-centre site, C1. The D1 jumps are the most prevalent at the lower temperatures. Then, with increasing temperatures, their contribution decreases but remains the major one up to 1425 K. A quantitative analysis, including the calculation of the atomic jump frequencies, indicates that the cations spend most of the time on regular lattice-sites. The combination of the various jumps results in a complex migration mechanism and the corresponding effective activation-enthalpy has been determined. All the results provide an extended view of the atomic-diffusion process in a superionic conductor.

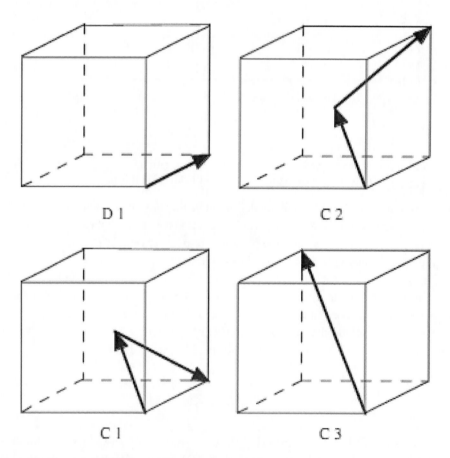

Figure 20. Definition of the different kinds of jumps drawn in the cationic sublattice cube. Jumps of types 1, 2 and 3 have lengths of $a/2$, $a\sqrt{2}/2$ and $a\sqrt{3}/2$, respectively. Arrows indicate the schematic paths of the jumps [46, 47].

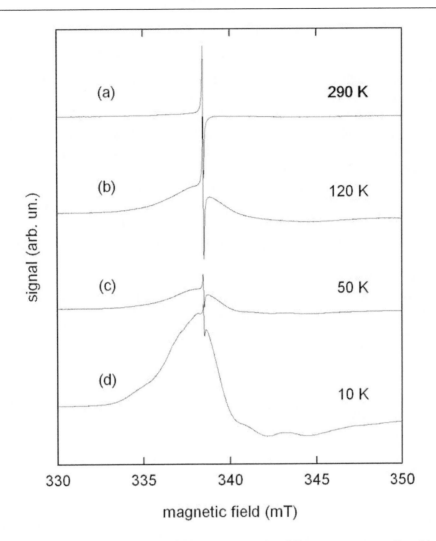

Figure 21. EPR spectra of irradiated Li_2NH powder measured at different temperatures T_m with the same microwave power P = 0.493 mW and modulation M = 20 μT; (a) T_m = 290 K, G=2 x10⁴; (b) T_m = 120 K, G=2 x10⁴; (c) T_m = 50 K, G=5 x10³; (d) T_m = 10 K, G=5 x10³[48].

In a subsequent paper, these authors completed their study by proposing a kinetic Monte Carlo code, simulating the lithium vacancy diffusion, and used to predict the correlation factor as a function of the atomic fraction of defects. There is a good agreement with the result directly obtained by MD. The analysis of the jump paths shows that the direct exchange between a vacancy and a migrating atom is the main part of the diffusion mechanism. The other atomic jumps, although complex, mostly imply vacancies. The Li^+ fast-diffusion proceeds by a vacancy mechanism involving several jump types.

9. LITHIUM IMIDE

We have extended our work on Li_2O to another lithium compound with the same antifluorite structure [48]. In the search for a light-weight, cheap, and easily practicable hydrogen-storage compound, the lithium amide/imide system has attracted notable interest, in particular in view of the reversible reaction $Li_2NH + H_2 \rightleftharpoons LiNH_2 + LiH$ occurring in the interesting range 150–200 °C. The crystal structure of lithium imide Li_2NH has been studied by neutron powder diffraction and by synchrotron X-ray diffraction and was established as a rather open cubic antifluorite structure, the NH ions forming the f.c.c. cell with the Li ions occupying its tetrahedral sites. We have thus irradiated Li_2NH powder with 2.5 MeV electrons at room temperature and investigated the introduced defects with electron spin resonance.

The resulting EPR spectrum is clearly composed of two very different signal components, as shown in Figure 21. The first one is a narrow line with lorentzian shape, a g-factor value of 2.0023 and a linewidth $\Delta H = 50$ µT; its intensity does not vary between 10 K and 290 K, following a Pauli behavior. All these data show that the narrow line stems from Li metal colloids created by irradiation, whose size lies somewhere between an upper limit of about 1 µm, from the non-dysonian shape of the line, and a lower one of a few nm, due to the absence of quantum effects.

The second and much broader EPR signal component ($\Delta H = 3$–4 mT) appears superimposed in Figure 21 upon the Li line at low T and has a Curie-type behavior, as seen in Figure 22.

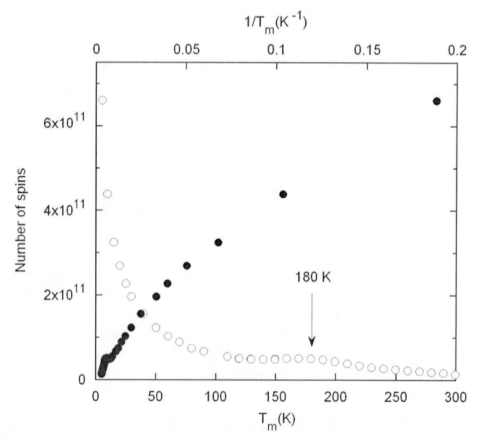

Figure 22. T dependence of the broad signal intensity in a direct plot (open signs, lower scale) and in a reciprocal plot (full signs, upper scale) [48].

The width of this broad line exhibits a complex T dependence with a break near 180 K. The defect responsible for this signal is certainly a paramagnetic center, but exhibits some anomalies, in particular seen as a break also near 180 K in the direct plot and a change of slope at the same temperature in the reciprocal plot. We are suggesting an anionic type defect in the NH-sublattice, with freezing of the H component below ~180 K, for its interpretation.

We have tried to anneal the radiation defects by heating the samples in their sealed glass tubes from 50°C on in steps of 25°C for 30 minutes each and recording the spectra at 300 K after each annealing. The samples bleach progressively, losing signal intensity at the same time, with practically complete disappearance after 175°C. As both the colloids and the color centers anneal simultaneously around 100°C, we think that this final annealing is probably related to chemical sample degradation due to hydrogen evolution.

10. BISTABLE CONDUCTION ELECTRON SPIN RESONANCE

Vigreux and coworkers [49] made an interesting experiment on electron-irradiated Li_2O polycrystalline pellets, samples prepared in a very similar way to ours, as described in detail in Section 3.

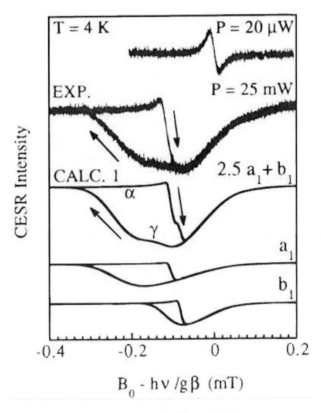

Figure 23. Experimental and calculated bistable conduction electron spin resonance spectra for colloidal lithium particles in irradiated Li_2O at T = 4 K and P = 25 mW. The unsaturated spectrum at P = 20 μW is shown at the top of the figure. The calculation (CALC 1) includes two populations A and B for the particles. The two spectra a_1 and b_1 represent the individual contributions of populations A and B to the total calculated spectrum [49].

In the samples irradiated at 1 MeV and 275 K, they detected a very narrow EPR line (ΔB_{pp} = 0.013 mT) clearly attributable to metal Li colloids with a size smaller than 1μm. In addition to the EPR parameters (narrow linewidth, free electron g factor, Pauli type intensity versus T), they added one more argument for this attribution: the observation of an ENDOR signal from ^{7}Li nuclei interacting with Li metal conduction electrons. The unsaturated (low rf power) signal at 4 K is shown in the upper spectrum of Figure 23.

There is an important change on the EPR line behavior when the rf power is increased, reaching the saturation region for the electron spins. In this case, as shown on the spectrum EXP of Figure 23, the line shifts towards low field values, its shape becomes much more complex, and one observes a very strange phenomenon: the signal shape is different when sweeping the magnetic field upwards or downwards. The authors give a detailed analysis of this spectacular behavior, attributed to what they call bistable conduction electron spin resonance: it is due to the Overhauser effect, an interaction between the conduction electrons and the nuclear spins via the hyperfine interaction. They propose several models to simulate the spectra, one is given in Figure 23. The analysis of this bistable conduction electron spin resonance line shape showed the existence of two populations of particles differing by their electron spin relaxation times T_2 and characterized by a distribution of nuclear relaxation times; these two populations being probably related to different particle sizes.

CONCLUSION

The interest shown by the scientific community for the ionic oxide Li_2O is related to its very high Li content, making this oxide a very good candidate for tritium generation under neutron irradiation in the future fusion reactors. In this framework, studying the properties of point defects, in particular after irradiation, is of high importance.

In this chapter, we analysed several studies of irradiation properties of Li_2O, either just after irradiation or after a subsequent annealing treatment. The main defects encountered are a color center, the F^+ center, and agglomerates of this center, easily detected by EPR measurements.

Large agglomerates of F^+ centers correspond to metallic Li precipitates or colloids. We described in detail the experimental conditions for the appearing of such colloids, together with the behavior of these colloids under isochronal annealing. We also listed different interesting and sometimes spectacular properties of these metallic colloids.

Finally, we showed that, in the anticipated temperature conditions of Li_2O breeding blanket in future fusion reactors, there is no risk of remaining stable metallic colloids.

REFERENCES

[1]   T. Tanifuji, D. Yamaki and S. Jitsukawa, *J. Nucl. Mat.* 329-333, 1266 (2004).
[2]   Y.Oishi , Y. Kamei, M. Akiyama and T. Yanagi, *J. Nucl. Mat.* 87, 341 (1979).
[3]   A.I. Popov, E.A. Kotomin and J. Maier, *Nucl. Inst. Meth.* B 268, 3084 (2010).
[4]   K. Noda, K. Uchida, T.Tanifuji and S.Nasu, *J. Nucl. Mat.* 91, 234 (1980).

[5] K. Uchida, K. Noda, T. Tanifuji, Sh. Nasu, T. Kirihara and A. Kikuchi, *Phys. Status Sol.*(a) 58, 557 (1980).

[6] K.Noda, K.Uchida, T.Tanifuji and S. Nasu, *Phys. Rev.* B 24, 3736 (1981).

[7] K. Noda, T. Tanifuji, Y. Ishii, H. Matsui, N. Masaki, S. Nasu and H. Watanabe, *J. Nucl. Mat.* 122/123, 908 (1984).

[8] K. Noda, Y. Ishii, H. Matsui and H. Watanabe, *J. Nucl. Mat.* 133/134, 205 (1985).

[9] K. Noda, Y. Ishii, H. Matsui and H. Watanabe, *Rad. Eff.* 97, 297 (1986).

[10] K. Noda, Y. Ishii, H. Matsui, H. Ohno, S. Hirano and H. Watanabe, *J. Nucl. Mat.* 155/157, 568 (1988).

[11] K. Noda, *J. Nucl. Mat.* 179/181, 37 (1991).

[12] K. Noda, Y. Ishii, H. Matsui, H. Ohno and H. Watanabe, *J. Nucl. Mat.* 179/181, 835 (1991).

[13] N.M. Masaki, K. Noda, H. Watanabe, R.G. Clemmer and G.W. Hollenberg, *J. Nucl. Mat.* 212/215, 908 (1994).

[14] H. Moriyama, S. Tanaka and K. Noda, *J. Nucl. Mat.* 258/263, 587 (1998).

[15] P. Vajda and F. Beuneu, *Nucl. Inst. Meth.* B 116, 183 (1996).

[16] P. Vajda and F. Beuneu, *Phys. Rev.* B 53, 5335 (1996).

[17] M. Lambert and A. Guinier, *C. R. Acad. Sci. Paris* 246, 1678 (1958).

[18] P.J. Ring, J.G. O'Keefe and P.J. Bray, *Phys. Rev. Lett.* 1, 453 (1958).

[19] Y.W. Kim, R. Kaplan and P.J. Bray, *Phys. Rev.* 117, 740 (1960).

[20] M. Lambert, Ch. Mazières and A. Guinier, *J. Phys. Chem. Sol.* 18, 129 (1961).

[21] W.T. Doyle, D.J.E. Ingram and M.J.A. Smith, *Proc. Phys. Soc.* 74, 540 (1959).

[22] F.E. Pretzel, D.T. Vier, E.G. Szklarz and W.B. Lewis, Los Alamos Scientific Laboratory Rep. N° LA-2463 (1961).

[23] A. Berthault, S. Bedere and J. Matricon, *J. Phys. Chem. Sol.* 38, 913 (1977).

[24] F. Beuneu and P. Vajda, *J. Appl. Phys.* 78, 6989 (1995).

[25] F. Beuneu and P. Monod, *Phys. Rev.* B 18, 2422 (1978).

[26] V. Grishmanov, S. Tanaka, J. Tiliks, G. Kizane, A. Supe and V. Grigorjeva, *Nucl. Inst. Meth.* B 134, 27 (1998).

[27] J. Shindo, S. Kimura, K. Noda, T. Kurasawa and S. Nasu, *J. Nucl. Mat.* 79, 418 (1979).

[28] F. Beuneu and P. Vajda, *Phys. Rev. Letters.* 76, 4544 (1996).

[29] F. Beuneu, P. Vajda, G. Jaskierowicz and M. Lafleurielle, *Phys. Rev.* B 55, 11263 (1997).

[30] P. Vajda and F. Beuneu, *J. Nucl. Mat.* 258-263, 495 (1998).

[31] G. Feher and F. Kip, Phys. Rev. 98, 337 (1955); F.J. Dyson, *Phys. Rev.* 98, 349 (1955).

[32] F. Beuneu and P. Vajda, *Radiation Effects and Defects in Solids* 150, 141 (1999).

[33] F. Beuneu, P. Vajda and O.J. Żogał, *Phys. Rev. Lett.* 83, 761 (1999).

[34] F. Beuneu, P. Vajda, O.J. Żogał, D. Massiot, J.P. Coutures and P. Florian, *Nucl. Inst. Meth.* B 166-167, 270 (2000).

[35] F. Beuneu, P. Vajda and O.J. Żogał, *Nucl. Inst. Meth.* B 141, 241 (1998).

[36] R.J. Meier, C.J. Schinkel and A. de Visser, *J. Phys.* C 15, 1015 (1982).

[37] R.L. Mills and E.R. Grilly, *Phys. Rev.* 99, 480 (1955).

[38] F. Beuneu, P. Vajda and O.J. Żogał, *Colloids and Surfaces* A 158, 83 (1999).

[39] G.C. Carter, L.H. Bennet and D.J. Kahan, Progress in Materials Science (Pergamon Press, Oxford, 1977), Vol. 20.

[40] R. Bertani, M. Mali, J. Roos and D. Brinkmann, *J. Phys.: Condens. Mat.* 2, 7911 (1990).

[41] O.J. Żogał, F. Beuneu, P. Vajda, P. Florian and D. Massiot, *Phys. Rev.* B 66, 064101 (2002).

[42] G.S. Smith, *J. Phys. Chem. Sol.* 36, 797 (1975).

[43] P. Vajda, F. Beuneu, G. Krexner, M. Prem, O. Blaschko and C. Maier, *Nucl. Inst. Meth.* B 166-167, 275 (2000).

[44] G. Krexner, M. Prem, F. Beuneu and P. Vajda, *Phys. Rev. Lett.* 91, 135502 (2003).

[45] M. Prem, G. Krexner, F. Beuneu and P. Vajda, *Physica* B 350 (Supplement), E999 (2004).

[46] M. Hayoun, M. Meyer and A. Denieport, *Acta Materialia* 53, 2867 (2005).

[47] M. Hayoun and M. Meyer, *Acta Materialia* 56, 1366 (2008).

[48] F. Beuneu, P. Vajda, Y. Nakamori and S. Orimo, *Phys. Rev.* B 74, 174122 (2006).

[49] C. Vigreux, L. Binet and D. Gourier, *J. Phys. Chem.* B 102, 1176 (1998).

In: Properties of Fluorite Structure Materials
Editors: Peter Vajda and Jean-Marc Costantini

ISBN: 978-1-62417-458-2
© 2013 Nova Science Publishers, Inc.

Chapter 5

RADIATION DAMAGE IN CUBIC-STABILIZED ZIRCONIA (ZrO_{2-x}) AND CERIA (CeO_{2-x})

Jean-Marc Costantini[*], *François Beuneu* *and William J. Weber*

[1]CEA, DEN, SRMA, Gif-sur-Yvette Cedex, France
[2]LSI, CEA-CNRS-Ecole Polytechnique, Palaiseau Cedex, France
[3]University of Tennessee, Knoxville, TN,
Oak Ridge National Laboratory, Oak Ridge, TN, US

ABSTRACT

Cubic zirconium dioxide, or zirconia (ZrO_{2-x}), generally stabilized by yttrium substitution, is a refractory material with a large oxygen sub-stoichiometry inducing a high ionic conductivity that can be used for solid oxide fuel cell (SOFC) applications, oxygen sensors and other electrochemical applications. Yttria-stabilized zirconia (YSZ) can be also used for nuclear applications as an inert matrix for actinide immobilization or transmutation. Indeed, the large amount of native oxygen vacancies also leads to a high radiation tolerance of this material owing to defect recombination occurring in the atomic displacements cascades induced by fast neutron irradiation or ion implantations. Molecular dynamics (MD) simulations of these collision cascades actually show that defect annihilation takes place due to recombination of oxygen interstitials with oxygen vacancies either in YSZ or ZrO_{2-x}. Amorphization cannot be obtained in YSZ either by nuclear-collision or electronic-excitation damage even at large fluences, just like in uranium dioxide or urania (UO_2). A kind of polygonization structure with slightly disoriented crystalline domains is obtained in both cases. Amorphization is reached in YSZ only by a chemical effect above a critical atomic fraction of implanted ions like Cs.

We discuss in details the different mechanisms of point-defect formation in YSZ by energetic photon, electron, and heavy-ion or neutron irradiations either via elastic (nuclear) collision, or inelastic (ionization) processes, on the basis of electron paramagnetic resonance (EPR) and UV-visible optical absorption data. In the first steps of damage, specific isolated point defects (like F^+-type color centers) and point-defect

---

[*] Email: jean-marc.costantini@cea.fr

clusters are produced by nuclear collisions with charged particles or neutrons leading to significant modifications of the electrical and mechanical properties. Further increase of damage leads to dislocation-loop formation then to collapse of the dislocation network into a polygonization structure. For swift heavy ion irradiations, a similar polygonization structure is obtained above a threshold stopping power value of about 20-30 keV nm^{-1}, depending on the ion velocity. Extended-defect production in cerium dioxide or ceria (CeO$_{2-x}$) by ion implantation is also discussed. MD simulations of ceria show that oxygen platelets in {111} planes are produced in collision cascades, in agreement with transmission electron microscopy (TEM). Similar extended defects are also observed by TEM in ion-implanted YSZ. The use of zirconia or ceria as non-radioactive surrogates for the behavior of actinide dioxides with the fluorite structure (e.g. urania) under irradiation is also addressed.

Keywords: Zirconia, ceria, non-stoichiometry, radiation effects, color centers, extended defects, molecular dynamics

INTRODUCTION

Non-stoichiometry is known to play a major role in ceramic-oxide structures and properties. It is particularly true for oxygen diffusion in transition metal oxides like zirconium dioxide or zirconia (ZrO$_{2-x}$) that can be stabilized at room temperature (RT) in the cubic fluorite (CaF$_2$) structure by substitution of Zr^{4+} with aliovalent cations such as Y^{3+} (yttria-stabilized zirconia, or YSZ) or Ca^{2+} (calcia-stabilized zirconia, or CaSZ) above a critical dopant concentration [1]. Substitutions with other trivalent (like rare earth or Sc^{3+}) or divalent (like Mg^{2+}) ions are also used to achieve such stabilization. In either case, a large number of charge-compensating oxygen vacancies (with the 2+ charge state, i.e. V$_O^{··}$ in the Kröger-Vink notation) are generated [2, 3, 4].

Non-stoichiometry has also a strong impact on the radiation tolerance of this material, as will be discussed further below. Actually, the large concentration of native (doubly-ionized) oxygen vacancies (V$_O^{··}$) acts as very effective recombination sites for defects produced by displacive damage [5]. Therefore, due to dynamic annealing, no amorphization of YSZ is produced in the displacement cascades generated by ion irradiations in the nuclear slowing down regime [6, 7] analogous to recoiling atoms induced by fast neutron irradiation. Likewise, YSZ cannot be amorphized by electronic excitations with swift heavy ion irradiations in the electronic slowing down regime [6, 8, 9] analogous to fission fragments. A kind of polygonization structure is found in both cases of damage [10, 11]. Nanocrystalline cubic zirconia undergoes some grain growth under extreme irradiation doses (approaching 35 displacements per atom, dpa) to saturation grain sizes on the order of 30 nm, but it retains the cubic structure, due to the formation of oxygen vacancies [12]. Moreover, enhancement of the ionic conductivity can also be achieved by neutron [13] or ion irradiations [14].

Both zirconia and ceria (CeO$_2$) are isostructural with urania (UO$_2$) and plutonia (PuO$_2$), which are the primary nuclear fuel materials of interest, as well as thoria (ThO$_2$), which is of interest for a thorium-based fuel cycle. Ceria is most often used as a non-radioactive surrogate for these actinide dioxide materials. All these oxides display a broad range of sub-stoichiometry leading to an intrinsic disorder due to large oxygen vacancy concentrations [15, 16].

In this Chapter, the major features of point-defect production and annealing in YSZ will be delineated, as well as the atomic lattice damage obtained with increasing fluences for charged-particle and neutron irradiations. The similarity with the behavior under radiation of other oxides like CeO_2 or UO_2 will be also considered, and the wide use of ceria as a surrogate for actinide dioxides with the fluorite structure will be discussed.

1. NATIVE DEFECTS AND PHASE STABILITY

The equilibrium phase of undoped ZrO_2 (baddeleyite) is monoclinic (α) under normal conditions up to ~ 1170°C and tetragonal (β) up to ~ 2370°C, and the high-temperature cubic (γ) phase is stable above 2370°C up to the melting point at ~ 2710°C [17]. A spread in the transition temperatures of the Zr-O phase diagram is encountered due to the variety of metastable states arising from sluggish kinetics of phase transformations even at 1000°C [18]. The high-temperature γ-phase can be fully stabilized at RT for yttria (Y_2O_3) contents larger than about 8 mol% [1, 19]. Below this critical content, zirconia is partially stabilized in the tetragonal β-phase at RT. In contrast to α- and β-phases, the cubic γ-phase exhibits a broad domain of stability in the Zr-O phase diagram with a wide range of oxygen sub-stoichiometry that leads to a large static disorder in the oxygen sub-lattice, similar to that observed in cubic CeO_{2-x} [20]. Along with the crystallite size [21], the major role of oxygen vacancies in the (meta-)stabilization of the three polymorphs of zirconia has been well known [22]. YSZ is a wide band-gap colorless solid (E_g~ 4.2 eV for 9.5 mol% Y_2O_3) [23] with the cubic fluorite structure (Fm3m space group and lattice parameter a_0~ 0.513 nm for 9.5 mol% Y_2O_3) [24]. It is widely used as a refractory material for high-temperature applications and as a solid-state electrolyte with a high ionic conductivity.

Ensuring charge neutralization of the lattice in YSZ entails that the (doubly-ionized) oxygen vacancy concentration must be half of that of Y^{3+} dopants: $[V_O^{\cdot\cdot}] = \frac{1}{2} [Y_{Zr}']$ (in the Kröger-Vink notation), which gives the formula $Zr_{1-2x}Y_{2x}O_{2-x}$ with $[V_O^{\cdot\cdot}] = x$. For 9.5 mol% yttria, it gives about 10 at% (x ~ 0.1) of native oxygen vacancies occupying ~ 4.5% of the oxygen sites. MD simulations show that Y^{3+} ions, which are oversized dopants, preferentially sit in the next-nearest neighbor (NNN) sites of oxygen vacancies with full eight-fold coordination, whereas Zr^{4+} ions can sit in nearest-neighbor (NN) sites with a lower coordination number [3, 4], which is consistent with recent *ab-initio* calculations on ordered structures in the ZrO_2-Y_2O_3 system [25] and with experimental EXAFS results [26]. Similar conclusions were reached at for Ca^{2+} ions in CaSZ [2].

Various speculations have been put forward to explain the cubic-phase stabilization. Four specific factors were considered to contribute to this stabilization, such as lattice distortions around oxygen vacancies, lowering of dielectric constant in the cubic phase, ionicity increase by the impurities, and removal of Zr 4d orbital degeneracy [27]. For the critical oxygen vacancy concentration, a phonon softening in the oxygen sub-lattice may induce an instability leading to a transition to the cubic phase [28]. The large amount of charge-compensating oxygen vacancies induces a translational disorder in the oxygen sub-lattice of YSZ causing a drastic reduction and (asymmetric) broadening of Raman scattering peaks [29] and absence of optical-phonon branches as seen by neutron scattering [30]. Actually, calculations show that the intrinsic static disorder in the pure cubic phase (γ-ZrO$_{2-x}$) might be of Schottky-type instead of mono-vacancies due to the larger atomic relaxation induced by vacancies [2]. This effect should be enhanced by the extrinsic disorder due to a larger amount of oxygen vacancies in YSZ.

Non-stoichiometry is also a key issue for applications to the SOFC materials requiring a high ionic conductivity, e.g. like cubic-stabilized zirconia or ceria [31, 32, 33, 34]. A maximum of conductivity is found for about 7-8 mol% yttria in YSZ solid-state electrolytes [31], arising from the increase of association of oxygen-vacancies with dopants ([$V_O^{\cdot\cdot} Y_{Zr}'$]$^{\cdot}$clustersin the Kröger-Vink notation) [3, 4] and the increased energy barriers for oxygen-vacancy migration above this maximum, as shown by Kinetic Monte-Carlo simulations of ionic transport [35]. The largest binding energy of [$V_O^{\cdot\cdot} Y_{Zr}'$]$^{\cdot}$clusters(0.35 eV) calculated for 8.3 mol% yttria is found for NNN positions [35].

Moreover, another important potential use of zirconia is as an inert matrix for actinide immobilization or transmutation in a nuclear reactor [36, 37, 38]. In this case, trivalent (Am, Cm) or tetravalent (U, Th, Pu) actinide elements can be substituted for Zr^{4+} and lead to full stabilization of the cubic phase above a critical concentration of trivalent cations (possibly including Y^{3+} and rare-earth ions) [39]. More recently, it has been shown that nanocrystalline zirconia can be stabilized in the cubic structure without aliovalent dopants and exhibits thermal stability up to 859°C [40], which increases the range of potential applications, including those in the nuclear fields.

2. POINT-DEFECT PRODUCTION AND RECOVERY

2.1. Photon Irradiations

Extensive studies have been performed on color center production by X-ray, UV or γ-ray irradiations of fully cubic-stabilized YSZ (with 9.5 mol% yttria) [41, 42, 43, 44, 45, 46, 47, 48, 49, 50, 51, 52, 53, 54], and CaSZ (with 15 mol% calcia, CaO) [55]. As usual, most of experimental evidence on point-defect production is given by EPR spectroscopy, UV-visible optical absorption spectroscopy, and photo- or thermo-luminescence. Two kinds of paramagnetic centers are observed: i) an electron center, the so-called T-center (after "trigonal" center) with a broad EPR signal (for g-factor $< g_e = 2.0023$) (Figure 1(a): spectrum (a)), and a broad optical absorption band centered at a wavelength $\sim$ 375 nm (at photon energy $\sim$ 3.3 eV) giving a yellow color, and ii) a hole center with a narrow EPR signal (for g-factor $> g_e$) and another broad optical absorption band centered at a wavelength $\sim$ 465 nm (at photon energy $\sim$ 2.7 eV), giving a brown coloration [50].

The former color center (T center) was assigned to a Zr^{3+} ion sitting in a trigonal environment (C$_{3v}$ point symmetry), and the latter one to an oxygen hole center (OHC), the so-called O$^-$ center sitting in an orthorhombic environment (C$_{2v}$ point symmetry). Upon electronic excitations and ionizations, electron-hole pairs are generated by above band-gap excitations (with E$_g \sim$ 4.2 eV [23]).It is liable to think that T centers are produced by free electron captures onto the lattice Zr^{4+}ions, whereas O$^-$ centers are produced by free hole captures onto the lattice O^{2-} ions.

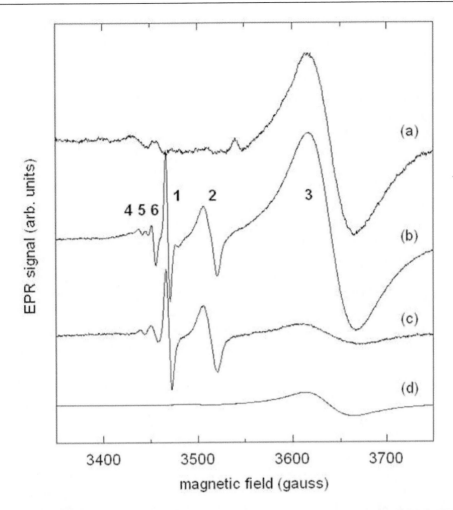

Figure 1(a): X-band EPR (9.5 GHz) spectra for an applied magnetic field B // <100> of (100) YSZ single crystals (9.5 mol% yttria): irradiated at RT with X-ray white spectrum (absorbed dose = 9.5 kGy) (a), 1.5-MeV electrons (sample z, fluence = 9.5x10^{18} cm^{-2}) (b), and 2.4-GeV Lead ions (fluence = 2.0x10^{12} cm^{-2}) (c), and after thermo-chemical reduction (TCR) under vacuum at 1100 °C (24 h) (d).

Complex charge-exchange kinetics between these two X-ray induced color centers were observed upon UV-light illumination, with photo-bleaching of both defects as a function of irradiation time [49].

The g-factor anisotropies were measured by EPR spectroscopy on (100) YSZ single crystals by rotating the <100> axis with respect to the applied magnetic field (B). The angular dependence of EPR lines shows quite different behaviors for the two defects. The T center has a large negative g-factor shift with an axial <111> anisotropy (C$_{3v}$ point symmetry) and two g-tensor principal values (g$_\perp$= 1.852, g$_{//}$ = 1.989) [42], whereas the O$^-$ center has an orthorhombic C$_{2v}$ point symmetry with one NN Y^{3+} ion ([O$'_O$ Y$'_{Zr}$]^{x}in the Kröger-Vink notation) and three g-tensor principal values (g$_x$ = 2.019, g$_y$ = 2.012, and g$_z$ = 2.004) [50]. Low-temperature optical measurements (down to 140 K) show that the broad T-center absorption band retains about the same full-width at half maximum (FWHM ~ 1 eV) [46]. A small oscillator strength value (f ~ 0.03) is found for the optical absorption of this center in agreement with the forbidden d-d inner-shell dipolar transitions.

The isochronal recovery stages of these two color centers are also completely different. The UV and X-ray induced T centers are bleached out at annealing temperatures above 600 K (first-order kinetics with an activation energy ~ 0.5 eV) [43, 50, 51], whereas the O$^-$ centers are bleached at RT after production by X-ray irradiation at liquid-nitrogen temperature [50, 51]. No clear influence of the yttria content (for 12 and 24 mol%) was found on the thermal annealing behavior of T centers [43, 45]. The broad thermo-stimulated luminescence (TSL) signal centered at ~ 550 K after X-ray irradiation was correlated with the T-center annealing stage [56].

Attempts have been made to calculate the specific spectral features of T centers by using crystal-field theory [44]. Good agreement was found for the g-factor shift and anisotropy of a Zr^{3+} ion (with the $4d^1$ electronic configuration) surrounded by two NN (doubly-ionized) oxygen vacancies ($V_O^{..}$) aligned along a <111> direction ([$V_O^{..} Zr'_{Zr} V_O^{..}$]$^{..}$ in the Kröger-Vink notation), giving the above-mentioned C_{3v} point symmetry. A quite similar defect (the so-called C-center) can also be observed by EPR with the same broad line as the T center (Figure 1(a): spectrum (d)) after thermo-chemical reduction (TCR) using high-temperature vacuum-annealing (or under hydrogen atmosphere), where extra oxygen vacancies are retained after quenching at RT [50, 51, 52, 57]. The so-called C-center (with an isochronal recovery stage at ~ 1000 K and activation energy ~ 0.1 eV) [45]) was assigned to a Zr^{3+} ion associated with only one native (doubly-ionized) oxygen vacancy ($V_O^{..}$) in the first coordination shell ([$V_O^{..} Zr'_{Zr}$]$^{..}$ in the Kröger-Vink notation) [50], also with a low oscillator strength (f ~ 0.01) for optical absorption [57]. The energy levels of the T centers and C centers lie at about 2 and 1.1 eV below the conduction-band edge, respectively [52]. These values are consistent with the trap-depth energy distribution (ranging between 0.8 and 1.3 eV) deduced from TSL data of X-ray irradiated YSZ [56]. The band-gap energy was found to increase from 4.23 to 4.96 eV in thermo-chemically reduced YSZ single crystals [23].

More recently, some more sophisticated first-principle calculations were performed to obtain the defect-level energies in the band gap and the optical transitions in pure ZrO_2 [58, 59, 60] and YSZ [61, 62, 63]. Calculated T-center energy levels range between 1.5 and 2.5 eV in YSZ below the conduction-band edge, for calculated E_g values ranging between 5.0 and 5.6 eV [62]. Allowed transitions close to 3.3 eV [63] are found in agreement with the experimental data on T-center optical absorption [46, 50]. Some authors raised the question of the intrinsic nature of this defect that could be linked to a Ti impurity often associated with Zr in the samples [53]. Recent calculations of both optical and magnetic properties of Zr^{3+} and Ti^{3+} (with the $3d^1$ electronic configuration) centers did not clearly discriminate between these two possibilities [62].

2.2. Charged-Particle and Neutron Irradiations

2.2.a. Experimental Data

T centers are equally produced in YSZ (with 9.5 mol% yttria) after electron or swift heavy ion irradiations (from 100 MeV to few GeVs) with about the same spectral features as with energetic photon irradiations (Figures 1(a)-(b): line 3): i.e. EPR line width, g-factor shift and <111> axial anisotropy, and g-tensor principal values ($g_\perp$= 1.859, $g_{//}$ = 1.989) [64, 65, 66].

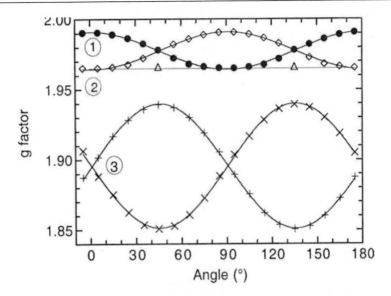

Figure 1(b). Angular variation in a {100} plane of g-factors of EPR lines 1-2-3 (Fig. 1(a)) for a (100) YSZ single crystal (9.5 mol% yttria) irradiated at RT with 2.5-MeV electrons (fluence = 9.0x10^{17} cm^{-2}). Solid lines are least-squares fitted curves [64].

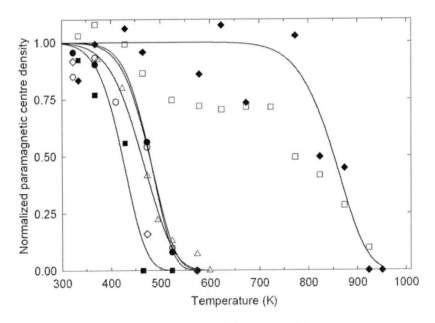

Figure 2. Normalized paramagnetic center density (N/N_0) versus isochronal annealing temperature (t_a = 30 min) for electron-irradiated YSZ single crystals; sample e (1.0-MeV, fluence = 9.7x10^{17} cm^{-2}): T centers (line 3, open triangles); sample j (1.0-MeV, fluence = 1.0x10^{19} cm^{-2}): F$^+$-type centers (line 1, full squares), T centers (line 3, open squares and full diamonds); sample s (2.0-MeV, fluence = 3.2x10^{18} cm^{-2}): F$^+$-type centers (line 2, full circles), T centers (line 3, open circles), OHCs (line 5, open diamonds). Lines are least-squares fits to the first-order kinetics with Eq (1) (see Table 1 for the sample characteristics) [68].

Table 1. EPR data of as-received (100) YSZ single crystals (with 9.5 mol% yttria) irradiated by electrons and ions with incident energies E: concentrations (N_0) of F$^+$-type centers, hole centers (HCs) and T centers, activation energies for recovery ($\Delta\varepsilon$), temperatures ($T_{1/2}$) at which 50% of defects are isochronally annealed out, on the basis of a first-order kinetics (single-stage recovery) with Eq (1) for the F$^+$-type and T centers, effective production cross-sections (σ), and concentrations at saturation(N_s) of the F$^+$-type centers (Eq (2))

Sample reference	Particle	E (MeV)	Fluence (cm^{-3})	N_0 (cm^{-3}) (F$^+$-type centers)	$\Delta\varepsilon$ (eV) (F$^+$-type centers)	$T_{1/2}$ (K) (F$^+$-type centers)	σ (cm^2) (F$^+$-type centers)	N_s (cm^{-3}) (F$^+$-type centers)	N_0 (cm^{-3}) (HCs)	N_0 (cm^{-3}) (T-centers)	$\Delta\varepsilon$ (eV) (T-centers)	$T_{1/2}$ (K) (T-centers)
e	e$^-$	1.0	9.7x10^{17}							1.7x10^{18}	0.41	479
j	e$^-$	1.0	1.0x10^{19}	8.0x10^{15}	0.45	436				2.0x10^{18}	1.28	870
z	e$^-$	1.5	9.5x10^{18}	6.2x10^{16}					1.2x10^{16}	2.4x10^{18}		
ff	e$^-$	2.0	1.5x10^{18}	1.7x10^{16}					2.4x10^{15}	1.9x10^{16}		
q	e$^-$	2.0	3.2x10^{18}	3.8x10^{16}					1.8x10^{16}	1.1x10^{18}		
s	e$^-$	2.0	3.2x10^{18}	3.5x10^{16}	0.59	492				1.3x10^{18}	0.54	492
f	e$^-$	2.5	9.8x10^{17}	1.9x10^{16}	0.65	434	3.2x10^{-19}	1.6x10^{17}		1.2x10^{18}	0.63	487
w	e$^-$	2.5	2.5x10^{18}	2.3x10^{16}			3.2x10^{-19}	1.6x10^{17}	8.5x10^{15}	4.8x10^{17}		
v	e$^-$	2.5	9.5x10^{18}	2.7x10^{16}			3.2x10^{-19}	1.6x10^{17}	7.4x10^{15}	5.3x10^{17}		
C-13	^{13}C	100	1.0x10^{14}	2.3x10^{17}	0.47	468	1.3x10^{-15}	1.8x10^{18}				
I-6	^{127}I	200	1.0x10^{12}	3.2x10^{17}	0.68	456	4.3x10^{-13}	2.6x10^{18}		1.4x10^{18}	0.55	478
AU-5	^{197}Au	200	1.0x10^{12}	4.9x10^{17}	0.66	449	9.0x10^{-13}	2.4x10^{18}				
AU-11	^{197}Au	200	2.5x10^{13}	2.8x10^{17}	0.70-0.83	532-562	9.0x10^{-13}	2.4x10^{18}				

Due to the large concentrations (N_0) found for this defect (up to $\sim 7\times10^{18}$ cm^{-3}, i.e. ~ 350 at. ppm, with the heavier ions), it is quite unlikely that it would be linked to any impurities, such as Ti ($<$ 1 at. ppm). The same isochronal recovery stage as the X-ray induced T centers (at ~ 500 K with an activation energy $\Delta\varepsilon\sim 0.5$ eV for a first-order kinetics, like the X-ray induced T center) is found for the low-fluence electron and ion irradiations (i.e. low defect concentrations), whereas it is similar to that of the TCR-induced C-centers (at ~ 1000 K) for the high-fluence irradiations (Figure 2) [67, 68]. Using the assumption that the frequency factor (ν) is thermally activated, gives a classical first-order kinetics for fitting the single-stage annealing curves (Figure 2):

$$N / N_0 = \exp(-\nu_0 t_a \exp(-\Delta\varepsilon / k_B T_a))$$ (1)

where N is the color-center concentration after annealing, ν_0 is a frequency factor, t_a is the annealing time, k_B is the Boltzmann's constant, T_a is the annealing temperature, and $\Delta\varepsilon$ is the activation energy for recovery (Table 1). This stage is characterized by the mid-temperature ($T_{1/2}$) at which half of the defects are annealed out (Table 1).

However, much more stable hole centers (with concentrations up to $\sim 2\times10^{16}$ cm^{-3} and an isochronal recovery stage at ~ 500 K) (Figure 2) than the X-ray induced O$^-$ centers (annealed at RT) are produced with a weak angular dependence of g-factors [68]. It seems that different OHCs are produced by electron or ion irradiations, although the g-factors of the three EPR lines (Figure 1(a): lines 4-5-6, with g = 2.014, 2.010, 2.007 respectively) are similar to those of the X-ray induced O$^-$ center (g$_x$ = 2.019, g$_y$ = 2.012, and g$_z$ = 2.004) [50]. The production of these OHCs was correlated to the inelastic stopping power (electronic excitations) of impinging particles [69]. When increasing the yttria content (from 9.5 to 18 mol%), the number of OHCs is greatly enhanced, probably because Y^{3+} ions can act as strong hole traps [70]. Clustering of yttrium ions is expected to occur for yttria contents larger than 10 mol% [71], and the number of highly stable neutral [Y$^{'}_{Zr}$ V$^{"}_O$ Y$^{'}_{Zr}$]^x clusters (in the Kröger-Vink notation) increases with the yttria content [3, 4].

Moreover, other paramagnetic electron centers with large concentrations (up to $\sim 2\times10^{18}$ cm^{-3} with heavy ions at large fluences) (Table 1) are also produced equally by electron or ion irradiations with an EPR signal that is quite different from the X-ray induced color centers (Figure 1(a): lines 1-2) [64, 65]. Larger concentrations of this defect are found in thermally-reduced samples having larger (doubly-ionized) oxygen vacancy concentrations (V$_O^{"}$) after TCR treatment prior to irradiations for the same irradiations [65, 67]. Little effect of the yttria content (from 9.5 to 18 mol%) is found on the production of these color centers [70], like for the X-ray induced T center [43, 45]. The color-center concentration (N) shows a saturation behavior as a function of ion fluence (ϕ):

$$N / N_s = 1 - \exp(-\sigma\phi)$$ (2)

where σ is an effective cross section, and N_s($\sim 10^{17}$-10^{18} cm^{-3}) is the concentration at saturation (Table 1), which is much larger than the major impurities. The latter cross section increases by about six orders of magnitude from electrons to Au ions. Such a behavior can be derived from first-order kinetics of defect annihilation [66].

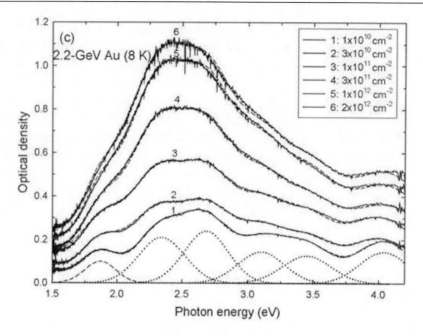

Figure 3. Transmission optical spectra of (100) YSZ single crystals (9.5 mol% yttria) irradiated at 8 K with 2.2-GeV Gold ions at various fluences. Dashed lines are trial-and-error fits with six Gaussian bands (dotted lines) centered at photon energies ~ 1.9, 2.3, 2.7, 3.1, 3.4, and 4.0 eV [72].

The angular dependence of these new EPR lines with a smaller negative g-shift exhibits a clear <100> axial symmetry with a weaker g-factor anisotropy (by rotating the <100> axis with respect to B) than the T center, either for electron or ion irradiations, with two g-tensor principal values ($g_\perp$= 1.972, $g_{//}$ = 1.996) (Figure 1(b): lines 1-2) [64, 65]. As will be shown further below, these new lines can be assigned to an F^+-type center. The recovery stage of this defect takes place for $T_{1/2}$~ 450 K with an activation energy $\Delta\varepsilon$~ 0.6 eV for a first-order kinetics (Figure 2) [67, 68] (Table 1), which is compatible with oxygen-vacancy migration energy data ranging between about 0.4 and 1 eV for ~ 9.5 mol% yttria [4, 32, 33]. An uncommon non-zero asymptotic behavior for long annealing times (t_a) is found for the isothermal annealing curves in this temperature range (and also RT ageing) of these color centers, as well as for the OHCs [68], with a time-dependence:

$$N/N_0 = N_\infty/N_0 + k \exp\left(- t_a/\tau\right) \tag{3}$$

where N_∞ is the asymptotic defect concentration, τ~v^{-1} is the decay time, and k is a constant ~ 1. Such a behavior may be due to equilibria between the various charged point defects.

This single-stage recovery process (denoted as type I) occurs for low color-center concentrations (viz. low fluences) in as-grown crystals (Figure 2). However, a complex two-stage recovery process (denoted as type II) takes place for high defect concentrations (viz. high fluences) in as-grown crystals, or for thermally-reduced single crystals [67]. In the latter type II process, after annealing above 600 K, these color centers are transformed into new paramagnetic centers showing a sharp EPR line with a larger g-factor value and a sextet hyperfine structure [66, 67, 68]. Full bleaching of all paramagnetic centers occurs eventually at 1000 K.

Low-temperature EPR line saturation measurements (from RT down to 10 K) permit to extract the spin-lattice relaxation time (T_1), which varies versus temperature (according to a $1/T$ dependence) [66]. It gives large T_1-values (~ 10 µs), either for electron or ion irradiations, with a very small variation of the spin-spin relaxation time ($T_2 \sim 2x10^{-8}$ s) with temperature, as deduced from the EPR line widths [65]. By contrast, the clear temperature-dependence of the EPR line widths between 120 K and RT for the X-ray induced T center was assigned to spin-lattice interactions [43].

A broad asymmetrical optical absorption band peaked at a wavelength ~ 450 nm (at photon energy ~ 2.5 eV) is found for all swift ion irradiations (Figure 3) giving a light purple color, whereas the electron-irradiated single crystals turn grey [65, 72]. This peculiar broad band was also observed after irradiations with ions in the 100-keV range [73, 74] and fast neutrons [75]. This absorption band was deconvoluted with two Gaussian contributions centered at photon energies of 2.4 and 3.1 eV [66, 72], the latter one being assigned to the T-center with a similar FWHM (~ 1.4 eV) as the X-ray induced T center (~ 1.6 eV) [50]. Both band integrated intensities increase linearly with the respective concentrations (N) of the two electron centers deduced from the EPR data, and show a saturation behavior like N in Eq. (2) [72]. Large oscillator strengths (f) of optical absorptions (f ~ 0.2-0.3) are obtained from the slopes of these plots for both color centers, in contrast to the X-ray induced T center (f ~ 0.01), on the basis of the Markham-Smakula's formula for Gaussian-shaped bands [76]:

$$N f \sim 0.87x10^{17} \{n/[(n^2 + 2)]^2\} \, \alpha_{max} \, W \tag{4}$$

where α_{max} is the maximum absorption coefficient deduced from the optical density, $n = 2.1585$ is the refractive index at 500 nm, and W is the FWHM.

Low-temperature optical measurements show that the two broad absorption components keep about the same FWHM from RT to 10 K, after swift heavy ion irradiation in the 100-MeV range at RT [65], like the X-ray induced T-center [46]. Such invariance was also found after irradiating with ions in the GeV range at 8 K and slowly warming up to RT [72]. As explained for the X-ray induced center, this invariance may arise from the disorder in the oxygen sublattice [46].

Moreover, the color-center production rate with fluence is much larger at 8 K than at RT. After heating up to RT, the defect recovery is not complete: the color center concentration is larger than the value for RT irradiation [72].

In contrast to the T centers, the production rate of these new electron centers is clearly correlated to the displacement damage rate of the various charged particles, i.e. the mean number of displaced atoms per particle, or likewise the dpa number [66]. The concentration of these color centers is significantly increased for heavy ions (Table 1), thereby explaining the difference in colors of ion and electron-irradiated samples.

A quite large oxygen displacement energy ($E_d \sim 120$ eV) was found by using electron irradiations with energies ranging between 1.0 and 2.5 MeV (with a large electron energy threshold ~ 1.0 MeV) [69, 70].

Finally, it is to be noted that charge equilibrium between electron centers and hole centers is not found (Table 1). This implies that extra EPR-silent diamagnetic centers must also be produced to make up for the charge imbalance.

2.2.b. Defect Identification

In contrast to the T center, which is well documented in the literature, the new color center produced by electron and ion irradiations is not found after energetic photon irradiations, as said above. Several features like: i) the small g-factor shift (small spin-orbit coupling constant like for a s-like wave function), ii) large T_1-values (weak coupling of the spin with the lattice-phonon modes), and iii) the large oscillator strength (allowed dipolar optical transitions like with standard F centers in the alkali halides) [76], hint to a F^+-type center with an electron trapped on a (singly-ionized) oxygen vacancy (with a 1+ charge state, i.e. $V_O^{\cdot}$ in the Kröger-Vink notation) [65, 66], similar to the F^+ center in MgO [77]. The 3-D wavelength-resolved TSL signal at a wavelength ~ 620 nm (i.e. photon energy ~ 2 eV close to the absorption band at ~ 2.4 eV) and temperature ~ 525 K is correlated with the annealing stage of these color centers in ion-irradiated YSZ (Figure 4) [78]. Like in MgO [79], this defect is produced by (elastic) nuclear collisions with electrons, ions and neutrons, as seen from the similar optical absorption bands [73, 74, 75].

The invariance of the optical absorption band FWHM with temperature is most probably linked to the lattice disorder for a large amount of randomly distributed native (doubly-ionized) oxygen vacancies (for 9.5 mol% yttria) [71], as was previously concluded for the X-ray induced T center [46]. The latter atomic disorder is reflected in the invariance of the fundamental absorption edge with temperature [80].

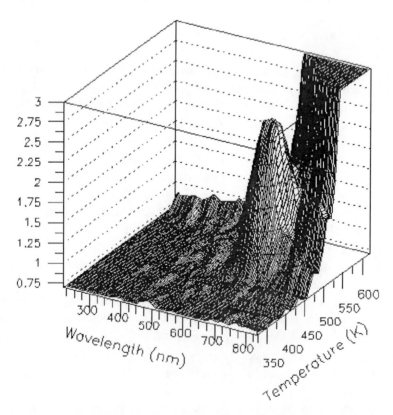

Figure 4. 3-D (wavelength-resolved) TSL spectrum of a (100) YSZ single crystal (9.5 mol% yttria) irradiated at RT with 2.6-GeV Uranium ions (fluence = 1.6×10^{12} cm^{-2}) [78].

Indeed, the "effective" band-gap energy depends mostly on the yttria content, not on temperature: $E_g \sim$ 4.2 eV for 9.5 mol% Y_2O_3, with an intrinsic absorption region for photon energies above $\sim$ 5.4 eV [80]. The increase of E_g with yttria content can be associated to an enhancement of native oxygen-vacancy ordering due to the increase of yttrium-oxygen vacancy $[Y'_{Zr} V_O^{\cdot\cdot} Y'_{Zr}]^x$ clustering [3, 4, 35], thereby reducing the (Urbach) band tails arising from disorder [80]. Such a disorder in the oxygen sublattice also results in an overall decrease and (asymmetric) broadeningof the first-order Raman scattering peaks in YSZ [29], due to the breakdown of selection rules in a non-periodic lattice. Rather, it corresponds to the projection of the phonon density-of-states at the Brillouin-zone center [30]. Such a static disorder also induces the disappearance of optical-phonon modes as seen by neutron scattering [30], and broad Gaussian-shaped TSL peaks [56, 79].

The large threshold displacement energy and the decoupling of the defect magnetic and optical properties from the lattice-phonon modes also hint to oxygen-vacancy clusters [66]. Actually, it was shown by *ab-initio* DFT calculations that the single F^+ center (i.e. $V_O^{\cdot}$ in the Kröger-Vink notation) should be unstable in YSZ due to a negative (Hubbard) U effect, which would lead to the defect reaction: $2 V_O^{\cdot} \rightarrow V_O^x + V_O^{\cdot\cdot}$ [61]. The same effect was also found by DFT calculations of formation energies of neutral and charged oxygen vacancies in undoped zirconia [81]. Actually, the present color center could be a 1+ charged oxygen divacancy (i.e. a F_2^+ center), possibly one paramagnetic vacancy associated to one NN neutral vacancy (i.e. $[V_O^{\cdot} V_O^x]^{\cdot}$ in the Kröger-Vink notation), thereby explaining the <100> axial symmetry of this defect [66]. Higher-order clusters (like trimers and so forth) seem quite unlikely due to this axial symmetry. No direct experimental evidence of a F_A-type center [76] associated to Y^{3+} impurities is found, due to the lack of a clear hyperfine splitting arising from NN [89]Y nuclei (with I = 1/2 nuclear spin) in the EPR spectra of this color center (Figure 1(a)). Although these color centers are primarily produced by elastic collision processes, as described above, the resulting singly-ionized oxygen vacancies must trap electrons to become EPR-active centers. Calculations for oxygen divacancies in YSZ give three allowed optical transitions with large oscillator strengths at photon energies of 1.93, 2.24, and 2.67 eV [60], whereas in pure ZrO_2 the main transitions for a single oxygen vacancy are found near 2.5 eV from a mid-gap state [63]. The latter value is consistent with the RT absorption band, while the former three values are in good agreement indeed with the measured three bands at photon energies of 1.87, 2.33, and 2.73 eVin the more resolved spectra recorded at 8 K after low-fluence swift heavy ion irradiations (Figure 3) [72]. Moreover, the calculated g-tensor principal values (g_x = 1.967, g_y = 1.981 and g_z = 1.995) [60] are consistent with the experimental values and the small negative g-shift of this electron center (Figure 1(b)) [65, 66]. The out-of-plane expansion measured by surface profilometry on YSZ single crystals is increasing linearly with the F^+-type center concentration for all ion species and energies (Figure 5) [8]. The large slopes of these linear plots, proportional to the defect volume, are also consistent with small oxygen-vacancy clusters [66]. As explained above, these color centers are found to transform into new paramagnetic defects after annealing above 600 K in the type II recovery process [67]. Appearance of a new line with a larger g-factor value and a sextet hyperfine splitting is analyzed as a transformation of divacancies into single oxygen vacancies with a different NN [91]Zr nucleus (with I = 5/2 nuclear spin) environment for high temperatures [67].

3. Extended Defect Formation and Lattice Damage

3.1. Damage Induced by Nuclear Collisions

Ballistic damage induced by heavy ions in the nuclear slowing down regime was quite extensively investigated at RT [6] by means of Rutherford backscattering spectrometry and channeling (RBS-C) [82], transmission electron microscopy (TEM) [7], and X-ray diffraction (XRD) [83]. It exhibits a three-step process (Figure 6) versus fluence of: i) point-defect accumulation and small defect-cluster formation, for doses < 5 dpa, ii) extended defect (dislocation loop) formation, and iii) collapse of loops into a kind of polygonization structure (with small disoriented crystalline domains of sizes ~ 100 nm), for doses > 5 dpa. This highly damaged state corresponds to a saturation of the disordered fraction at about 50% in the Zr sublattice after 4-MeV Au ion implantation, and at 80% after rare-gas ion implantations in the 100-keV range (as measured by RBS-C for doses > 10 dpa) [7]. A similar damage evolution is found for the O sublattice but with larger damage fractions for the same fluences [82]. The difference of maximum damage fraction in step III is accounted for by annealing of defects by electronic excitations for the heavier ions (Figure 6) [7]. The damage kinetics is modeled by using different phenomenological approaches, e.g. the multiple-step damage accumulation (MSDA) model applied to YSZ after noble-gas [84] and Au ion implantations [7], for which the damage fraction (f_d) dependence versus fluence (ϕ) is given by:

$$f_d = \sum_{i=1}^{n} (f_{d,i}^{sat} - f_{d,i-1}^{sat})\ G\left[1 - \exp(-\sigma_i(\phi - \phi_{i-1}))\right] \tag{5}$$

where n is the number of steps in the damage accumulation process (n typically varies from 1 to 3), $f_{d,i}^{sat}$ is the level of damage saturation in the i-th step, σ_i is the damage cross-section in i-th step, ϕ_i is the threshold fluence for the i-th transformation, and G is a function which transforms negative values into zero, and leaves positive values unchanged.

Such a microstructure is obtained without any cold work and subsequent thermal annealing like in the standard recovery processes of strained metallic materials [85]. There is no consistent modeling of such a process taking place upon irradiation. A similar effect (without any amorphization) was found in UO_2 single crystals showing a fine-grained polycrystalline state after 300-keV Xe ion implantation above a threshold fluence due to over-pressurized gas bubble formation [86]. This is quite similar to the microstructural evolution of high burn-up urania fuels [87, 88, 89, 90]. In this peculiar respect, YSZ may be considered as a surrogate for the microstructural evolution of urania.

Amorphization is thus not achieved in YSZ by point-defect build-up for Xe ion implantation in the 100-keV range [10] or other heavy ion (such as Au) implantations in the MeV-range [7]. The resistance to amorphization most likely stems from the dynamic annealing due to the large number of defect recombination in the displacement cascades, thereby precluding the formation of amorphous domains by direct impact or by defect accumulation with cascade overlaps (see section 5) [5, 91, 92].

However, amorphization can be obtained in a fourth step at high fluences [84] by a chemical effect where the implanted ions (e.g. Cs$^-$) substitute for Zr^{4+}, leading to the collapse of the fluorite structure above a large implanted ion concentration (10-20 at%) [93].

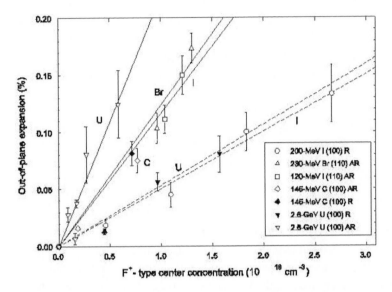

Figure 5. Out-of-plane expansion measured by surface profilometry on (100) and (110) YSZ single crystals (9.5 mol% yttria) irradiated at RT with heavy ions as a function of the F$^+$-type center concentration deduced from EPR spectra. Solid and dashed lines are linear regressions for as-received (AR) samples and thermo-chemically reduced (R) samples (pre-annealed at 1100°C under vacuum), respectively [8].

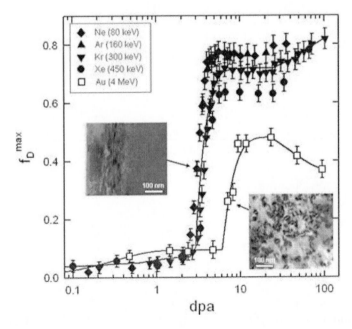

Figure 6. Maximum damage fraction (f_d^{max}) in (100) YSZ single crystals (9.5 mol% yttria) deduced from RBS/C data as a function of dpa for various ions. Solid lines are least-squares fits using the MSDA model (Eq. (5) with n = 3). The TEM micrographs correspond to the second step (n = 2) of steep increase of damage [7].

This probably arises from the charge imbalance that cannot be made up for by oxygen vacancies, leading eventually to the formation of Cs precipitates [94], or definite ternary compounds such as Cs_2ZrO_3 [95].

RBS/C data show that the substitutional fraction along <100> axis is larger than 40% for 150 and 300-keV Cs ion implantation, whereas it reaches 10% at most for 150-keV I ions and remains very small for 450-keV Xe ions regardless of fluence up to 10^{16} cm^{-2} [82, 94]. The decrease of Cs atom substitutional fraction for high fluences is correlated with the ternary phase formation. High-temperature (750°C) 300-keV Cs ion implantations strongly modify the damage accumulation kinetics and resulting microstructure seen by TEM, but with no secondary phase formation up to 3 at% [96]. High-temperature rare gas (30-keV Ne) ion implantations also show a dependence of microstructural evolution on the irradiation temperature (up to 1200°C) [97]. At 700°C, TEM images show the formation of dislocation loops and gas bubbles that grow upon subsequent thermal annealing, whereas no dislocations are seen at 1200°C.

A peculiar effect is obtained by electron irradiation (in an high-voltage electron microscope) of pre-existing ion-induced damage in YSZ single crystals (with 13 mol% yttria), giving rise to some extended defect (coherent oxygen platelets in {111} planes) formation involving charged oxygen interstitial diffusion to the charged dislocation loops [98, 99]. An effect of electronic excitations was speculated to account for the large defect cluster growth rate [98]. A similar kind of interstitial oxygen clusters seems to be produced in strained YSZ single crystals (with 9.4 mol% yttria) in which dislocations have been formed prior to the electron irradiations [100].

3.2. Damage Induced by Electronic Excitations

In the case of swift heavy ion irradiations, in the electronic slowing down regime, no amorphization of YSZ is obtained either way. A similar polygonization structure is observed by TEM [9] above a threshold electronic stopping power ~ 20-30 keV nm^{-1} (for 9.5 mol% yttria) (Figure 7) [8, 9]. No significant difference is found between as-grown and thermo-chemically reduced single crystals. Above the latter threshold, the lattice disorder measured by RBS-C increases with fluence up to a saturation value corresponding to the formation of a polygonization structure, similar to that of nuclear-collision damage, but for lower damage fractions (< 40%). In contrast to the nuclear-collision damage, this process occurs in a single step of damage accumulation, with the damage fraction (f_d) given as:

$$f_d = 1 - \exp(-\sigma' \phi) \tag{6}$$

Eq. (6) corresponds to $n = 1$ in Eq. (5), for a one-step direct-impact process with a damage cross section σ'.

Reciprocal space mapping by XRD near the (220) and (440) diffraction spots confirms that there is no amorphization of (110) YSZ single crystals (with 9.5 mol% yttria) above the threshold (Figure 8) [11]. The broad distribution of scattered X-ray intensity around these symmetrical Bragg reflections was assigned to the small lattice plane disorientations (< 0.4°) induced in polycrystalline samples by swift heavy ion irradiations [9].

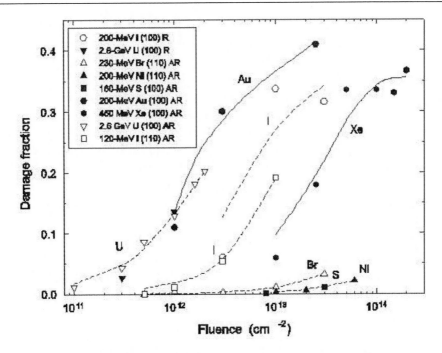

Figure 7. Damage fraction (f_d) in (100) and (110) YSZ single crystals (9.5 mol% yttria) deduced from RBS/C data as a function of fluence for various ions in the electronic slowing down regime (AR: as-received samples; R: thermo-chemically reduced samples by pre-annealing at 1100°C under vacuum). Solid lines are least-squares fits to a single-impact saturation law (Eq. (6)), and dashed lines are linear regressions [8].

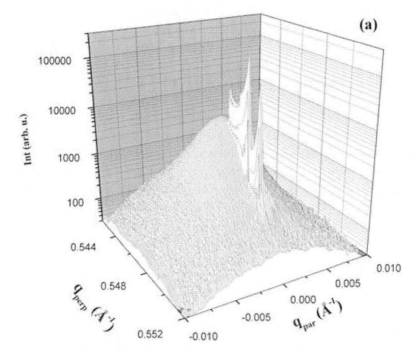

Figure 8. Reciprocal space mapping by XRD near the (220) Bragg reflection of a (110) YSZ single crystal (9.5 mol% yttria) irradiated at RT with 200-MeV Gold ions (fluence = 2.5x10^{13} cm^{-2}) [11].

The small (positive) perpendicular lattice strain ($< 0.5\%$) deduced from the XRD data [11] is consistent with the small above-mentioned out-of-plane expansion (leveling off at about 0.15%) (Figure 5) assigned to F^+-type center formation, with no large volume change due to a phase change or amorphous phase formation [8].

A similar dependence is found for the ion-induced out-of-plane expansion as in Eq (2), with cross sections similar to those found for F^+-type center production (Table 1) [8].

However, the same kind of microstructure seems to be produced with a similar low out-of-plane strain ($< 0.7\%$) as in the case of nuclear damage [10, 83], although it corresponds to different disordered fractions. Thermal-spike modeling accounts for ion-track formation above the threshold $\sim$ 20-30 keV nm^{-1} depending on the ion velocity [9]. However, there is no complete modeling of this process for conversion of electronic excitations into atomic motion leading to the polygonization structure.

A similar behavior was also observed in urania single crystals at high electronic stopping power $\sim$ 20-30 keV nm^{-1} [101] with a strong disordering of both U and O sublattices even at low fluence without amorphization [102], and with a small volume swelling ($< 1.5\%$) [101]. Thermal-spike modeling also accounts for track formation above this threshold [103].

4. MODIFICATIONS OF PHYSICAL PROPERTIES

As said in the introduction, modifications of the electrical properties can be achieved by neutron or ion irradiations. The mobility of oxygen ions in oxygen sensors using YSZ (with 8 mol% yttria) electrolyte increases and the activation energy decreases after fast neutron irradiation to a fluence of $\sim 10^{19}$ cm^{-2} [13]. The electro-motive force of oxygen sensors using YSZ and CaSZ (with 11 mol% calcia) electrolytes was also significantly decreased after neutron irradiation. A new electric-dipole relaxation process with a significantly smaller activation energy (0.62 eV) than in the pristine YSZ material (1.33 eV) was found in the ac-impedance data. This probably arises from charge exchange between oxygen-vacancies with different charges (see section 2.2). A significant conductivity increase of YSZ films was also obtained in ac-impedance measurements after 150-keV Ar ion irradiation and heat treatment at 800°C [14]. The increase in ionic conductivity may be due in this case to the formation of a dense dislocation network (acting as grain boundaries) seen by TEM.

Modifications of the mechanical properties have been studied in fully stabilized zirconia single crystals [104, 105, 106] and polycrystalline samples [107] after ion irradiations. After 240-keV Xe ion implantation, Knoop indentation tests first show an increase of hardness of YSZ single crystals (with 9.4 mol% yttria) for low fluences, then a decrease at larger fluences. TEM shows that point defects and dislocation networks are formed in the hardening regime. For high fluences, where softening occurs, electron diffraction hints to the formation of solid Xe. Similar evolutions of Knoop micro-hardness were observed for other noble-gas (Ne, Ar) and heavy ion (N, Si, Ti, W) implantations in the 100-keV range showing a maximum at low fluences [104, 106]. This maximum can be very nicely correlated to the steps of damage of YSZ, as was done for spinel ($MgAl_2O_4$) after irradiation with Ar ion in the 100-keV range in which a maximum of hardness coincides with the end of step II of damage [108]. The microhardness evolution was rescaled as a function of the nuclear-collision damage energy for the various ion species [104].

For swift heavy ion (940-MeV Pb) irradiations of YSZ sintered samples (with 9.4 mol% yttria), Vickers indentation tests exhibit a monotonic increase of the microhardness [107], in agreement with the single step of damage [8, 9]. The strengthening was interpreted as an effect of the in-plane residual compressive stresses induced at the sample surface by irradiation [107].

5. MOLECULAR-DYNAMICS SIMULATIONS OF DAMAGE

While there have been numerous studies on MD simulations of radiation damage processes in related fluorite-type oxides [92, 109], there are few MD studies of radiation damage in zirconia. In a study of 30 keV Zr recoil cascades in zirconia and YSZ [5], dynamic defect recombination during the thermal spike of the cascade was shown to be very effective in zirconia and even more effective, particularly for oxygen defects, in the presence of the oxygen structural vacancies present in YSZ. Oxygen interstitials in YSZ undergo nearly complete annihilation with the structural vacancies. However, even without structural vacancies, ZrO_2 exhibited substantial interstitial recombination due to the high mobility of the oxygen vacancies. It was also shown that recovery of cation defects is assisted by the recovery and high mobility of oxygen defects. In a subsequent study of YSZ [91], it was reported that Y is preferentially displaced compared to Zr, with about 44% of the cation interstitials being Y interstitials. Lastly, MD simulations show that the threshold displacement energy (E_d) for oxygen is quite large (in excess of 200 eV), in agreement with the experimental data, whereas Zr atoms can be displaced for $E_d = 80$ eV [72].

MD simulations have also been used to investigate threshold displacement energies and Frenkel pair recombination in CeO_2 [110]. The minimum threshold displacement energies were determined to be 27 and 56 eV for O and Ce, respectively. The recombination of oxygen Frenkel pairs occurs either spontaneously, or through thermally-activated processes, and cerium Frenkel pairs undergo athermal recombination for all Frenkel pair configurations considered.

6. USE OF ZIRCONIA OR CERIA AS SURROGATES FOR ACTINIDE DIOXIDES

Besides its potential use as a high-performance SOFC material [34, 111], ceria is widely used as a non-radioactive surrogate for either urania (UO_2) or plutonia (PuO_2) because of its similar fluorite structure and sensitivity to valence change under reducing conditions and irradiation. One of the earliest studies on irradiation effects in ceria was a comparative study with UO_2 and PuO_2 on response to α-particle damage [112], which demonstrated a similarity in point-defect production and recovery for CeO_2, UO_2 and PuO_2. More recently, CeO_2 is often used as a non-radioactive surrogate for either UO_2 or PuO_2.

High-voltage electron microscopy has been used to study the electron-energy dependence of dislocation-loop formation in CeO_2 [113]. At low energies (200 to 1250 keV), the formation of interstitial-type nonstoichiometric loops from the aggregation of oxygen interstitialswas observed, while at higher energies (1500 to 3000 keV), perfect dislocation loops were formed. Based on the results, the threshold displacement energies were estimated to be lower than 33 eV for oxygen and between 44 and 58 eV for cerium. This is in reasonable agreement with the results of MD simulations that determined threshold displacement energies of 27 and 56 eV for oxygen and cerium, respectively [110]. Based on the decreased growth behavior of perfect dislocation loops at elevated temperatures [113] the migration energy for Ce vacancies was also estimated to be greater than 2.1 eV, which is in reasonable agreement with the value of 2.3 eV determined in post-irradiation annealing studies [112]. MD simulations of oxygen Frenkel pairs [114] show that interstitial oxygen platelets are formed in {111} planes in agreement with the TEM observations, like in ion-implanted YSZ [98].

Because much of the restructuring of nuclear fuels comes from the damage caused by the high-energy (70 to 210 MeV) fission products (FPs) produced by nuclear fission, there have been extensive investigations of high-energy heavy ion damage in CeO_2, in order to develop a better understanding of the crystallographic restructuring that is observed in nuclear fuels [87, 88, 89, 90]. This restructuring, which occurs most prominently in the rim region of nuclear fuel pellets, is commonly described at the "rim effect". In this high-energy regime of FPs, most of the radiation damage is from high-density electronic excitations along the FP tracks. A polygonization structure is obtained as in UO_2 single crystals for swift heavy ion irradiations above a threshold electronic stopping power even at low fluences [86, 102], with pore formation at high fluences [86]. In this particular respect, CeO_2 can also be regarded as a surrogate of UO_2 behavior under irradiation, similar to YSZ as noted above.

CONCLUSION

Radiation damage in cubic-stabilized, and more specifically yttria-stabilized zirconia (ZrO_2: Y^{3+}) or YSZ, has been extensively studied over the last 20 years, as regards point-defect and extended-defect production, and lattice damage. Ceria (CeO_{2-x}) was also investigated but to a lesser extent, as yet. Both oxides with a cubic crystal structure are characterized by a broad domain of stability with a large oxygen sub-stoichiometry. EPR and UV-visible optical absorption spectroscopy data show that F^+-type centers (involving singly-ionized oxygen vacancies) are produced in YSZ by elastic-collision processes with charged particle or neutron irradiations. These defects are most likely paramagnetic oxygen di-vacancies (i.e. F_2^+ centers). Another color center (the so-called T center), assigned to a Zr^{3+} ion, is produced in YSZ by electronic excitations with energetic photon or charged particle irradiations.

A striking point is that amorphization cannot be achieved either by nuclear collisions or dense electronic excitations in YSZ. The end point of lattice damage is a kind of polygonization structure, after collapse of the dislocation-loop network in the case of displacive damage at high fluences. These findings are consistent with MD simulations of the first steps of damage showing that point-defect annihilation takes place in the collision cascades, due to the large number of recombination with native oxygen vacancies. The formation of segregated oxygen atoms in coherent [111] platelets is also observed for both YSZ and ceria. The similarity of the behavior of zirconia and ceria with urania (UO_2), plutonia (PuO_2) and thoria (ThO_2) is highlighted for their application as surrogates for studying the irradiation response of these fluorite-structured actinide dioxides and mixed actinide dioxides, such as $(U, Pu)O_2$ and $(Th, Pu)O_2$, in advanced nuclear energy systems.

REFERENCES

[1]   T. H. Etsell, and S. N. Flengas, *Chem. Reviews* 70 (1970) 339.

[2]   A. Dwivedi, and A. N. Cormack, *Philos. Mag.* 61 (1990) 1.

[3]   M. O. Zacate, L. Minervini, D. J. Bradfield, R. W. Grimes, and K. E Sickafus, *Solid St. Ionics* 128 (2000) 243.

[4]   R. Devanathan, W. J. Weber, S. C. Singhal, and J. D. Gale, *Solid St. Ionics* 177 (2006) 1251.

[5]   R. Devanathan, and W. J. Weber, *J. Mater. Res.* 23 (2008) 593.

[6]   K. E. Sickafus, Hj. Matzke, Th. Hartmann, K. Yasuda, J. A. Valdez, P. Chodak III, M. Nastasi, and R. A. Verrall, *J. Nucl. Mater.* 274 (1999) 66.

[7]   S. Moll, L. Thomé, G. Sattonnay, A. Debelle, F. Garrido, L. Vincent, and J. Jagielski, *J. Appl. Phys.* 106 (2009) 073509.

[8]   J. M. Costantini, C. Trautmann, L. Thomé, J. Jagielski, and F. Beuneu, *J.Appl. Phys.* 101 (2007) 073501.

[9]   S. Moll, L. Thomé, L. Vincent, F. Garrido, G. Sattonnay, T. Thomé, J. Jagielski, and J. M. Costantini, *J. Appl. Phys.* 105 (2009) 023512.

[10] J. Cheng, and F. B. Prinz, *Nucl. Instr. and Meth.* B 227 (2005) 577.

[11] J. M. Costantini, F. Guillet, S. Lambert, D. Grébille, F. Beuneu, and C. Trautmann, *J. Appl. Phys.* 104 (2008) 073504.

[12] Y. Zhang, W. Jiang, C. Wang, F. Namavar, P. D. Edmondson, Z. Zhu, F. Gao, J. Lian, and W. J. Weber, *Phys. Rev. B* 82 (2010) 184105.

[13] N. Hiura, Y. Endo, T. Yamaura, T. Hoshiya, N. Niimi, J. Saito, S. Sozawa, N. Ooka, and M. Kobiyama, *J. Nucl. Mater.* 258-263 (1998) 2041.

[14] J. Cheng, R. Pornprasertsuk, H. Huang, Y. Saito, and F. B. Prinz, Proceedings of the Materials Research Society, *Fall Meeting* (2009), vol. 801 (BB6.10).

[15] G-Y. Adachi and N. Imanaka, *Chem. Rev.* 98 (1998)1479.

[16] C. Guéneau, A. Chartier, and L. V. Brutzel, Chapter 2.02: "Thermodynamic and thermophysical properties of the actinide oxides" p. 21-59, Vol.2: Material Properties/Oxide Fuels for Light Water Reactors and Fast Neutron Reactors in: Comprehensive Nuclear Materials, R. J. M. Konings Editor (Elsevier, Amsterdam, 2012).

[17] R.C. Garvie, *"Zirconium dioxide and some of its binary systems"*, in: A.M. Alper, Editor, *"High Temperature Oxides"* Part II (Academic, New York, 1970), p. 117.

[18] M. Yashima, M. Kakihana, and M. Yoshimura, *Solid St. Ionics* 86-88 (1996) 1131.

[19] A. H. Heuer, and M. Rühle, *"Advances in Ceramics"* vol. 12, in: N. Claussen, M. Rühle, and A. H. Heuer Editors (American Ceramic Society, Colombus, 1983).

[20] O. T. Sørensen, in *"Nonstoichiometric Oxides"*, O. T. Sørensen Editor (Academic, New York, 1981), pp. 1-59.

[21] R. C. Garvie, *J. Phys. Chem.* 69 (1965) 1238.

[22] J. Livage, K. Doi, and C. Mazières, *J. Am. Ceram. Soc.* 51 (1968) 349.

[23]   V. R. PaiVerneker, A. N. Petelin, F. J. Crowne, and D. C. Nagle, *Phys. Rev. B*40 (1989) 8555.

[24]   Landolt-Börnstein, "Numerical Data and Functional Relationships in Science and Technology" New series, Vol. 7 Crystal Structure Data of Inorganic Compounds, Part b1, K.-H. Hellwege and A. M. Hellwege Editors (Springer, Berlin, 1975), pp 336-338.

[25]   A. Predith, G. Ceder, C. Wolverton, K. Persson, and T. Mueller, *Phys. Rev. B* 77 (2008) 144104.

[26]   P. Li, I.-W. Chen, and J. E. Penner-Hahn, *J. Am. Ceram. Soc.* 77 (1994) 118.

[27]   E. V. Stefanovich, A. L. Shluger, and C. R. A. Catlow, *Phys. Rev. B* 49 (1994) 11560.

[28]   S. Ostanin, E. Salamatos, A. J. Craven, D. W. McComb, and D. Vlachos, *Phys. Rev. B* 66 (2002) 132105.

[29]   A. Je. Semjonow, and E. Anastassakis, *Physica A* 201 (1993) 416.

[30]   D. W. Liu, C. H. Perry, A. A. Feinberg, and R. Currat, *Phys. Rev. B* 36 (1987) 9212.

[31]   S. P. S. Baldwal, *Solid St. Ionics* 52 (1992) 23.

[32]   K. Sasaki, and J. Maier, *Solid St. Ionics* 134 (2000) 303.

[33]   M. Kilo, C. Argirusis, G. Borchardt, and R. A. Jackson, *Phys. Chem. Chem. Phys.* 5 (2003) 2219.

[34]   M. Belmonte, *Adv. Engineer. Mater.* 8 (2006) 693.

[35]   R. Pornprasertsuk, P. Ramanrayanan, C. B. Musgrave, and F. B. Prinz, *J. Appl. Phys.* 98 (2005) 103513.

[36]   K. E. Sickafus, R. J. Hanrahan Jr, K. J. McClellan, J. N. Mitchell, C. J. Wetteland, D. P. Butt, P. Chodak III, K. B. Ramsey, H. T. Blair, K. Chidester, Hj. Matzke, K. Yasuda, R. A. Verall, and N. Yu, *Am. Ceram. Soc. Bull.*78 (1999) 69.

[37]   W. L. Gong, W. Lutze, and R.C. Ewing, *J. Nucl. Mater.* 277 (2000) 239.

[38]   C. Degueldre, M. A. Pouchon, M. Döbeli, K. E. Sickafus, K. Hojou, C. Lederberger, and S. Abolhassani-Dadras, *J. Nucl. Mater.* 289 (2001) 115.

[39]   C. Degueldre, T. Arima, and Y. W. Lee, *J. Nucl. Mater.* 319 (2003) 6.

[40]   F. Namavar, G. Wang, C. L. Cheung, R. F. Sabirianov, X. C. Zeng, W. N. Mei, J. Bai, J. R. Brewer, H. Haider, and K. L. Garvin, *Nanotechnology* 18 (2007) 415702.

[41]   K. K. Ermakovich, V. N. Lazukin, I. V. Chepeleva, and V. I. Aleksandrov, *Sov. Phys. Solid State* 18 (1976) 1022.

[42]   C.B. Azzoni, and A. Paleari, *Phys. Rev. B*40 (1989) 6518.

[43]   C.B. Azzoni, and A. Paleari, *Phys. Rev. B* 40 (1989) 9333.

[44]   C. B. Azzoni, and A. Paleari, *Phys. Rev. B*44 (1991) 6858.

[45]   C. B. Azzoni, and A. Paleari, *Solid St. Ionics* 44 (1991) 267.

[46]   C. B. Azzoni, L. Bolis, A. Paleari, G. Samoggia, and F. Scardina, *Phys. Rev B* 51 (1995) 15942.

[47]   C. B. Azzoni, L. Bolis, A. Paleari, and F. Scardina, *J. Magn. Magn.Mater.* 140-144 (1995) 175.

[48]   C. B. Azzoni, L. Bolis, P. Camagni, G. C. Campagnoli, and M. De Simone, Radiat. *Effects and Defects in Solids*134 (1995) 485.

[49]   C. B. Azzoni, and A. Paleari, *Phys. Rev B* 53 (1996) 5.

[50]   V. M. Orera, R. I. Merino, Y. Chen, R. Cases, and P. J. Alonso, *Phys. Rev. B* 42 (1990) 9782.

[51]   V. M. Orera, R. I. Merino, Y. Chen, R. Cases, and P. J. Alonso, *Radiat.Eff. and Defects Solids* 119-121 (1991) 907.

[52] R. I. Merino, and V. M. Orera, *Radiat. Eff. and Defects Solids* 137 (1995) 273.

[53] R. I. Merino, V. M. Orera, E. E. Lomonova, and S. Kh. Batygov, *Phys. Rev B* 52 (1995) 6150.

[54] L. Fuks, and C. Degueldre, *J. Nucl. Mater.* 280 (2000) 360.

[55] C. B. Azzoni, L. Bolis, and A. Paleari, *Nucl. Instr. and Meth B* 116 (1996) 191.

[56] J. M. Costantini, F. Beuneu, M. Fasoli, A. Galli, A. Vedda, and M. Martini, *J. Phys.: Condens. Matter* 23 (2011) 455901.

[57] R. Ben-Michael, D. S. Tannhauser, and J. Genossar, *Phys. Rev. B* 43 (1991) 7395.

[58] A. S. Foster, V. B. Sulimov, F. Lopez-Gejo, A. L. Shluger, and R. M. Nieminen, *Phys. Rev B* 64 (2001) 224108.

[59] J. Robertson, Ka Xiong, and B. Falabretti, *IEEE Trans. on Device andMaterials Reliability* 5 (2005) 84.

[60] D. Muñoz-Ramo, P. V. Sushko, J. L. Gavartin, and A. L. Shluger, *Phys. Rev B* 78 (2008) 235432.

[61] G. Stapper, M. Bernasconi, N. Nicoloso, and M. Parrinello, *Phys. Rev. B* 59 (1999) 797.

[62] F. Pietrucci, M. Bernasconi, C. Di Valentin, F. Mauri, and C. J. Pickard, *Phys. Rev B* 73 (2006) 134112.

[63] D. Muñoz-Ramo, and A. L. Shluger, *J. Physics: Conf. Series* 117 (2008) 012022.

[64] J. M. Costantini, F. Beuneu, *Radiat. Eff. and Defects Solids* 157 (2002) 903.

[65] J. M. Costantini, F. Beuneu, D. Gourier, C. Trautmann, G. Calas, and M. Toulemonde, *J. Phys.: Condens. Matter* 16 (2004) 3957.

[66] J. M. Costantini, and F. Beuneu, *J. Phys.: Condens. Matter* 23 (2011) 115902.

[67] J. M. Costantini, and F. Beuneu, *Nucl. Instr. and Meth. B* 230 (2005) 251.

[68] J. M. Costantini, and F. Beuneu, *J. Phys.: Condens. Matter* 18 (2006) 3671.

[69] J. M. Costantini, and F. Beuneu, *Phys. Stat. Sol.*(c) 4 (2007) 1258.

[70] J. M. Costantini, F. Beuneu, S. Morrison-Smith, R. Devanathan, and W. J. Weber, *J. Appl. Phys.* 110 (2011) 123506.

[71] J. P. Goff, W. Hayes, S. Hull, M. T. Hutchings, and K. N. Clausen, *Phys. Rev. B* 59 (1999) 14202.

[72] J. M. Costantini, F. Beuneu, K. Schwartz, and C. Trautmann, *J. Phys.:Condens. Matter* 22 (2010) 315402.

[73] I. V. Afanasyev-Charkin, V. T. Gritsina, D. W. Cooke, B. L. Bennett, and K. E. Sickafus, *Ceram. Trans.* 107 (2000) 535.

[74] S. Zhu, X. T. Zu, X. Xiang, Z. G. Wang, L. M. Wang, and R. C. Ewing, *Nucl. Instr. and Meth. B* 206 (2003) 1092.

[75] B. Savoini, D. Cáceres, I. Vergara, R. Gonzáles, and J. E. Muñoz-Santiuste, *J. Nucl. Mater.* 277 (2000) 199.

[76] *"Physics of Color Centers"*, W. Beal Fowler editor (Academic, New York, 1968).

[77] B. Henderson, and J. E. Wertz, *"Defects in the Alkaline Earth Oxides"* (Taylor and Francis, London, 1977).

[78] J. M. Costantini, F. Beuneu, M. Fasoli, A. Galli, A. Vedda, and M. Martini, *J. Phys.: Condens. Matter* 23 (2011) 115901.

[79] Y. Chen, D. L. Trueblood, O. E. Schow, and H. T. Tohver, *J. Phys. C: Solid St. Phys.* 3 (1970) 2501.

[80] P. Camagni, P. Galinetto, G. Samoggia, and N. Zema, *Solid St.Commun.*83 (1992) 943.

[81] A. Eichler, *Phys. Rev. B* 64 (2001) 174103.

[82] L. Thomé, J. Fradin, J. Jagielski, A. Gentils, S. E. Enescu, and F. Garrido, *Eur. Phys. J. Appl. Phys.* 24 (2003) 37.

[83] A. Debelle, and A. Declémy, *Nucl. Instr. and Meth. B* 268 (2010) 1460.

[84] J. Jagielski, and L. Thomé, *Appl. Phys. A* 97 (2009) 147.

[85] J. Friedel, "*Dislocations*" (Pergamon, Oxford, 1964).

[86] Hj. Matzke, A. Turos, and G. Linker, *Nucl. Instr. and Meth. B*91 (1994) 294.

[87] T. Sonoda, M. Kinoshita, Y. Chimi, N. Ishikawa, M. Sataka, and A. Iwase, *Nucl. Instr. and Meth. B* 250 (2006) 254.

[88] T. Sonoda, M. Kinoshita, N. Ishikawa, M. Sataka, Y. Chimi, N. Okubo, A. Iwase, and K. Yasunaga, *Nucl. Instr. and Meth. B* 266 (2008) 2882.

[89] N. Ishikawa, Y. Chimi, O. Michikami, Y. Ohta, K. Ohhara, M. Lang, and R. Neumann, *Nucl. Instr. and Meth. B* 266 (2008) 3033.

[90] M. Kinoshita, K. Yasunaga, T. Sonoda, A. Iwase, N. Ishikawa, M. Sataka, K. Yasuda, S. Matsumura, H. Y. Geng, T. Ichinomiya, Y. Chen, Y. Kaneta, M. Iwasawa, T. Ohnuma, Y. Nishiura, J. Nakamura, and Hj. Matzke, *Nucl. Instr. and Meth. B* 267 (2009) 960.

[91] R. Devanathan, *Nucl. Instr. and Meth. B* 267 (2009) 3017.

[92] R. Devanathan, W. J. Weber, and J. D. Gale, *Energy and Environ. Sci.* 3 (2010) 1551.

[93] L. M. Wang, S. X. Wang, S. Zhu, and R. C. Ewing, *J. Nucl. Mater.* 289, 122 (2001).

[94] L. Thomé, J. Jagielski, A. Gentils, and F. Garrido, *Nucl. Instr. and Meth. B* 175-177 (2001) 453.

[95] M. A. Pouchon, M. Döbeli, C. Degueldre, and M. Burghartz, *J. Nucl. Mater.*, 274 (1999) 61.

[96] L. Vincent, L. Thomé, F. Garrido, and O. Kaitasov, *Nucl. Instr. and Meth. B* 257 (2007) 480.

[97] T. Hojo, J. Aihara, K. Hojou, S. Furono, H. Yamamoto, N. Nitani, T. Yamashita, K. Minato, and T. Sakuma, *J. Nucl. Mater.* 319 (2003) 81.

[98] K. Yasuda, C. Kinoshita, S. Matsumura, and A. I. Ryazanov, *J. Nucl. Mater.* 319 (2003) 74.

[99] A. I. Ryazanov, K. Yasuda, C. Kinoshita, and A. V. Klaptsov, *J. Nucl.Mater.*,323 (2003) 372.

[100] D. Gomez-Garcia, J. Martinez-Fernandez, and A. Dominguez-Rodriguez, *Phil. Mag. Lett.* 81 (2001) 173.

[101] Hj. Matzke, P. G. Lucuta, and T. Wiss, *Nucl. Instr. and Meth. B* 166-167 (2000) 634.

[102] F. Garrido, C. Choffel, J. C. Dran, L. Thomé, L. Nowicki, and A. Turos, *Nucl. Instr. and Meth. B*127-128 (1997) 634.

[103] T. Wiss, Hj. Matzke, C. Trautmann, M. Toulemonde, and S. Klaumünzer, *Nucl. Instr. and Meth. B*122 (1997) 583.

[104] E. L Fleischer, W. Hertl, T. L. Alford, P. Børgesen, and J. W. Mayer, *J. Mater. Res.* 5 (1990) 385.

[105] E. L Fleischer, M. Grant Norton, M. A. Zaleski, W. Hertl, C. Barry Carter, and J. W. Mayer, *J. Mater. Res.* 6 (1991) 1905.

[106] K. E. Sickafus, C. J. Wetteland, N. P. Baker, N. Yu, R. Devanathan, M. Nastasi, and N. Bordes,*Mater. Sci. Eng. A* 253 (1998) 78.

[107] V. Menvie-Bekale, G. Sattonnay, C. Legros, A. M. Huntz, S. Poissonnet, and L. Thomé,*J. Nucl. Mater.* 384 (2009) 70.

[108] J. Jagielski, L. Thomé, P. Aubert, O. Maciejak, A. Pietkowska, and R. Groetzschel, *Nucl. Instr. and Meth. B* 266 (2008) 2902.

[109] L. Van Brutzel, M. Rarivomanantsoa, and D. Ghaleb, *J. Nucl. Mater.* 354 (2006) 28.

[110] A. Guglielmetti, A. Chartier, L. van Brutzel, J.-P. Crocombette, K. Yasuda, C. Meis, and S. Matsumura, *Nucl. Instr. and Meth. B* 266 (2008) 5120.

[111] T. Hibino, A. Hashimoto, T. Inoue, J-i. Tokuno, S-i. Yoshida, and M. Sano, *Science* 288 (2000) 2031.

[112] W. J. Weber, *Radiation Effects* 83 (1984) 145.

[113] K. Yasunaga, K. Yasuda, S. Matsumura, and T. Sonoda, *Nucl. Instr. and Meth. B* 266 (2008) 2877.

[114] K. Shiiyama, T. Yamamoto, T. Takahashi, A. Guglielmetti, A. Chartier, K. Yasuda, S. Matsumura, K. Yasunaga, and C. Meis, *Nucl. Instr. andMeth. B* 268 (2010) 2980.

In: Properties of Fluorite Structure Materials
Editors: Peter Vajda and Jean-Marc Costantini

ISBN: 978-1-62417-458-2
© 2013 Nova Science Publishers, Inc.

Chapter 6

RADIATION EFFECTS IN ACTINIDE COMPOUNDS WITH THE FLUORITE STRUCTURE

Thierry Wiss and Rudy Konings*

European Commission, Joint Research Centre,
Institute for Transuranium Elements, Karlsruhe

LIST OF ABBREVIATIONS

LWR:	Light Water Reactor
FBR:	Fast Breeder Reactor
PWR:	Pressurized Water Reactor
MA:	Minor Actinides
HBRP:	High Burnup RIM Project
dpa:	Displacement per atom
HBS:	High Burnup Structure
FPs:	Fission Products
LFP:	Light Fission Product
HFP:	Heavy Fission Product
SRIM:	Stopping and Range of Ions in Mater
SEM:	Scanning Electron Microscope
TEM:	Transmission Electron Microscope

ABSTRACT

Radiation damage in actinide compounds with the fluorite structure and especially on UO_2 and $(U, Pu)O_2$ has been extensively studied for more than 50 years in view of the better understanding of the behavior of these materials as fuel for nuclear power reactors.

---

* Email: Thierry.WISS@ec.europa.eu

The studies cover single effects from various damage sources (mostly by ion implantation) up to combined effects in e.g. irradiated nuclear fuels.

The second practical issue related to the understanding of the damage formation in UO_2 but also in mixed oxides fuels (MOX) lies in the forecast of its long term behavior (several millenaries and beyond). The minor actinides present in the spent fuel will produce alpha-damage and radiogenic helium that will impact the long term properties of the spent fuel. The prediction of the long term behavior of such compounds is therefore of major importance for safety assessments of storage/disposal facilities.

A third aspect of radiation damage in minor actinide (MA) compounds (with the fluorite structure) becomes more and more important and namely the use of fuel with MA. The key issue for reducing the MA radiotoxicity is their partitioning and transmutation in fast neutron reactors or accelerator driven systems. This implies to know how these compounds will behave not only against their self-irradiation damage build-up but also how they will be affected by their irradiation in reactor systems.

Basic processes of energy loss are described and stopping power and ranges of various ions/particles defined for the specific case of UO_2. The radiation effects produced by these ions/particles are subsequently described as well as their impact on the physico-chemical properties of the nuclear fuel UO_2.

The PuO_2 has also been studied more in detail as radio-isotopic thermal generator (RTG) to be used for satellite batteries for example but also as stockpile from weapon material after the conversion into oxide. Some studies on the aging of PuO_2 due to alpha-decay and helium formation are discussed hereafter.

As a global outcome of studies concerning the fluorite structure based actinide compounds it could be shown that they exhibited generally a remarkable resistance against radiation effects, hardly ever amorphizing. Nevertheless the stability of these compounds degrades in the order PuO_2, AmO_2, CmO_2, CfO_2 as can be also observed for their thermal stability.

Also the irradiated fuel UO_2 and MOX shows a remarkable resistance to radiation damage build-up considering the tough irradiation conditions.

Keywords: Radiation damage, radiation effects, Energy loss, defects, UO_2, nuclear fuel

1. INTRODUCTORY REMARKS

As the most common material used as nuclear fuel, UO_2 has been extensively studied with regard to its response to in-reactor fission irradiation damage but also with respect to the aging of this material due to the accumulation of alpha-damage in spent fuel storage/disposal conditions. This is also true for the PuO_2 that is used in MOX fuel but also as Radio-isotopical Thermal Generators (RTG) for satellites for examples, especially for the shorter living isotope [238]Pu. Actinide dioxides with the fluorite structure have been extensively studied [1-6] in the early seventies especially the higher actinides dioxide forms like CmO_2, BkO_2 and CfO_2. These results however are limited when compared to the uranium and plutonium dioxide.

In the series of the actinides many compounds exhibit the fluorite structure and this is particularly true for the dioxides up to the californium dioxide. For the minor actinides however, studies on radiation damage are more limited and mostly swelling and lattice parameter have been recorded as a function of alpha-damage. Many other compounds of actinides with the fluorite structure are known and effects of radiation were only studied little.

These materials are also often ternary compounds like $AmO-ThO_2$, $AmO-ZrO_2$ to a small extend $AcOF$, Pa_2O_5/ThO_2 [7] and will not be discussed here.

The following sections will focus on the most studied compounds i.e. the dioxides and more specifically of uranium and plutonium. The results from the higher actinides are somehow biased because of the very high alpha-activity of these elements which due to the production of the daughter atoms affect some of the measured properties (e.g. lattice parameter). Also the reduction of compounds like CmO_2 or CfO_2 due to a strong self-radiation producing a preferential sputtering of oxygen atoms affects some property measurements such as deviation from the fluorite structure for example. Several compounds with the fluorite structure and incorporating actinides have been widely studied as potential matrices for the conditioning of nuclear waste (e.g. $Nd_2Zr_2O_7$ [8]) but also as candidate inert matrices for the transmutation of minor actinides (e.g. ZrO_2 [9]). These compounds will not be treated here but some aspects of radiation resistance of zirconia, for example, are described in chapter 5 of this book.

The macroscopically, observable and often technologically crucial results from the exposure to energetic particles are collectively known as *radiation effects*. The primary microscopic events that precede the appearance of gross changes in the solid are called *radiation damage*. This branch of the physics attempts to predict the number and the configuration of the point defects (vacancies and interstitial atoms) produced by the bombarding particles but also their evolution towards extended defects resulting from their coalescence.

UO_2 is today's most commonly used fuel material in nuclear power reactors. Nuclear fuels have to operate safely for years under severe conditions of radiation damage. Heat production in the nuclear fuel in order to generate electricity ensues mostly from the slow down of the fission products (FPs) i.e. high energy heavy ions but also from their further radioactive decay most frequently by gamma or beta decay. The heat dissipated in the lattice of the crystalline material constituting the conventional nuclear fuels is a primary effect from the energy losses of the fission fragments by nuclear or electronic interactions on the atoms constituting the fuel. As a direct consequence, there are also defects created along the path of the fission fragments leading to modification of the physical properties of the fuel.

In addition to the fission process, damage is also created by alpha-decay particularly in the fuel containing strong alpha-emitters (minor actinides) but also from beta and gamma decay from the fission products.

Basic processes of energy loss will be described and stopping power and ranges of various ions/particles defined for the specific case of UO_2. The radiation damage produced by the passage of these ions/particles will be conceptually related. The impact of defect creation on the physico-chemical properties of UO_2 will then be described with particular emphasis on its use as nuclear fuel. Fuel operating conditions will be taken into account in addition to concomitants effects of damage sources when discussing the overall behaviour of UO_2 during irradiation but also during (long term) storage.

Uranium dioxide has been extensively studied and an exhaustive list of publications related to the radiation effects is impossible. The reader will be referred to more detailed publications covering both UO_2 properties by J. Belle [10], radiation damage processes in UO_2 by C. Lemaignan [11] or processes of damage in nuclear fuel by D. Olander [12] for example.

The study of the physical processes of radiation damage has started soon after the discovery of radioactivity by Henri Becquerel in 1896. There were very soon interests in how particles from radioactive decay were slowed down in matter. Marie Curie has stated that "les rayons alpha sont des projectiles susceptibles de perdre de leur vitesse en traversant la matière" (alpha-rays might lose part of their speed while travelling through matter) [13]. J. Thomson, N. Bohr and E. Rutherford (see [14] by E. Rutherford and R. Owens for example) were pioneers in studying the effect of particle interaction with matter. The development of ion accelerators allowed performing extensive studies on radiation damage in all types of materials. Linked to the use of the monte-carlo code SRIM for the estimation of energy loss, range and damage, the description of the main processes of particle/ion interactions with matter are described in [15]. The investigation of irradiated fuel being more difficult, numerous studies were performed on ion-irradiated UO_2 in order to understand the basic mechanisms of damage evolution.

2. THE SLOWING DOWN OF ENERGETIC PROJECTILES IN UO_2

In the context of physical processes occurring in nuclear fuels involving energy dissipation all type of radiation should be considered. When the conditions are met for a fission to occur, about 200-MeV energy is dissipated in the fuel lattice. Most of this high energy is carried by the fission products (FPs) that cover the mass range from A = 75 to 160, i.e. elements between Ga and Dy. The FPs fall into two groups: the light ones, typically Kr, with about 100 MeV energy, and the heavy ones, typically Ba, with about 70-MeV energy. Intense neutron fluxes, produced by the fission reactions themselves, with energies ranging from eV to MeV are necessary to sustain the controlled nuclear chain reaction. An intense ß.γ-radiation field is also present because most FPs are radioactive with different decay energies and very different half-lives. Moreover, alpha-decays are produced from the original actinides, and in addition by large amounts of "minor actinides," e.g., Np, Am, and Cm that are formed by successive neutron capture during the operation of the fuel. The alpha-decay has to be accounted for not only during reactor irradiation (at elevated temperature), but also during storage before and after reactor irradiation, i.e. under conditions where thermally activated damage recovery is largely or fully absent. These alpha-decaying actinides are soluble in the UO_2 matrix and will occupy lattice positions of the fluorite structure.

In terms of energy release two major processes have to be considered, i.e. inelastic collisions and ballistic (elastic) collisions depending on the projectile type and its characteristics like energy and mass. Under the given conditions both processes can occur simultaneously in different proportions. The next paragraphs summarize these aspects with particular emphasis on the UO_2 nuclear fuel.

2.1. Main Processes

Energetic charged particles interact independently with the nuclei and the electrons in a solid. Basically the energy loss of a charge particle can occur by four processes:

- Inelastic collisions with an electron (main process of energy loss producing excitation and ionization).
- Inelastic collisions with a nucleus (Bremsstrahlung and coulombic excitation).
- Elastic collisions with a nucleus (Rutherford scattering).
- Elastic collisions with an electron

2.1.1. Nuclear Energy Loss

When the energy of a given particle/ion is sufficiently low, elastic collisions with nuclei occur. The main process called Rutherford scattering results from the transfer of kinetic energy from the impinging particle/ion to a target atom.

The subsequent effects (described extensively in the next paragraphs) are the displacements of atoms from their regular lattice site. If such a knock-on atom has gained sufficient kinetic energy from the collision it can itself generate a new collision hence displacement. The energy necessary to displace an atom from its lattice site is called threshold displacement energy with values in UO_2 of 20 eV and 40 eV for oxygen and uranium atoms respectively [16]. If the total energy from an incident particle is high enough the succession of such collision-displacement sequences produces collision cascades. Figure 1 shows such a collision cascade produced by a recoil nucleus during an alpha-decay (the energy is typically 100 keV). The cascade has been calculated with SRIM2003 [15]. The "size" of the knock-on atoms represents the energy transferred during the collisions. In a collision cascade the typical energy transferred is 50 eV but some collisions with a large cross-section can produce energy transfer of some keV which explains the formation of sub-cascades. The resulting displaced atoms either recombine or leave permanent defects that will be discussed in a further section.

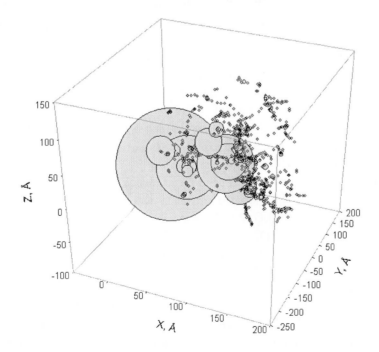

Figure 1. Collision cascade produced by a recoil nucleus during an alpha-decay (the energy is typically 100 keV). The cascade has been calculated with SRIM2003 [15]. The grey spheres represent uranium atoms and the black spheres oxygen atoms displaced from their lattice site.

2.2.2. Electronic Energy Loss

Electronic energy losses and their effects have been extensively described. Different concepts have been proposed in order to explain the formation of ion tracks in matter by the slowing down of swift heavy ions in the electronic stopping power regime. The "ionic spike" model for insulators of Fleischer et al. [17] assumes a high ionization rate of the lattice atoms surrounding the path of the incoming ion, which leads to a local explosion due to high Coulomb repulsions. However, it has been shown that the electronic stopping power threshold deduced from the etching of several insulators cannot be scaled by the parameters governing this model, but can be rather related to the thermal conductivity of the material. This led many authors to reconsider the thermal-spike model. The basic assumption in the thermal-spike model originally proposed by Seitz and Koehler [18] is that a high temperature region is formed in the material around the trajectory of the high-energy ion. The maximum temperature reached in a cylinder around the ion trajectory may surpass the melting point T_f of the material, as e.g. in UO_2 (with $T, = 3150$ K). In a model revisited by Toulemonde et al. [19] thermodynamic parameters of UO_2 have been taken into account to calculate the radius of observed ion tracks in UO_2. This model considers that energetic ions transfer their energy in a first step to the target electrons and then to the lattice via electron-phonon interactions leading to a heating of the lattice. It is assumed that the effect of the electron-phonon coupling can be described by the parameter λ, the mean diffusion length of the energy deposited on the electrons. This parameter is linked to the electron-phonon coupling constant, g, by the relation $\lambda^2 = D_e \tau_a$ where $\tau_a = C_e/g$ is the mean electron-phonon interaction time, C_e is the specific heat of the electrons (($D_e \sim 2$ $cm^2.s^{-1}$ and $C_e \sim 1$ $J.cm^{-3}.K^{-1}$), and D, is the electron diffusivity. As suggested by Baranov et al. [20] the values of C_e, and D_e, can be assumed to be constant since the hot electrons in the conduction band of an insulator will behave like in metals. Using different values of λ as parameter, the track radius was calculated as a function of (dE/dx). For a value of $\lambda = 6$ nm, Figure 2 shows the calculated lattice temperature as a function of time and radial distance from the ion path for a I- ion of 72 MeV in UO_2. The peak temperature of the spike increases to its maximum value within a very short time of 10^{-13} s and then it decreases and the spike broadens as a result of heat conduction [21]. A similar calculation for 173 MeV Xe ions with (dE/dx), = 29.1 keV/nm and for 11.4 MeV/u U-ions with (dE/dx) = 60 keV/nm also shows a good correlation between measured and calculated track radii, demonstrating, at least for the values of dE/dx studied in our work, that this model can be successfully applied to UO_2.

These results add thus further evidence to the existence of thermal-spike effects produced by fission fragments in UO_2. The previous evidence was (i) TEM observations of a fission-spike induced phase change in U_4O_9 needles existing in UO_{2+x} (this transformation occurs at $T = 1150°C$)[22], (ii) fission-enhanced diffusion of U in UO_2 can only be explained by thermal and pressure effects of fission spikes [23] (iii) the same is true for the observed fission gas resolution (destruction of fission gas bubbles) due to passing fission products [24].

Recently the formation of ion tracks caused by energetic heavy ions as well as a dislocation cell structure in fluorite (CeO_2) due to electronic excitation and the motion of dislocations caused by overlapping energetic heavy ion tracks was presented in [25] and more recently for UO_2 in [26]. The drastic changes of surface morphology and inner structure in UO_2 indicate that the overlapping of ion tracks will produce point defects, enhance the diffusion of point defects and dislocations, and form the sub-grains at relatively low temperature. These findings have been used to describe the mechanism of the High Burnup Structure (HBS) formation in nuclear fuel as summarized in section 6.2.

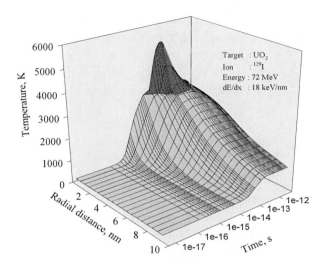

Figure 2. Calculated evolution of the UO_2 radial temperature distribution along a track in UO_2 as a function of time. The calculations are for 72 MeV I- ions in the first nm of the target, i.e. $dE/dx = 18$ keV/nm with $\lambda = 6$ nm and a melting temperature of $T_f = 3150$ K.

In another model the formation of ion track in UO_2 has been described by the propagation of a pressure wave created along the path of an energetic fission fragment under specific conditions of geometry. It is shown that a large fraction of the fission fragment electronic losses is converted in strong shock waves whose passage in the solid is too fast for producing atomic displacements, but which can release high energy by unloading on free surfaces. The subsequent matter displacements have been shown to have important effects on the structural properties of the nuclear fuel. Surface tracks could be explained by the expelling of material when these pressure waves reach the surface [27].

2.3. Main Damage Sources

2.3.1. Energy Loss and Displacements Produced by Neutrons

In nuclear reactors three types of neutrons are considered: the thermal neutrons with energy E < 1 eV (0.025 eV), the epithermal neutrons with, 1 eV < E < 10 keV and the fast ones with E > 10 keV. In the energy domain where neutrons from fission are emitted, only elastic collisions and capture are considered. The energy loss by the neutrons in the moderator is the *sine qua non* condition for a controlled fission reaction chain to occur (in Light Water Reactors essentially) while the remaining fast neutrons (not thermalized) produce damage in the fuel and on the structure materials. A neutron of mass m = 1 and of energy E_n, while passing through a medium of mass M_1, will occasionally collide (mean free path ~ 1 cm) with a lattice atom, imparting to it an energy (depending on the impact parameters) up to a *maximum* energy given by

$$E_{max} = \frac{4mM_1}{(m+M_1)^2} E_n \qquad \text{or} \qquad \sim \frac{4E_n}{M_1} \qquad \text{for } M_1 \gg m$$

The *maximum* pka (primary knock-on atom) energies for a neutron of energy $E_n = 1$ MeV are thus for UO_2: 17 keV for U, and 250 keV for O, but most interactions with neutrons will lead to a smaller energy transfer. The *minimum* neutron energy to produce one displacement is given by $E_{max} = E_d$, where E_d is the displacement energy threshold (for example 20 eV for O and 40 eV for U in UO_2 [16]. Hence

$$E_n^{min} \sim 0.1 \text{ keV}$$

Thermal (low energy) neutrons do thus not produce direct displacements, .only indirect ones through recoil after capture by some nuclei.

2.3.2. Energy Loss and Displacements Produced by (β,γ)-Decays

For beta decays of the fission products in nuclear fuels the energy distribution is a continuum with $E_{\beta max}$ (typically 2.6 keV $< E <$ 10.4 MeV). The e^- and e^+ produce ionisation and excitation along their path and the nuclear scattering is very large. The Rutherford scattering cross-section is proportional to $(M_1/m_0)^2$ and the cross-section ratio $\sigma_{e^-}/\sigma_{p^+} = 4 \cdot 10^6$. In fact σ can be extremely large and target e- has to be considered. Electrons can also produce isolated displaced atoms if their energy is high enough. The minimum energy, E_e^{min}, to displace a lattice atom is given by

$$E_d = 2\frac{m_0}{M}\frac{E_e^{min}}{m_0 c^2}\left(E_n^{min} + 2m_0 c^2\right)$$

where m_0 is the electron mass, M the mass of the displaced atom and c the velocity of light. β-decay causes thus very few, isolated point defects.

The emission of photons, γ but also X-rays in nuclear fuel will be neglected in this section. Heating effects and ionization are in any case produced but their consequences compared to the other damage sources during operation of nuclear fuel, for example, are negligible.

2.3.3. Energy Loss and Displacements Produced by α-Decay

The α-decay results in two damaging sources:

- a He-ion (α-particle) of ~ 5.5 MeV, with mainly electronic stopping, producing about 200 displacements, most of them as largely isolated defects at the end of its range of some 10-20 μm
- a heavy recoil atom, e.g. Np^{237} in the decay of Am^{241} which receives a recoil energy E due to conservation of momentum, $ME = mE_\alpha$, hence typically ~ 100 keV (or 91 keV in the decay of Am^{241}). These recoil atoms show predominantly nuclear

stopping and produce a dense collision cascade with typically ~ 1500 displacements within a short distance of ~ 20 nm. Defect clustering can occur stabilizing the damage.

As already described, ions passing through matter lose energy via two processes, either by direct collisions with the atoms of the matter (elastic collisions) or by dissipating their energy on the electrons (inelastic collisions), hence nuclear energy loss $(dE/dx)_n$ leading directly to displaced atoms, or ionizations (electronic energy loss $(dE/dx)_e$). Any given radiation source can exhibit these two types of energy loss. The case of α-decay in UO_2 is partially included in Figure 1 showing a displacement cascade produced by the recoil atom of the decay of Pu^{238} i.e. ^{234}U. Figure 3 shows the energy loss of the alpha-particle which is predominantly electronic by comparison with the recoil nucleus (see also table 1). The effects of alpha-damage in UO_2 have been studied for decades either by external irradiation with alpha-particles or heavy ions simulating the recoil nucleus [28] or by doping UO_2 with strong alpha-emitters (e.g. ^{238}Pu) [29-31]. The formation of point defects and their evolution into extended defects but also the consequences on the UO_2 lattice (e.g. lattice swelling) and on the modification of thermo-physical properties have been assessed [32]. The studies on alpha-damage aim also at determining what is the long term evolution of spent nuclear fuel during storage and more specifically what has to be expected from its integrity or behaviour against corrosion if contacted with water [33-35].

2.3.4. Impact of Fission Fragments

For the specific case of the higher actinides not only neutron-induced fission will occur depending also on the energy spectrum but spontaneous fission. Fission produces two fission products, FPs, (plus 2-3 neutrons). These FPs fall into two groups, the light ones (LFP, typically Mo or Kr with ~ 95 MeV energy) and the heavy ones (HFP, typically I or Ba with ~ 70 MeV energy). Further typical values (for the case of UO_2) are given in Table 1 and in the sketch below: range, number of defects produced etc. The exact values depend on the substance used (e.g. displacement energy, E_d, atomic number, density etc.). Because of the high energy deposition rate, typically 20 to 30 keV/nm, a locally (over-) heated track (fission spike or thermal spike) may be formed. Such fission tracks are visible in transmission electron microscopy in many materials. Most of the energy deposition is by electronic energy loss, in particular for the more energetic light FP. This, in addition to causing local heating up to or above the melting point, can cause the formation of additional defects and/or rearrangement of existing defects. An extreme case is the destruction of pre-existing fission gas bubbles by the passage of a fission spike, known to occur in the conventional nuclear fuel, UO_2.

A short description of the sequence of events in the fission spike is the following:

- Primary phase or ballistic phase - the passage of the fission fragment - is very short but it defines the initial size and shape of the spike. Most Frenkel defects are produced by secondary collision cascades. The deposited Coulomb energy is dissipated into local heating through electronic interactions with recoiling ions to produce a thermal spike.

- Second or quenching phase - recombination of vacancies and interstitials occurs when the spike comes to thermal equilibrium. An interstitial-rich outer zone and a vacancy-rich inner zone form. The hydrostatic pressure field originally created by the molten core of the spike - contributing to the separation of interstitials from the vacancies of the Frenkel pairs formed in the primary phase - is replaced by compressive stresses in the outer zone and dilatational stresses in the core.
- Third or track annealing phase - more recombination occurs, some vacancy clusters are stabilized by fission gases forming embryos for later bubbles.

The processes in these three phases are repeated many times through the whole fuel volume in a homogeneous fuel. All of such a fuel is affected after a rather short time, the level of one displacement per atom, dpa, being typically reached within less than one day. The consequences are a significant fission-enhanced diffusion, fission-enhanced creep, re-solution of fission gas from bubbles, etc.

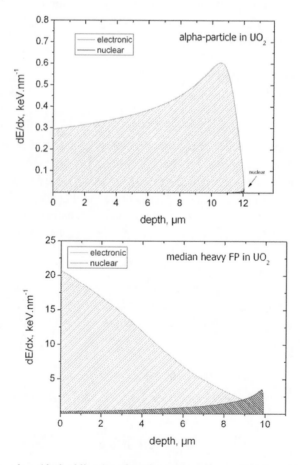

Figure 3. lectronic energy loss (dashed lines) and nuclear energy losses (black area) of a typical α-particle (upper part) and of a median fission product (lower part) in UO_2.

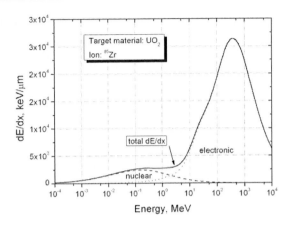

Figure 4. Energy loss of a typical light fission product as function of its energy.

Figure 3 shows the large difference in electronic energy loss, $(dE/dx)_e$, between the alpha-particles and the fission products. The energy loss curves show the electronic stopping only, i.e. the ionization part, with high values of 18 to 22 keV/nm at the point of fission (full ion energy) for the case shown, i.e. UO_2.

The nuclear, i.e. the displacement damage part, peaks at the end of the range (~ 1 keV.nm^{-1}) and is very small (but still present) at the point of fission (~ 0.1 keV.nm^{-1}). The ratio of nuclear to electronic stopping is always low for those high energies, but it varies between 1:180 at the fission site and some 1:3 toward the end of the range, or even $< 1:1$ at the very end.

Table 1. Displacements induced in UO_2 by different damaging sources

	Energy, keV	Range, µm	Fraction of energy lost by elastic (nuclear) / inelastic collisions (electronic)	Number of defects formed, N
Light fission product	~95000	9	0.03 / 0.97	40000
Heavy fission product	~70000	7	0.06 / 0.94	60000
α-particle	5500	15	0.01 /0.99	200
Recoil atom	95	0.02	0.90 / 0.10	1500

The recoil atoms of the α-decay and the high defect density produced by their slowing down are not included in the Figure 3 below because of the large difference in range: about 1500 displacements are formed along a very short track of only ~ 20 nm, as shown in Figure 1. Figure 4 shows the energy loss of a typical light fission fragment as a function of the energy of the fragment. In this figure the energy displayed covers a range beyond fission energy to show that when increasing the energy above an energy corresponding to the coulombic barrier, the energy loss decreases. This is attributed to the fact that the fission fragment is fully ionized and that when increasing energy the velocity also increases, reducing the energy transfer for a given unit length. Two energy losses can indeed correspond to two different ion energies. The energy losses in UO_2 for different projectiles can result in the formation of defects with numbers of different proportions as a function of their nature.

The ballistic effects can be easily converted in a certain number of instantaneous defects formed (although instantaneous recombination is not easy to quantify). The electronic energy losses result generally in less quantifiable effects for a single projectile. The next paragraphs will offer more insights on these phenomena.

2.4. Range of Different Projectiles in UO_2

Because of numerous collisions with energy transfer to the target atoms a given ion or particle will have a defined trajectory with a given length.

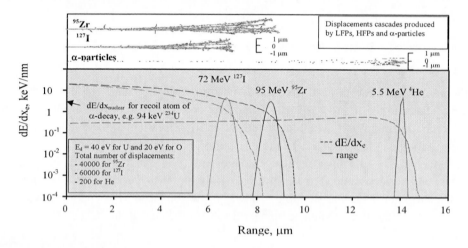

Figure 5. Range and energy loss (electronic) of different projectiles in UO_2. The upper inset shows the straggling and the cascades produced from several projectiles, all having a normal incidence relative to the surface.

From the energy losses, either elastic or inelastic, one can determine the range of a given particle. Whereas the high energy particles/ions experience only few scattering events (low cross-section for nuclear scattering) and hence are almost not deviating from their original direction, the low energy ones might experience high angle scattering.

This is shown in the upper inset in Figure 5 for the case of fission products or alpha-particles having an almost straight path in a material contrary to the alpha-recoil shown in Figure 1.

Moreover it can be noted that the range of the particle/ion decreases with increasing mass directly correlated with the charge of the ions at the considered energy. When the ions are fully ionized at certain energy, hence at a given speed, the energy loss decreases and the range proportionally increases again.

3. BASIC EFFECTS OF RADIATION DAMAGE

During the slowing down of a particle/ion in a target the history of the particle has to be followed, hence the knowledge of the energy loss of this particle, its range and the interactions through the media it is passing. As interactions one has to primarily consider the displacements, recombination, ionization, excitations in order to assess the radiation damage build-up. Additionally, complexes can be formed between different kinds of point defects, e.g. point defects can be assembled to give origin to line defects.

3.1. Point Defect Formation

Contrary to perfect lattices, all real crystals contain defects distinguished according to their dimension.

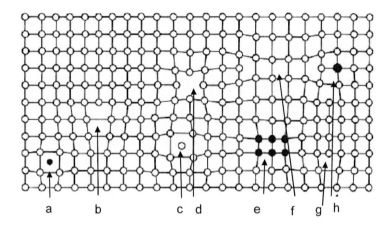

Figure 6. Various crystal lattice defects: (a) interstitial impurity atom, (b) edge dislocation, (c) self-interstitial atom, (d) vacancy, (e) precipitate of impurity atoms, (f) vacancy-type dislocation loop, (g) interstitial-type dislocation loop, (h) substitutional impurity atom, an atom lodged in a position between normal lattice atoms; that is in an interstice.

The defects in a crystal can be triggered by the different kind of damage processes as described in the previous sections. The zero-dimensional defect is called a point defect, implying that it involves only one atom surrounded by an otherwise perfect lattice.

However, the presence of a point defect may affect the properties of its nearest neighbours, and by elastic or electric interactions, a sizable spherical region of the lattice around the defect. Two point defects are intrinsic to the material, meaning that they form spontaneously in the lattice without any external intervention. These two are the vacancy and the self-interstitial, shown schematically in Figure 6 and referenced (d) and (c) respectively. The vacancy is simply an atom missing from a lattice site, which would be occupied in a perfect lattice. The qualification "self" indicates that the interstitial atom is of the same type as the normal lattice atoms. The defects referenced (a) and (h) in Figure 6 show the two basic mechanisms by which a foreign or impurity atom exists in the crystal lattice of a host element. Large impurity atoms, usually of the same category as the host atoms (e.g., Pu in UO_2), replace the host atoms on regular lattice positions. These are called substitutional impurities. The structure of the lattice is not disturbed, only the identity of the atoms occupying the lattice sites is different. Small atoms that are also chemically dissimilar from the host atoms occupy interstitial positions and do not appreciably distort the surrounding host crystal (for example He in UO_2). They are termed interstitial impurities.

Self-interstitials and vacancies occur naturally in ionic crystals as well as in elemental solids. However, because in UO_2 the cations (U) and anions (O) carry electrical charges (+4 and -2 respectively) vacancy and interstitial formation are not independent processes. To create a vacancy on the anion sublattice by moving the anion to the surface, for example, would leave the surface negatively charged and the interior around the vacancy with a net positive charge. This violation of local electrical neutrality prevents such a process. Similar arguments apply to cation vacancies or self-interstitials of either ionic type. In UO_2 two anion vacancies need to be created for each cation vacancy, forming a Schottky trio. However, the dominant point defects in ideally pure stoichiometric UO_2 are anion Frenkel defects , O^{2-} vacancies and O^{2-} interstitials [36].

3.2. Modelling of Point Defects

Electronic structure calculations by *ab initio* techniques enable us to determine quantities inaccessible to experiments because of either a too small length scale or the impossibility to isolate the contribution of a given factor to the studied physical properties. In particular, *ab initio* calculations allow to study separately different types of point defects in a solid and to determine for each of them its stability (formation energy) or its influence on the crystal structure (atom relaxation around the defect, swelling of the crystal). Much work has recently contributed to assess the energy associated to these different defects in UO_2 but also in non-stoichiometric UO_2 [37, 38] The study of the primary damage state (for example point defects caused be an □-decay in UO_2) is essential to understand how the material ages. Molecular dynamics (MD) simulations have also been successfully applied to model this phenomenon in various materials used in nuclear science applications [39]. In a recent thesis [40] simulation techniques based on empirical potentials have been used, focusing in a first stage on pure uranium dioxide to describe the behaviour of point defects but also the estimation of elastic and melting properties. Thus, it could be determined that simple defects such as interstitials occupy the large empty zone 4 b in the unit cell.

However, for positive deviation from stoichiometry, Willis determined that oxygen interstitials tend to cluster, which have a binding energy of about 1.7±0.6 eV [41].

The structure that best fitted experimental neutron diffraction patterns is a 2:2:2 cluster, consisting of 2 interstitials and two oxygen atoms displaced from their regular lattice position, creating two additional interstitials and two vacancies. Yakub *et al.* [38] have studied the formation and stability of different types of clusters in hyperstoichiometric UO_{2+x}, including Willis's 2:2:2 interstitial dimers as well as cuboctahedral tetra- and pentamers under static and dynamic conditions based on a partly-ionic model. A 'Free Hopping Approximation' for small polarons has been proposed and implemented in a molecular dynamic simulation computer code [38]. Lattice parameter and other equilibrium properties of UO_{2+x} were calculated and compared with existing experimental data in a wide range of temperature and stoichiometry [38].

The modelling of radiation damage has also been used to predict the evolution of some microstructural aspects like the evolution of gas (helium) bubbles exposed to dense cascades from the alpha-recoil nucleus [42] but also the mobility of defects has been used to model the diffusion of gas [43].

The formation of point defects and their study by modelling via *ab initio* and molecular dynamics is now also considering the oxygen behaviour which is the very fast diffusing species in UO_2 but nevertheless has impact on many of the macroscopic properties notably affecting the transport properties. By means of an ab initio plane wave pseudopotential method, the behavior of helium in UO_2, PuO_2, AmO_2 and $(Am_{0.5}Pu_{0.5})O_2$ and of xenon in UO_2 is studied. It was shown that a pseudopotential approach in the generalized gradient approximation (GGA) can satisfactorily describe the cohesive properties of these actinide dioxides [39]. Formation energies of point defects (vacancies and interstitials), as well as incorporation and solution energies of helium in UO_2, PuO_2, AmO_2 and $(Am_{0.5}Pu_{0.5})O_2$, and of xenon in UO_2 have been calculated and the results discussed according to the incorporation site of the gas atom in the fluorite lattice and according to the dioxide stoichiometry [39].

The challenges of modelling actinide based nuclear material systems lie in the complicated bonding characters of the materials, where the 5f electrons strong correlations play a major role.

The complicated bonding characters are reflected in the multi-valency states of U ions in UO_2, as well as the strong covalency bonds between U ions and O-ions. These features are difficult to model by empirical potential approaches such as large-scale molecular dynamics simulations. DFT studies help to identify correctly the charge transfer and charge compensation mechanisms associated with defects and defects clusters, as well as in defect transport processes. In the latter case, the inherent electronic structure determination from DFT and DFT+U studies allow to describe the mixed valence state as well as the complex directional bonding dependence in these materials like also in PuO_2 [44]. Using DFT, steady progress has been made in the understanding of defects properties, defect–defect interactions, fission product stability, and fission product transport in nuclear fuels [45]. Gryaznov et al. also used the density functional theory (DFT) calculations for UO_2, PuO_2 and MOX containing He atoms in octahedral interstitial positions. In particular, basic MOX properties and He incorporation energies as functions of Pu concentration within the spin-polarized, generalized gradient approximation (GGA) DFT have been calculated [46].

In general, modelling of defect has become a wide research area and the complex electron system of the actinides a challenging aspect of describing the evolution of the structure of these materials.

3.3. Extended Defects

Once point defects start diffusing within the solid, they can interact with each other and form extended defects (linear, planar or 3-dimensional defects) so as to reduce the total energy.

These extended defects are the following:

- dislocation-type defects: In general, dislocation-type defects are loops which can exhibit edge, screw and mixed dislocation character within a single loop, or can be prismatic (interstitial- or vacancy-type dislocation loop). The latter is a direct consequence of production and diffusion of interstitials and vacancies in the U and O sublattices. The former is a plastic deformation under external loading and is not a direct product of the fission process.

- voids: These are formed by vacancy absorption and are more stable than vacancy loops.

3.3.1. Ionic Configurations of Dislocations in UO₂

The geometry of slip in a single crystal is fully defined by the slip system, which designates the slip plane (reticular plane in which surface atomic density is maximum) and the slip direction (reticular direction in which linear atomic density is maximum). The dislocation is generally a mixture of screw and edge components in the shape of a loop. However, important deformation properties, such as the creep rate and the yield stress (or usually called the critical resolved shear stress), are controlled primarily by the edge components of the dislocation. Consequently, the nature of edge dislocations in UO_2 has received the most attention in the literature. In 1960, Rapperport and Huntress [47] examined the macroscopic slip of UO_2 monocrystals deformed in compression between 700 °C and 1900 °C. The most active slip system, highlighted by the analysis of slip trace and the Laue stereotypes, is {100}<110>. The planes {110} and {111} become active when the temperature increases, the slip direction remaining <110>. The planes {111} are often activated by cross-slip. In 1963, Ashbee confimed these results, by means of TEM observations, and defined the Burgers vector as a/2 <110> [48]. The distance a/2 <110> effectively corresponds to the shortest period of the fluorite network. Primary slip planes in UO_2 are not the densest ones, i.e. {111} planes as classically observed in fcc metals. The most important slip system in UO_2 is the one which rather confers on the crystal a minimum electrostatic energy than a minimum elastic energy. The easy slip along {100}<110> tends to minimize the intense repulsive force between cations. The anions then screen during such translations. The ionic configurations of dislocations in UO_2 have been investigated by Evans [49] in order to identify the peculiarities that may influence the deformation characteristics of this material.

Ashbee [48] has observed dissociated dislocations into partial dislocations. However, these stacking faults might have been identified in non-stoichiometric UO_2 due to the TEM observation conditions which induced a local reduction of the oxide. This excess uranium ions could stabilize stacking faults according to calculations based on an ionic model [50]. The same calculations showed that the stacking fault energy was much too high to consider the dissociation of dislocations into partial dislocations in UO_2.

3.3.2. Prismatic Loops

Another type of loop is called a prismatic loop. This type is fundamentally different from the shear loop; the only feature the two types have in common is their circular shape and their ability to expand or contract radially.

Figure 7 shows a TEM micrograph of a UO_2 sample having cumulated 10^{-5} dpa alpha-damage. Prismatic dislocation loops are clearly visible in this sample. A study as function of the alpha-damage has shown that the loops grow in size and concentration [32, 51]. Corresponding to the two types of point defects, vacancies and interstitials, there are two types of prismatic loops.

The interstitial loop consists of a disk-shaped layer of atoms formed by assembling free interstitial atoms from the bulk solid. The atom-layer agglomeration is thermodynamically more stable than the same number of atoms dispersed in the lattice as self-interstitials. Interstitial loops form only in solids bombarded by high energy radiation (e.g., fission fragments) because only this environment produces sufficient quantities of self-interstitials. In common with the interstitial loop, the periphery of the vacancy loop is a circular edge dislocation with a Burgers vector perpendicular to the plane of the loop. However, the Burgers vectors of the two types are of opposite sign. By definition, an interstitial loop grows/shrinks by absorption of interstitials/vacancies, whereas the vacancy loop grows/shrinks by absorption of vacancies/interstitials.

However, vacancy loops shrink by self-interstitial atom absorption at all temperatures and shrink by vacancy emission at high temperatures. This means that vacancy loops are intrinsically unstable at all temperatures. Rather than forming loops in the shape of a disc, vacancy condensation results in voids, which are in turn a perfect trap for gas atoms (see next paragraph and Figure 10).

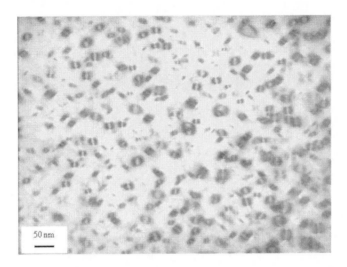

Figure 7. TEM micrograph of 10 wt% ^{233}U-doped UO_2 showing the presence of prismatic loops resulting from the alpha-damage © European Atomic Energy Community, reproduced with permission.

3.3.3. Void Nucleation and Growth

Because of preferential absorption of self-interstitials at dislocations, a slight excess of vacancies is left in the solid to first nucleate and then grow voids (a void does not contain gas). Voids, as well as prismatic loops, can nucleate homogeneously or heterogeneously. Homogeneous nucleation refers to the build-up of small clusters by random encounters of individual point defects executing random walks in the solid. The stability of these clusters relative to the individual point defects of which they are composed (i.e., voids contain vacancies and perhaps gas atoms whereas loops contain interstitials) is the driving force for nucleation. None of the structural features of the solid are needed to cause agglomeration of the point defects. Heterogeneous nucleation refers to the appearance of voids on distinct structural features of the solid. These features can be pre-existing gas bubbles, incoherent precipitate particles or dislocations.

The depleted zones created in the collision cascade can also act as heterogeneous nucleation sites for void formation. The latter is considered to be the most important nucleation mechanism in irradiated UO_2 fuels.

Nucleation and growth are often treated as sequential steps in the overall process of void formation. During the nucleation period, the number density of cavities increases with time, but the sizes remain small.

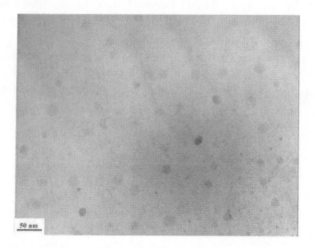

Figure 8. TEM micrograph of a 10wt% ^{238}Pu-doped UO$_2$ (2.4 dpa) annealed at 1100 K © European Atomic Energy Community, reproduced with permission.

During the growth period that follows, the number density stabilizes and the void size increases with time. The void is assumed to be spherical and its growth is controlled by diffusion of vacancies and interstitials from the bulk of the solid to the void surface. In most situations, gas atoms will stabilize the voids/cavities. Figure 8 shows a TEM micrograph of a heavily alpha-damaged (U, Pu)O$_2$ sample where voids have formed by diffusion of vacancies and stabilized by the radiogenic helium. The interstitial loops formed as shown in Figure 7 have been annealed.

4. PuO$_2$

Plutonium dioxide is another fluorite based actinide which is of great interest as single compound but also as a component of the MOX fuels. The behaviour of PuO$_2$ as a constituent of MOX is subsequently discussed in chapter 6. When considered as a waste form, the structural stability of the plutonium oxide ceramic forms is of major importance when considering its potential accidental radiolytic reaction when coming into presence of water. The surface area eventually exposed to humidity will be one of the main parameters determining the production of hydrogen and all the other effects associated with radiolysis [52]. Depending on the original form of the PuO$_x$ (pellets, agglomerates, powder) the surface area potentially exposed to humidity could span over several orders of magnitude. The main process that would modify intrinsically the microstructure during storage is the radiation damage due to alpha-decay. The alpha-particle emitted during the decay, and, even more importantly, the recoil nucleus produce defects in the PuO$_x$ lattice (mostly Frenkel pairs). Moreover, when the alpha-particle comes to rest it produces a helium atom that can be retained in the PuO$_x$ lattice, but can also contribute to increase the strain, especially when He bubbles form. Additionally to hydrogen produced by radiolysis it should also be considered that some generated helium could be released from the PuO_x matrix during storage and contribute to increasing the pressure in the container.

In this section the available knowledge on radiation damage build-up in PuO_x and its consequences in terms of physical property changes is reviewed, with the final aim of assessing the possibility of predicting the structural stability of PuO_x and/or highlighting gaps and needs for further investigation in this area. Figure 9 shows a SEM micrograph highlighting the strong sputtering effect from the alpha-activity of ^{238}Pu. In this plutonium dioxide dendrites have formed during the storage time resulting in a total cumulated dose of about 110 dpa.

The alpha-damage and the helium formation and consequence on the stability of this type of compounds are discussed.

4.1. Radiation Damage Effects in PuO_2 and MOX

The self-radiation effects on the lattice parameter of PuO_x have been studied on $^{238}PuO_x$ samples [5, 29]. Lattice parameter increase was determined for samples stored at ambient temperature in oxygen or in vacuum, for samples stored at liquid nitrogen temperature and for samples containing 5% Fe (III) and kept under pure oxygen at room temperature.

The ingrowth of damage is frequently described by a simple exponential function. The lattice parameter change $\Delta a/a_0$ can be described by:

$$\Delta a/a_0 = A(1 - e^{-B \cdot t}) \tag{1}$$

where

λ: decay constant

t: time

A: value at saturation

B: rate constant for simultaneous annealing of defects.

The value A can be influenced by the history of the specimen used [53, 54]. The effects due to atomic displacements are rather complex functions describing the relative sink strengths of a given specimen for interstitials and vacancies. The formation of extended defects like dislocation loops [51] or of helium bubbles [55, 56] can provide additional sinks. Local maximum and minimum values observed for the lattice parameter as a function of accumulated damage before reaching a saturation level have been attributed to the trapping of interstitials into (helium) sinks. At saturation, the recombination rate is equal to the production rate of Frenkel defects.

In the experiments of Chikalla and Turcotte [1] saturation is observed for lattice expansion of ~0.3 %. This value is in substantial agreement with the measurements of Noe and Fuger [5] in various systems where a lattice expansion at saturation of 0.28 % was measured. The lattice expansion at saturation of a sample pre-annealed at high temperature (1540 °C), hence having no initial point defect damage or helium content was 0.32 % [53]. Although all point defects and helium should have been removed by the pre-annealing treatment, it can be speculated that nano-sized empty cavities had remained after helium desorption, constituting sinks for defects segregation, hence resulting in slightly higher saturation level for the lattice expansion.

Figure 9. SEM image of the RTG sample showing dendrites on the surface of the grains formed by sputtering of material caused by the strong alpha-activity © European Atomic Energy Community, reproduced with permission.

The similar resulting cavities left after annealing are visible in the TEM micrograph in Figure 8. The annealing of samples whose lattice expansion has reached saturation occurs in two steps starting at 450 °C. The first stage at ~400 °C is characterized by low activation enthalpy (~0.17 eV) implying short range annihilation of defects near sinks [53]. Isochronal anneals revealed an increased ease of recovery with increasing helium concentration. Weber [29] described two recovery stages for self-damaged PuO_2, the first occurring at 450 °C (with an activation energy of 1.9 eV) corresponding to oxygen-interstitial diffusion and the second at 675 °C (with an activation energy of 2.5 eV) corresponding to Pu-vacancy diffusion.

Redistribution of oxygen has an important impact in fuel-cladding interaction (in the case of spent fuel), but also more generally on mass transport properties. For hypostoichiometric PuO_{2-x} solid state thermal diffusion of oxygen vacancies occurs towards the high temperature region in a thermal gradient [57]. Oxygen diffusion in PuO_{2-x} proceeds via vacancy diffusion and shows a marked dependence on x [58]. Since helium diffusion can be directly associated with the anion mobility it is important to assess the self-diffusion of oxygen to evaluate long term storage conditions. Because of the technological importance of mixed oxides fuel some studies have been performed on non-irradiated MOX fuel subjected to self-damage from alpha-decays. The lattice parameter for samples of MOX powders and pellets that had been left in the air for up to 32 years was measured. The lattice parameter increased and was saturated at about 0.29% in the same range as other actinide dioxides as presented in ref [59]. The change in lattice parameter was formulated as a function of self-radiation dose. Three stages in the thermal recovery of the damage were observed in temperature ranges of below 673 K, 673–1073 K and above 1073 K. The activation energies in each recovery stage were estimated to be 0.12, 0.73 and 1.2 eV, respectively, and the corresponding mechanism for each stage was considered to be the recovery of the anion Frenkel defect, the cation Frenkel defect and a defect connected with helium, respectively [59].

Lattice expansion due to self-radiation with MOX was small compared with those for UO_2 and PuO_2, and it was explained by the fact that lattice expansion of MOX, due to oxygen interstitial atoms, was smaller than that of other actinide oxides. In the [238]Pu-doped UO_2 however it was observed that increase and saturation of the lattice parameter was earlier and higher respectively [35]. This is most probably attributed to the formation of complexes helium-vacancies formed earlier due to the short half-life of [238]Pu.

4.2. Helium Behaviour in PuO_2

More generally, radiogenic helium formation due to the alpha-decay of actinides has to be tightly correlated to the damage. Large quantities of helium far above the solubility [55] are typically generated in short times and can cause the formation of tiny bubbles acting as sinks for vacancies, hence modifying the mobility of which would in turn affect the diffusion of helium [60] but also the damage pattern.

Technologically, disposal of fuel or of old stocks of PuO_2 implies transport/diffusion of helium out of the considered material under storage condition.

The initial grain size or particle size and the potential disintegration of the original structure are one of the key parameters for the determination of helium release. Although the thermal diffusion of helium is some orders of magnitude faster than that of other noble gases like e.g. xenon (relevant in case of spent fuel storage/disposal), it remains low in the temperature range expected for storage and/or disposal ($8 \cdot 10^{-7} \exp(-167 \text{ kJ mol}^{-1}/RT)$ [61]).

Several experiments on helium thermal desorption have been performed. Some helium release experiments have been performed on [238]PuO_x from Radioisotopic Thermal Generator (RTG) used for space applications [60]. Figure 10 shows for example the helium desorption spectrum from a [238]PuO_2 sample in form of a pellet aged of 37 years hence having cumulated 110 dpa. A major helium fraction is released between 800 K and 1000 K followed by a second release at 1600 K likely from bubbles.

In another experiment plasma-melted PuO_x microspheres have been annealed isothermally between 100 and 1300 °C, but also in transients (for the transient-tested microspheres it was more difficult to derive a diffusion equation; thus these experiments will not be described in this work). Two samples were prepared with particle size range 177-210 μm and 74-88 μm, respectively.

The samples were heated in a steady-state furnace for the release in isothermal conditions. The helium release was measured using a mass spectrometer [60]. The effective diffusion parameter determined from 14 steady-state release experiments did not depend on the size of the microspheres indicating that the diffusion length is much smaller than the microspheres. In terms of retention, the experiments showed that about 65 % of the total inventory of the helium produced over 10 months was retained. From these experiments it could be determined that helium release is complete at 1300 °C within 10-20 minutes.

The diffusion of helium showed two regimes, one below 1100 °C and one above. At low temperature it was suggested that helium diffuses with low activation energy through vacancies resulting from damage, whereas at high temperature it diffuses as bubbles by vacancy diffusion controlled by Pu diffusion in PuO_2.

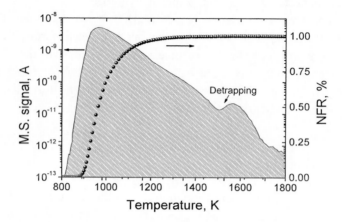

Figure 10. Helium thermal desorption spectrum from a $^{238}PuO_2$ sample (RTG) with 110 dpa.

In a more recent paper, El-Genk et al. have estimated the gas release from $^{238}PuO_2$ fuel particles for radioisotope heat sources and heater units [62]. The release mechanisms of helium in/from small-grain (7-40 μm) plutonia pellets were reviewed and the applicability of these mechanisms for large-grains (>300μm) fuel kernels was examined. In transient-tested pellets (small grains) the release rate increase and the fraction released depend on the maximum temperature reached during the transient. The experiments showed that no release occurred below 900 K. The apparent diffusion coefficient depended on the available surface area, the temperature reached and the initial helium inventory. In experiments with 7 months old plutonia samples (30-50 μm grains) heated slowly to 1300 K a sequence of processes leading to helium release was described as follows:

- a region below 900 K where less than 1 % of the helium inventory was released by atomic diffusion
- a region up to 1150 K with growing intergranular bubbles and trapping of helium at triple points of grains before interconnection/coalescence of bubbles (additionally to atomic diffusion)
- formation of networks of open tunnels causing some grain separation.

Helium release was measured from isothermal heating of plutonia pellets aged between 6 months and 2 years and then isothermally heated to 1273-1873 K up to 12 hours [63]. Below 1273 K or after very short time at higher temperatures tiny bubbles had formed. Further heating produced larger bubbles often resulting in complete saturation of the grain boundaries. Precipitation at the grain boundaries can enhance gas desorption through tunnels and further fragilize grain boundaries leading to their potential de-cohesion. The helium release from small-grain at 1723 K would be ~ 80 % decreasing to less than 10 % at 1042 K whereas the release from large grains could be as low as ~ 0.8 % at 1042 K.

The helium desorption of a 25 years old $^{239}PuO_x$ pellet showed a rather low activation enthalpy (~40 kcal.mol^{-1}) for helium atomic diffusion. The helium retained amounted up to

80-90 % of the inventory. Embrittlement of the original pellets occurring during storage was observed [61].

In very recent experiments [55] helium release from a very old (37 years old) $^{238}PuO_2$ powder sample was measured. The release starts at 950 K (in good agreement with the observation reported by El-Genk) and takes place in 3 steps. The first release (950-1100 K) is attributed to the helium adsorbed on the surface. At 1150 K a second release is attributed to the helium trapped in pores between the agglomerated grains. This fraction is low and its contribution to the total release is negligible. The main release peak is observed between 1150 and 1600 K due to release of the helium located in the grains, probably precipitated in tiny bubbles, which diffuses, via grain boundaries, to the surface [55]. The total helium quantity measured during this release experiment, $2.43 \cdot 10^{-7} \pm 5 \cdot 10^{-9}$ mol, represents only about *3 %* of the helium generated during the storage period, corresponding to an "apparent solubility" of $2.85 \cdot 10^{-5} \pm 5 \cdot 10^{-7}$ mol g^{-1} [55]. This would indicate that powder material would readily release essentially all the helium generated to the free volume of a storage container. However, in [64] it is reported that the majority of the helium generated by alpha decay in powdered plutonium oxide apparently remained trapped within the oxide particles. This discrepancy can probably be explained by considering the actual size and structure (agglomeration, etc.) of the PuO_2 particles used in different tests. The total quantity of helium generated in the experiments described in [64] would have led to a total pressure increase (if all helium released) of only 0.12 bars. The quantity generated and corresponding damage are probably not significant enough at such an early stage to extrapolate it in a reliable way to longer storage times and higher helium quantities formed. This is an area where further work could be envisaged to draw unequivocal conclusions as to what are the boundary conditions for long-term retention of helium in the oxide matrix. These examples highlight the influence of the state of the material on the total release of helium. The key parameter is the grain size and size/density of the ceramic matrix. Very large grains are apparently better suited to avoid early mechanical failure of the sintered ceramic. A powder with small grain size would lead to the release of a large fraction of the radiogenic helium starting earlier at rather high damage rate (i.e. high specific activity of the material) and would be more significant in case of sub-stoichiometric PuO_{2-x}.

Depending on the strategy adopted concerning the final destination of stored PuO_x, advantages and disadvantages of having the material as powder versus sintered monoliths (e.g. pellets) should be evaluated. Monoliths would require an additional fabrication process, but may result in better retention of the He and a lower surface area for radiolytic processes (hydrogen buildup, radiolysis, etc.), thus turning out better suited for very long storage/disposal concepts. Specific experiments and calculations could be envisaged to tackle this issue.

5. RADIATION DAMAGE IN THE HIGHER ACTINIDE OXIDES, AM, CM, BK, CF

The effects of self-radiation on the lattice parameter evolution have been studied for $^{244}CmO_2$ by Noe and Fuger [5, 65] for example and for $^{241}AmO_2$ by the same authors but also by Hurtgen and Fuger [4, 65] and by Mendelssohn *et al.* [2]. The effects of the self-irradiation damage induced in ^{244}CmO$_2$ have been studied by following the evolution of the lattice parameter of this compound as a function of time. Samples kept at room temperature undergo an expansion of the lattice parameter, limited to a saturation value, which is reached in a few days. The expansion of the samples kept in a vacuum of 133x10^{-6} Pa appears slightly different from that of samples kept under 1 atmosphere of oxygen pressure. At liquid nitrogen temperature, a further expansion can be observed, only with the samples sealed in oxygen. This low temperature expansion anneals out at room temperature, in two days, whereas the complete annealing of the initial room temperature expansion needs a treatment of ten days at 360°C [4]. In the case of ^{244}CmO$_2$ there was a larger difference observed between samples kept in vacuum or under oxygen, attributed to losses of oxygen by self-irradiation [4]. Freshly prepared samples, kept in atmosphere of oxygen, for one month, at 360°C, do not show any lattice expansion. The losses of oxygen by self-irradiation are extremely important on the surface by direct sputtering in the collision cascades from the recoil. This effect which is shown in the SEM micrographs in Figure 11 for the ^{244}CmO$_2$ but also previously in Figure 9 for the case of ^{238}PuO$_2$ results in the restructuring of the surface forming dendrites. This effect was observed to be extremely large for californium where a sample of ^{249}CfO$_2$ turned to ^{249}CfO$_{1.8}$ after only twenty days of storage in air [66].

Figure 11. SEM micrograph of a ^{244}CmO$_2$ sample after 20 years of storage showing the formation of dendrites due to the strong sputtering from the alpha-decays © European Atomic Energy Community, reproduced with permission.

Comparison with berkelium is more difficult since the most produced isotope ^{249}Bk is essentially a soft beta-emitter. Freshly prepared samples, kept in an atmosphere of oxygen, for one month, at 360°C, did not show any lattice expansion. Some values of A and B obtained from different experiments performed on PuO$_2$, AmO$_2$ (see for example the SEM micrograph in Figure 13) and CmO$_2$ as calculated from eq. (1) are summarized in table 2 below. Work has also been performed on the thermal conductivity of plutonium and americium oxides allowing determining the saturation for point defects threshold in AmO$_2$ [68]. It appears clearly as also observed in ^{238}Pu-doped UO$_2$ that the saturation in the variation of thermal conductivity is much faster than that for saturation of lattice parameter change. The defects contributing to these two property changes are hence of different nature.

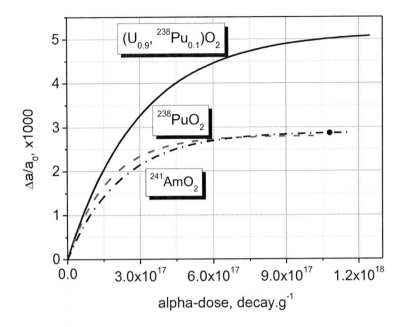

Figure 12. relative lattice parameter evolution as function of accumulated alpha-damage for UO_2 samples doped with 10 wt% of ^{238}Pu, $^{241}AmO_2$ stored in vacuum from ref. [4] and $^{238}PuO_2$ stored in vacuum from ref.[5] respectively.

Figure 13. SEM micrograph of americium dioxide powder © European Atomic Energy Community, reproduced with permission.

The early appearance of point defects (frenkel pairs) acting as phonon scattering centres has a strong effect on the thermal diffusivity degradation whereas the formation of extended defects most probably result only on the increase of the lattice parameter. A study on the

Impact of auto-irradiation on the thermophysical properties of oxide nuclear reactor fuels shows evidence for this phenomenon as shown in ref. [32].

Table 2. values of A parameter (saturation) of eq. (1) for different self-irradiated actinide-compounds

Compound	$A \times 10^3$	Reference
$^{239}PuO_2$	3.38	[2]
$^{238}PuO_2$	2.8	[5]
$^{241}AmO_2$	2.89	[4]
$^{241}AmO_2$	2.82	[67]
$^{244}CmO_2$	2.33	[65]
$(U_{0.9}, {}^{238}Pu_{0.1})O_2$	5.15	

6. RADIATION EFFECTS IN NUCLEAR FUELS

Most electricity-producing nuclear power stations use uranium dioxide (UO_2) as fuel, enriched in ^{235}U to about 5%, and some also use in MOX (mixed oxide) fuel, i.e., UO_2 with about 5% of PuO_2 replacing the UO_2. The fuel consists of sintered pellets of about 1 cm in diameter. These pellets are used to produce long stacks that are sheathed in tubes (cladding) of a Zr-alloy.

Uranium dioxide fuel is subjected to all the radiation and damaging sources for about 5 years, covering γ and X-rays, neutrons, electrons, fission fragments, alpha-decaying elements. During this period, fission products concentrations increase in and change both chemical and physical properties. Any treatment of damage effects has to allow for such changes that occur even in the absence of damage buildup. The most interesting damage effect in UO_2 fuel at high burn-up (expressed in GWd/tU or in percent fissions of the heavy metal atoms) is polygonization, the formation of about 10^4 small submicrometer grains from each original UO_2 grain. Polygonization is the term used to describe the rearrangement of those dislocations formed in the earlier stage of irradiation that do not annihilate each other into walls of dislocations, forming low-energy "subboundaries" and perfect but slightly misaligned subgrains.

A well-known consequence of accumulated radiation damage are damage-induced phase changes, most notably amorphization (or metamictization) of originally crystalline matter, or polygonization, also named grain subdivision—a process that transforms a typical grain of an originally well-crystallized ceramic into thousands of small grains in the submicron range. Polygonization occurs in several nuclear fuels, including UO_2.

When discussing damage accumulated by fission, or to a lesser extent, by radioactive decay, one has to consider the simultaneous changes in chemistry. Each fission, besides producing the above 100,000 displacements, also produces two fission products: new chemical elements between Ga and Dy, including volatile elements such as Br, I, Kr, Xe, Cs, etc., accumulating to often more than 10 at% at the end of life of the nuclear fuels. Or in α-decay where daughter atoms, e.g., Np in the decay of Am and He atoms formed in addition to the displacements, the He atoms may precipitate into bubbles, thus causing the specimens to swell.

Similarly, in ß-decay, new elements are formed. For example, Cs, a high-abundance fission product, decays into Ba with another valence state and a different chemical behavior. Therefore, we deal with complex phenomena that explain why interest is still high in understanding damage effects and mechanisms that exist not only in new but also in conventional nuclear fuels, despite the large amount of work devoted to this subject in the past five decades.

6.1. Change in Bulk Physical Properties

UO_2 does not become amorphous under any damage source. Fission damage and the ingrowth of fission products can eventually cause polygonization, i.e. both single crystals and sintered specimens are transformed into a material consisting of very small grains of about 0.1–0.3 mm grain size. In UO_2 fuel about 10^{-4} subgrains are formed from each original UO_2 grain. This phenomenon has already been observed in early test irradiations and was called grain subdivision. It has received renewed attention in the 1980s when power reactors increased the fuel burn-up.

Between 130 °C and 1000 °C, the diffusion of U and Pu is completely athermal, i.e. independent of temperature. These facts have been explained by the formation of thermal spikes along the trajectory of the fission fragments in combination with a pressure gradient. Because of the high-energy deposition rate a locally (over)heated track (fission spike or thermal spike) may be formed. Such fission tracks are seen in transmission electron microscopy in thin UO_2 foils and with the replica technique at UO_2 surfaces but not in TEM samples prepared from the bulk [21, 22]. This indicates that the threshold for the formation of observable tracks must be close to the energy loss value of fission products, i.e. 18–22 keV/nm. An extreme case of fission spikes interacting with the fuel matrix is the destruction of pre-existing fission gas bubbles by a fission spike that is passing by.

The phenomenon is called "re-solution" of fission gas and was known for about 40 years. It was explained by the above-mentioned hydrostatic pressure component [24] of the thermoelastic stress field of the fission spike interacting with the bubbles. The pressure gradients also serve to explain the surprisingly high U and Pu diffusion coefficients. To decrease these gradients, the highly mobile uranium interstitials are pushed away from the spike axis, thus increasing the U-diffusion to values higher than those calculated for atomic mixing and thermal spike effects alone. Like diffusion, in-pile creep of UO_2 was shown to be athermal and fission-enhanced below 1273 K as well [69].

Mechanical properties can also vary as a function of damage accumulation in UO_2. Figure 14 shows the evolution of the Vickers hardness as function of accumulated damage for the two alpha-doped compounds. The two materials accumulate decay damage at a rate differing by two orders of magnitude. The combined data for the two materials span over six order of magnitudes of damage, providing insight on different stages of radiation damage accumulation. The initial trend for the UO_2 doped with 0.1 wt% of ^{238}Pu shows essentially no clear changes of the hardness. A relatively sharp transition occurs around 10^{-2} dpa, indicating that this is a threshold level at which the accumulation of microscopic defects produces evident macroscopic changes. This level of damage corresponds to spent fuel at discharge from the reactor or during the first months/years of cooling. In spite of the different decay rates, the evolution of the hardness shows an essentially continuous evolution independently from the time necessary to reach a given displacements per atom (dpa) level. This important finding is confirmed by other types of analysis: for instance, microstructure analysis by transmission electron microscopy revealed that the damage accumulation pattern up to a few dpa is characterized by the production of dislocation loops as shown in Figure 7.

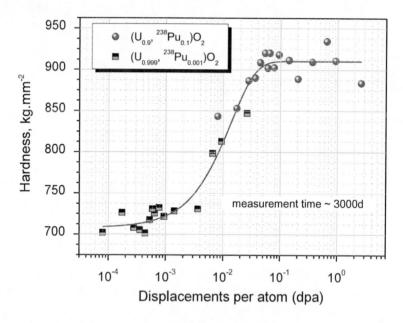

Figure 14. Hardness evolution for two alpha-doped materials expressed as a function of cumulated damage (dpa).

6.2. The High Burnup Structure

In the late 1950s it was observed that a strong capture by ^{238}U of neutrons in the resonance range occurs at the periphery of the nuclear fuel leading to the production of ^{239}Np and therefore of ^{239}Pu [70]. The consequence of the increase of the fissile density is a local increase of the burnup. The area typically concerned by this phenomenon is the annular outer part of the fuel pellet of about 200 mm thickness, representing about 8% of the fuel volume at a (radially averaged) burnup of 60 MWd/kgU. The local enrichment then decreases almost exponentially towards the centre of the fuel. The original grains with size of around 10 mm in typical LWR fuels tend to subdivide into thousands of smaller grains with sizes of about 100-200 nm. This restructuring of the grains is associated with the formation of a local porosity that can reach values above 20 %.

The coarsened micrometric size porosity contains almost all of the fission gases. For power reactors this phenomenon has been observed in the 1980s. Two structures, rounded grains at open surfaces and (bulk) polyhedral grains, have been identified in the high-burnup region of the fuel [71]. The formation of smaller grains at open surfaces (e.g. pores) shows a fractal appearance with the smaller grains having a size of less than 10 nm as can be seen in Figure 15 and Figure 16.

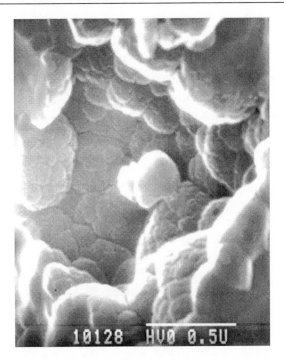

Figure 15. Secondary electron image of a restructured UO$_2$ fuel showing the occurrence of rounded shaped sub-grains inside pores © European Atomic Energy Community, reproduced with permission.

Figure 16. TEM bright field micrograph showing the HBS in a fuel sample with 75MWd/kg irradiated at 900 °C © European Atomic Energy Community, reproduced with permission.

The surface reorganization has been observed by scanning electron microscopy [72, 73] and is accompanied by a bulk restructuring that is also observable by scanning electron microscopy but is mostly investigated by transmission electron microscopy [74]. The fuel transforms by a sub-division process in polyhedral grains surrounding pores. The newly formed tiny grains are often found to be slightly disoriented (a few degrees) [75].

The exact mechanisms responsible for the formation of the high burnup structure are still under investigation. The formation of defects in combination with the presence of the fission gases appears to play a key role in the process and several scenarios have been suggested [76].

Nogita and Une [77, 78] proposed a formation mechanism of the HBS that is directly related to the accumulation of radiation damage. Tangled dislocation networks are formed by the inhomogeneous accumulation of dislocations after the development of interstitial-type dislocation loops. At the same time, intragranular fission products gas bubbles are formed by the clustering of vacancies and of fission gases Xe and Kr. With increasing burn-up, tangled dislocations are organized into sub-divided grains with high angle boundaries [77]. Then, some of them are recrystallized, sweeping out small intragranular bubbles. In this approach, recrystallization refers to a series of steps, i.e. formation of subgrains, growth of the subgrains into recrystallization nuclei, and growth of the recrystallized grains. In line with this, Spino et al. [79] have tentatively attributed the formation of the HBS to the local start of recrystallization around pores (characteristic of the HBS). This interpretation has been opposed by the results of the High Burnup Rim Project (HBRP) in which a set of irradiated UO_2 disks of different burnup and temperature were analyzed extensively [80]. On the basis of the results of this project Matzke [81] concluded that (a) there is no instantaneous recrystallization due to the accumulation of gas and radiation damage, (b) an increased temperature is needed for recrystallization, and (c) if occurring, recrystallization does not necessarily sweep gases. The latter three facts disagree with the formation mechanisms proposed by Nogita and Une.

TEM observations of HBRP samples [82] showed that in the HBS the initial grains are sub-divided and not recrystallized. Figure 16 shows a TEM image of a re-structured UO_2 fuel sample. The sub-divided grains with sizes as small as 50 nm for some of them are clearly visible. The subdivision process proceeds further with increasing burnup as recently observed by the SEM examination of a very high burnup specimen [83]. Sonoda et al. [82] thus concluded that the restructuring is initiated by the accumulation and mutual interaction of (1) radiation damage including point defects and dislocations, (2) fission products including gas bubbles and metal particles, (3) stored energy caused by electronic excitation and nuclear collision which may cause radiation-enhanced diffusion of interstitials and vacancies, and (4) the growth of dislocation loops.

In spite of the different views on its formation mechanism, there is now agreement that the HBS has a high fission gas retention capacity. In particular, the HBS does not evolve toward an open system of interconnected channels, even when porosity reaches very high values (e.g. 35% in a FBR fuel, 50% in a PWR MOX agglomerate) [84]. As a technological spin-off of this result, the HBS could be considered to retain effectively the fission gases occluded in pores up to relatively high local burn-ups (>300 MWd/kgHM) because only at these burnup values porosity fractions greater than 0.3 may be reached, for which incipient pore interconnection might just appear. A consequence of the influence of HBS on thermal conductivity is that the high burn-up fuel will run cooler in the reactor than would be assumed from its thermal conductivity vs. porosity behavior at low burnup, leading to lower fission gas release [85].

In the Fast Reactor (FR) fuels, due to the extreme operating conditions (temperature, radiation dose), the original microstructure of the fuel material undergoes significant changes during the irradiation, often called fuel restructuring. In the outer rim of the pellet because of moderated operating temperature the original fuel structure is preserved whereas in an intermediate region some recrystallized grains form. The central region is typically formed by elongated (columnar) grains that form by vaporization-condensation processes [86] and in extreme conditions a central void is formed due to a redistribution of the initial porosity.

The high operating temperature also affects the oxygen migration and typically the stoichiometry of the fuel decreases in the centre. As a consequence the oxygen content in the periphery of the initially slightly sub-stoichiometric fuel increases hence the local thermal conductivity resulting in better heat exchange with the coolant.

The central part of the fuel would, however, become more sensitive to defect formation and also to re-distribution of some actinides (see next paragraph) even if the overall stability and behaviour of the FR fuel does not appear to be fundamentally affected.

6.3. Actinide Bearing Nuclear Fuels

As an option for the management of the highly active actinides formed during the irradiation of the conventional UO_2 or MOX it is envisaged to incorporate minor actinides (MA) in so-called MA-bearing fuels with the aim of transmuting them into homogeneous or heterogeneous recycling in Fast Breeder Reactors (FBR) or in Accelerator Driven systems (ADS) [87]. There is limited experience with minor actinide fuel for fast reactors and the feasibility of irradiating this type of fuel has been performed in the past in the SUPERFACT [88] experiment for example and more recently in an irradiation in the JOYO reactor in Japan [89] where the development of a central hole and redistribution of the americium after a very short-term irradiation was observed.

Prunier et al. (1997) report the results of the irradiation experiment (SUPERFACT) in which the irradiation behaviour of mixed actinide oxide fuels was studied in the frame of transmutation research. Low minor actinide content ($U_{0.741}Pu_{0.242}Np_{0.015}O_{1.973}$, $U_{0.745}Pu_{0.237}Am_{0.018}O_{1.957}$) and high minor actinide content fuels ($U_{0.552}Np_{0.448}O_{1.996}$, $U_{0.596}Np_{0.212}Am_{0.192}O_{1.926}$) were irradiated in the Phénix fast reactor (France) and subjected to extensive post-irradiation examinations. The results indicated that the low minor actinide content fuel behaved very similar in comparison to standard mixed oxide fuel. A central hole was formed with columnar grains around it.

This was not observed for the high minor actinide content fuel, due to the lower operational power in the absence of plutonium [88]. The stability of this type of fuel need to be more thoroughly investigated and the relation between irradiation effects and chemical and thermo-physical properties investigated.

Different types of fuels [90] are currently considered including oxides, metals but also composites like CERMET (ceramic-metal) or IMF (inert matrix fuel) like zirconium based fuels having also the fluorite structure like the oxide forms considered.

CONCLUSION

Radiation damage in actinide compounds with the fluorite structure and especially on UO_2 and $(U, Pu)O_2$ has been extensively studied for more than 50 years. The studies cover single effects from various damage sources up to combined effects in e.g. irradiated nuclear fuels. UO_2 is the most commonly used fuel in nuclear reactors and a thorough knowledge of its behaviour under irradiation is extremely important to ensure a safe exploitation of this energy production source. The safety and economic issue have especially triggered the research on the microstructural evolution of the fuel at high burnup.

The second practical issue related to the understanding of the damage formation in UO_2 lies in the forecast of its long term behaviour as a waste form in the option of direct disposal. The spent fuel that will be disposed off will not be in equilibrium due to radioactive decay during millenaries. The alpha-damage will be essentially due to all the minor actinides present in the spent fuel. The alpha-damage will impact the long term properties of the spent fuel and the comprehension of the mechanisms of damage formation will help to predict its behaviour.

As a global outcome of studies concerning the fluorite structure based actinide compounds it could be shown that they exhibit generally a remarkable resistance against radiation effects, hardly ever amorphizing. Nevertheless the stability of these compounds degrades in the order PuO_2, AmO_2, CmO_2, CfO_2 as can be also observed for their thermal stability. This aspect needs to be thoroughly investigated when considering minor actinide bearing fuels for the next generation of nuclear reactors.

In parallel to somewhat cumbersome aspects on the handling of actinide materials, modeling tools are developed to better describe these elements and particularly by integrating the specificity of the 5f electrons in the models.

REFERENCES

[1]   T.D. Chikalla, R.P. Turcotte, Self-radiation damage ingrowth in $^{238}PuO_2$, *Radiat. Eff.,* 19 (1973) 93-98.

[2]   K. Mendelssohn, E. King, J.A. Lee, M.H. Rand, C.S. Griffin, R.S. Street, Plutonium 1965, in: A.E.K.a.M.B. Waldun (Ed.), Chapman and Hall, London, 1967, pp. 189-204.

[3]   H. Matzke, in: H.B.a.R. Lindner (Ed.) Plutonium and other Actinides, North-Holland, Amsterdam, 1976, pp. 801-831.

[4]   C. Hurtgen, *J. Fuger, Inorg. Nucl. Chem. Lett.,* 13 (1977) 179-188.

[5]   M. Noe, J. Fuger, Self-radiation effects on the lattice parameter of $^{238}PuO_2$, *Inorganic and Nuclear Chemistry Letters,* 10 (1974) 7-19.

[6]   W.J. Nellis, *Inorganic and Nuclear Chemistry Letters,* 13 (1977) 393-398.

[7]   L.R. Morss, N.M. Edelstein, J. Fuger J.J. Katz (Eds.)The Chemistry of the Actinides and Transactinides Elements, 4th ed., Springer, Dordrecht, 2010.

[8]   S. Lutique, D. Staicu, R.J.M. Konings, V.V. Rondinella, J. Somers, T. Wiss, Zirconate pyrochlore as a transmutation target: Thermal behaviour and radiation resistance against fission fragment impact, *J. Nucl. Mater.,* 319 (2003) 59-64.

[9]   F. Garrido, L. Vincent, L. Nowicki, G. Sattonnay, L. Thomé, Radiation stability of fluorite-type nuclear oxides, Nuclear Instruments and Methods in Physics Research Section B: *Beam Interactions with Materials and Atoms,* 266 (2008) 2842-2847.

[10] J. Belle, Uranium Dioxide: Properties and Nuclear Applications, in: N.R. Handbooks (Ed.), United States Atomic Energy Commission, 1961.

[11] C. Lemaignan, Science des Matériaux pour le Nucléaire, EDP Sciences, 2004.

[12] D. Olander, Fundamental aspects of nuclear fuel elements, in, Office of Public Affairs Energy Research and Development Administration, Springfield, Virginia, 1976.

[13] M.P. Curie, *Comptes Rendus,* 130 (1900) 76.

[14] E. Rutherford, R.B. Owens, Thorium and uranium radiation, *Trans. R. Soc. Can.,* 2 (1899) 9-12.

[15] J.F. Ziegler, J.P. Biersack, U. Littmark, The Stopping and Range of Ions in Solids, Pergamon Press, Oxford, 1985.

[16] J. Soullard, A. *Alamo, Radiat. Eff.,* 38 (1978) 133.

[17] R. Fleischer, P. Price, R. Walker, Nuclear Tracks in Solids, in, University of California Press, Berkeley, 1975.

[18] F. Seitz, J. Koehler, *Solid State Phys.,* 2 (1956) 305.

[19] M. Toulemonde, E. Paumier, C. Dufour, *Radiat. Eff. Solids,* 126 (1993) 205.

[20] I.A. Baranov, Y.V. Martynenko, S. Tsepelevitch, Y.N. Yavlinskii, *Sov. Phys. Usp.,* 31 (1988) 1015.

[21] T. Wiss, H. Matzke, C. Trautmann, S. Klaumünzer, M. Toulemonde, Swift heavy ion damage in UO2, Nucl. Instr. Meth. B, 122 (1997) 583.

[22] C. Ronchi, *J. Appl. Phys.,* 44 (1973) 455.

[23] H. Matzke, *Radiat. Eff.,* 75 (1983) 317.

[24] H. Blank, H. Matzke, *Radiat. Eff.,* 17 (1973) 57-64.

[25] T. Sonoda, M. Kinoshita, Y. Chimi, N. Ishikawa, M. Sataka, A. Iwase, Electronic excitation effects in CeO2 under irradiations with high-energy ions of typical fission products, *Nucl. Instrum. Meth. B,* 250 (2006) 254-258.

[26] T. Sonoda, M. Kinoshita, N. Ishikawa, M. Sataka, A. Iwase, K. Yasunuga, Clarification of high density electronic excitation effects on the microstructural evolution in UO2, *Nucl. Instrum. Meth. B,* 268 (2010) 3277-3281.

[27] C. Ronchi, T. Wiss, Fission-fragment spikes in uranium dioxide, *J. Appl. Phys.,* 92 (2002) 5837-5848.

[28] H. Matzke, O. Meyer, A. Turos, damage recovery in the U-sublattice of ion implanted UO_2 between 5 K and 2000K, *Radiation Effects and Defects in Solids,* 119-121 (1991) 885-890.

[29] W. Weber, Alpha-irradiation damage in CeO_2, UO_2 and PuO_2, *Radiat. Eff.,* 83 (1984) 145-156.

[30] W.J. Weber, Ingrowth of lattice defects in alpha irradiated UO_2 single crystals, *J. Nucl. Mater.,* 98 (1981) 206-215.

[31] W.J. Weber, Thermal recovery of lattice defects in alpha-irradiated UO_2 crystals, *J. Nucl. Mater.,* 114 (1983) 213-221.

[32] D. Staicu, T. Wiss, V.V. Rondinella, J.P. Hiernaut, R.J.M. Konings, C. Ronchi, Impact of auto-irradiation on the thermophysical properties of oxide nuclear reactor fuels, *J. Nucl. Mater.,* 397 (2010) 8-18.

[33] V.V. Rondinella, H. Matzke, J. Cobos, T. Wiss, *Mat. Res. Soc. Symp. Proc.,* 556 (1999) 447-454.

[34] V.V. Rondinella, J. Cobos, T. Wiss, D. Staicu, Studies on spent fuel alterations during storage and effects on corrosion behaviour, in: Proceedings - 10th International Conference on Environmental Remediation and Radioactive Waste Management, ICEM'05, Glasgow, UK, 2005, pp. 1418-1424.

[35] V.V. Rondinella, T. Wiss, J.P. Hiernaut, D. Staicu, Dose rate effects on the accumulation of radiation damage, in: ICEM'07: The 11th International Conference on

Radioactive Waste Management and Environmental Remediation, Oud Sint-Jan Hospital Conference Center, Bruges, Belgium, 2007.

[36] A. Lidiard, *J. Nucl. Mater.,* 19 (1966) 106.

[37] M. Freyss, T. Petit, J.-P. Crocombette, Point defects in uranium dioxide: Ab initio pseudopotential approach in the generalized gradient approximation, *J. Nucl. Mater.,* 347 (2005) 44-51.

[38] E. Yakub, C. Ronchi, D. Staicu, Computer simulation of defects formation and equilibrium in non-stoichiometric uranium dioxide, *J. Nucl. Mater.,* 389 (2009) 119-126.

[39] M. Freyss, N. Vergnet, T. Petit, Ab initio modeling of the behavior of helium and xenon in actinide dioxide nuclear fuels, *J. Nucl. Mater.,* 352 (2006) 144-150.

[40] K. Govers, Atomic scale simulations of noble gases behaviour in uranium dioxide, in: Faculté des sciences appliquées, Université Libre de Bruxelles, Bruxelles, 2008.

[41] B.T.M. Willis, *J. Chem. Soc. Faraday Trans.,* 2 (1987) 1073.

[42] D.C. Parfitt, R.W. Grimes, Predicted mechanisms for radiation enhanced helium resolution in uranium dioxide, *J. Nucl. Mater.,* 381 (2008) 216-222.

[43] K. Govers, S. Lemehov, M. Verwerft, In-pile Xe diffusion coefficient in UO2 determined from the modeling of intragranular bubble growth and destruction under irradiation, *J. Nucl. Mater.,* 374 (2008) 461-472.

[44] H. Nakamura, M. Machida, M. Kato, LDA+U study on Plutonium Dioxide with Spin-Orbit Coupling, *Progress in Nuclear Science and Technology,* 2 (2011) 16-19.

[45] X.-Y. Liu, D. Andersson, B. Uberuaga, First-principles DFT modeling of nuclear fuel materials, *J. Mater. Sci.,* 47 (2012) 7367-7384.

[46] D. Gryaznov, S. Rashkeev, E. Kotomin, E. Heifets, Y. Zhukovskii, *Nucl. Instr. Meth. B,* 268 (2010) 3090-3094.

[47] E.J. Rapperport, A.M. Huntress, Deformation modes of single crystal uranium dioxide from 700 °C to 1900 °C, in, U.S. At. Energy Comm., 1960, pp. 1-29.

[48] K.H.G. Ashbee, Stacking faults in uranium dioxide, in: Proceedings of the Royal Society of London, 1964, pp. 37-46.

[49] A.G. Evans, P.L. Pratt, Dislocations in The Fluorite Structure, *Philosophical Magazine,* 20 (1969) 1213-1237.

[50] J.M. Lefebvre, J. Soullard, R.J. Gaboriaud, J. Grilhe, Calcul d'énergie de fautes d'empilement dans le dioxide d'uranium, *J. Nucl. Mater.,* 60 (1976) 59-65.

[51] J. Jonnet, P. Van Uffelen, T. Wiss, D. Staicu, B. Rémy, J. Rest, Growth mechanisms of interstitial loops in a-doped UO_2 samples, Nuclear Instruments and Methods in Physics Research, Section B: Beam Interactions with Materials and Atoms, 266 (2008) 3008-3012.

[52] V.V. Rondinella, J. Cobos, H. Matzke, T. Wiss, P. Carbol, D. Solatie, Leaching behavior and ?-decay damage accumulation of UO_2 containing short-lived actinides, in: Materials Research Society Symposium - Proceedings, 2001, pp. 391-398.

[53] R. Turcotte, Chikalla;T, Annealing of self-radiation damage in $^{238}PuO_2$, *Radiat. Eff.,* 19 (1973) 99-108.

[54] J. Fuger, H. Matzke, Self-radiation effects in the actinides and their compounds: basic studies and practical implications, in: A.J. Freeman, C. Keller (Eds.) Handbook on the Physics and Chemistry of the Actinides, Elsevier Science Publishers B.V., 1991, pp. 641 -684.

[55] E. Maugeri, T. Wiss, J.P. Hiernaut, K. Desai, C. Thiriet, V.V. Rondinella, J.Y. Colle, R.J.M. Konings, Helium solubility and behaviour in uranium dioxide, *J. Nucl. Mater.*, 385 (2009) 461-466.

[56] V.V. Rondinella, H. Matzke, J. Cobos, T. Wiss, Leaching behaviour of UO_2 containing alpha-emitting actinides, *Radiochimica Acta*, 88 (2000) 527-531.

[57] C. Sari, G. Schumacher, *Nucl. Technol.*, 28 (1976) 256-260.

[58] H. Matzke, Atomic mechanisms of mass transport in ceramic nuclear fuel, *J. Chem. Soc. Faraday Tran.*, 86 (1990) 1243.

[59] M. Kato, A. Komeno, H. Uno, H. Sugata, N. Nakae, K. Konashi, M. Kashimura, self-radiation damage in plutonium and uranium dioxide, *J. Nucl. Mater.*, 393 (2009) 134-140.

[60] P. Angelini, R.E. McHenry, J.L. Scott, W.S. Ernst Jr., J.W. Prados, Helium release from $^{238}PuO_2$ microspheres, in, Oak Ridge National Laboratory, Oak Ridge, TE, 1970.

[61] C. Ronchi, J.-P. Hiernaut, Helium diffusion in uranium and plutonium oxides, *J. Nucl. Mater.*, 325 (2004) 1-12.

[62] M. El-Genk, J.M. Tournier, Estimates of helium gas release in $^{238}PuO_2$ fuel particles for radioisotope heat sources and heater units, *J. Nucl. Mater.*, 280 (2000) 1-17.

[63] R.N.R. Mulford, B.A. Mueller, Measurement of helium release from materials containing 238Pu, in, Los Alamos National Laboratory, Los Alamos, NM, 1973.

[64] K. Veirs, Gas generation by pure and impure plutonium dioxide materials., in: M.S. Coonley (Ed.) Actinide Research Quarterly, Los Alamos, Nuclear Materials Technology/Los Alamos National Laboratory, 2004.

[65] M. Noe, *J. Fuger, Inorg. Nucl. Chem. Lett.*, 7 (1971) 421.

[66] R.D. Baybarz, R.G. Haire, J.A. Fahey, *J. Inorg. Nucl. Chem.*, 34 (1972) 557.

[67] T.D. Chikalla, L. Eyring, *J. Inorg. Nucl. Chem.*, 30 (1968) 133.

[68] H.E. Schmidt, J. Richter, H. Matzke, J. Van Geel, The Effect of Self-Irradiation on the Thermal Conductivity of Plutonium and Americium Oxides, in: T.W. Tong (Ed.) Thermal Conductivity 22, Technoic Publ. Co., Lancaster, PA, 1994, pp. 920-925.

[69] D. Brucklacher, J. Dienst, *J. Nucl. Mater.*, 42 (1972) 285.

[70] D. Klein, W. Baer, G.G. Smith, *Nucl. Sci. Eng.*, 3 (1958) 698.

[71] N. Lozano, L. Desgranges, D. Aymes, J.C. Niepce, *J. Nucl. Mater.*, 257 (1998) 78-87.

[72] H. Matzke, H. Blank, M. Coquerelle, K. Lassmann, I.L.F. Ray, C. Ronchi, C.T. Walker, *J. Nucl. Mater.*, 166 (1989) 165.

[73] K. Une, K. Nogita, S. Kashibe, M. Imamura, *J. Nucl. Mater.*, 188 (1992) 65.

[74] K. Une, K. Nogita, T. Shiratori, K. Hayashi, *J. Nucl. Mater.*, 288 (2001) 20-28.

[75] I.L.F. Ray, H. Matzke, H. Thiele, M. kinoshita, *J. Nucl. Mater.*, 245 (1997) 115-123.

[76] V.V. Rondinella, T. Wiss, The high burn-up structure in nuclear fuel, Mat. Today, 13 (2010) 24-32.

[77] K. Nogita, K. Une, *Nucl. Instrum. Meth. B,* B91 (1994) 301.

[78] K. Nogita, K. Une, *J. Nucl. Mater.*, 226 (1995) 302.

[79] J. Spino, D. Baron, M. Coquerelle, A.D. Stalios, High burn-up rim structure: evidences that xenon-depletion, pore formation and grain subdivision start at different local burn-ups, *J. Nucl. Mater.*, 256 (1998) 189-196.

[80] M. Kinoshita, T. Sonoda, S. Kitajima, A. Sasahara, T. Kameyama, T. Matsumura, E. Kolstad, V.V. Rondinella, C. Ronchi, J.P. Hiernaut, T. Wiss, F. Kinnart, J. Ejton, D. Papaioannou, H. Matzke, High Burnup Rim Project: (III) properties of rim-structured

fuel, in: 2004 International Meeting on LWR Fuel Performance, ANS, Orlando, Fl, USA, 2004, pp. 207-213.

[81] H. Matzke, Range, energy loss, energy straggling and damage production for alpha-particles in uranium dioxide, *J. Nucl. Mater.*, 270 (1999) 49-54.

[82] T. Sonoda, M. Kinoshita, I.L.F. Ray, T. Wiss, H. Thiele, D. Pellottiero, V.V. Rondinella, H. Matzke, Transmission electron microscopy observation on irradiation-induced microstructural evolution in high burn-up UO2 disk fuel, Nuclear Instruments and Methods in Physics Research Section B: *Beam Interactions with Materials and Atoms*, 191 (2002) 622-628.

[83] J.P. Hiernaut, T. Wiss, J.Y. Colle, H. Thiele, C.T. Walker, W. Goll, R.J.M. Konings, Fission product release and microstructure changes during laboratory annealing of a very high burn-up fuel specimen, *J. Nucl. Mater.*, 377 (2008) 313-324.

[84] J. Noirot, L. Desgranges, J. Lamontagne, Detailed characterisations of high burn-up structures in oxide fuels, *J. Nucl. Mater.*, 372 (2008) 318-339.

[85] D. Staicu, C. Cozzo, G. Pagliosa, D. papaioannou, S. Bremier, V.V. Rondinella, C.T. Walker, A. Sasahara, *J. Nucl. Mater.*, 412 (2011) 129-137.

[86] R.J.M. Konings, T. Wiss, C. Guéneau, Nuclear Fuels, in: L.R. Morss, N.M. Edelstein, J. Fuger (Eds.) The Chemistry of the Actinides and Transactinides Elements, *Springer, Dordrecht*, 2010, pp. 3665-3811.

[87] F. Lebreton, D. Prieur, A.l. Jankowiak, M. Tribet, C. Leorier, T. Delahaye, L. Donnet, P. Dehaudt, Fabrication and characterization of americium, neptunium and curium bearing MOX fuels obtained by powder metallurgy process, *J. Nucl. Mater.*, 420 (2011) 213-217.

[88] C. Prunier, F. Boussard, L. Koch, M. Coquerelle, *Nucl. Technol.*, 119 (1997) 141-148.

[89] T. Kosuke, M. Shuhei, S. Isamu, H. Takashi, O. Hiroshi, K. Shin-ichi, Y. Hiroshi, T. Kenya, Microstructure and elemental distribution of americium-containing uranium plutonium mixed oxide fuel under a short-term irradiation test in a fast reactor, *JNM*, 385 (2009) 407-412.

[90] J. Somers, Minor Actinide Bearing Fuels: Fabrication and Irradiation Experience in Europe, *Energy Procedia*, 7 (2011) 169-176.

INDEX

D

E

K

L

M

N

T

U